Labels
for
Less

West One
PUBLISHING

© West One (Trade) Publishing Ltd. 1999

ISBN 1-900327 35 X

A CIP catalogue record for this book is available from the British Library.

Printed and bound in Slovenia.

Published by

West One (Trade) Publishing Ltd, Kestrel House, Dukes Place, Marlow, Bucks SL7 2QH

Telephone: 01628 487722 Fax: 01628 487724 Email: sales@west-one.com

London and South-East England

Bedford

Matalan

Unit C, Interchange Retail Park, Ampthill Road,
Kempston, Bedford, Bedfordshire, MK42 7AZ
Tel: 01234 365077

Women's and children's clothes

Hours Mon–Fri 10–8, Sat 9–6, Sun 11–5

Discount up to

50%

Dunstable

The Vanity Box

16 Church Street, Dunstable, Bedfordshire, LU5 4RU
Tel: 01582 600969

Designer clothes for ladies and accessories

Hours Mon–Sat 9:30–5, Thur 10–4

Labels Jaeger, Mondi, Bianca

Discount up to

50%

Leighton Buzzard

Gossard Factory Shop

Grovebury Road, Leighton Buzzard, Bedfordshire,
LU7 8SN
Tel: 01525 851122 / 850088

All underwear for women

Hours Mon–Sat 9:30–5:30

Discount

25%–75%

Parking Yes, & Yes

Luton

Crystal Art

320 Selbourne Road, Luton, Bedfordshire, LU4 8NY
Tel: 01582 494904 Fax: 01582 494911
Email: crystal-art@breathemail.net

Crystal animals and hanging crystal. Photo frames for
special occasions. Baby gifts, Feng Shui crystal, mirrors,
glass displays. Glass domes, collectors' cases for the home,
some available with halogen lights

Hours Mon–Fri 10–4

Closed Christmas and New Year

➡ M1 J11 follow signs to Luton. Left into Waller Avenue.
Straight over roundabout, 200 yards turn left into
Selbourne Road

Discount

Parking 10 Spaces, & No, **Group Tours** Yes, **Mail order** No,
Catalogue Yes, **Internet Sales** No

Luton

Kangol

46 Church Street, Luton, Bedfordshire, LU1 3JG
Tel: 01582 405000

Hats for all occasions for men and women

Hours Mon–Fri 9–4:30, Sat 9:30–4

See ad on page 243

Discount see text

Luton

Walter Wright Factory Shop

29 Albion Road, Luton, Bedfordshire, LU2 0DS
Tel: 01582 721616

Hats

Hours Mon–Fri 9–7

Discount see text

Ascot

The Really Good Deal Fashion Sale

The Pavilion, Ascot Racecourse, Ascot, Berkshire
Tel: 01367 860017

Women's clothes

Hours Please telephone to apply for a mailing list

Discount see text

Ascot

The Stock Exchange

1 High Street, Sunninghill, Ascot, Berkshire, SL5 5NQ
Tel: 01344 25420

Designer and High Street labels for ladies, men and children

Hours Mon–Fri 9–5:30, Sat 9–4:30

Labels C. Klein, Boss, YSL

Discount see text

Cookham

Kid2Kid

High Street, Cookham, Berkshire, SL6 9SH
Tel: 01628 531804 Fax: 01628 531804

Nearly new children's clothes. NEW discounted ex-stock. PLUS nearly new maternity wear. Nearly new baby equipment

Hours Mon–Sat 10–5:30

Closed Christmas and New Year

➜ M4 exit J8/9. Follow signs to Cookham

Public Transport Railway station at Cookham

Discount

Labels Numerous labels

25%–50%

Parking Street, & Yes, **Group Tours** No, **Mail order** No, **Catalogue** No, ✕ Restaurants, pubs, cafés, **Internet Sales** No

Cookham

Seconds Out

High Street, Cookham, Berkshire, SL6 9SQ
Tel: 01628 850371

Middle to upper range of designer labels and accessories

Hours Mon–Sat 9–5:30, Thur late until 9

Discount

Labels Armani, Versace, Chanel, Escada, Tomasz Starzewski

see text

& Yes, **Group Tours** No, **Mail order** No, **Catalogue** No, ✕ Refreshments on site, **Internet Sales** No

Reading

Freelance Fabrics (Reading) Limited

130 Crockhamwell Road, Woodley Shopping Centre, Reading, Berkshire, RG5 3JH
Tel: 0118 9699611 Fax: 0118 9442603

Curtain, upholstery and dress fabrics. Foam cut to size. Polystyrene beads and Dacron. Upholstery accessories, haberdashery, net curtains, ready mades, tracks and poles, curtain lining and heading tape. Bargain remnants. Making up service

Hours Mon–Sat 9–5, Sun 10–4

Closed Christmas Day

➜ M4 J10 to Reading. Off at spur for Winnersh. Follow signs to Earley then at traffic lights signs to Reading A329. By the 'George' pub turn right, Loddon Bridge Road, follow Woodley signs

Public Transport Bus stop in Headley Road near 'Chequers' pub.

Discount

Labels SMD, Rectella, Prestigious, Romo, Marson, Gilbey, Leon, Homemaker, Richard Barrie

10%–30%

Parking 10 Spaces, & Yes, **Group Tours** Yes, **Mail order** No, **Catalogue** Yes, ✕ Coffee shop opposite, **Internet Sales** No

Reading

Matalan

Rose Kiln Lane, Reading, Berkshire, RG2 0SN
Tel: 01189 391958

Women's and children's clothes

Hours Mon–Fri 10–8, Sat 9–6, Sun 11–5

Discount up to

50%

Reading

TK Maxx

Broad Street Mall, Broad Street, Reading, Berkshire, RG1 7QE
Tel: 01189 511117

Clothing for all the family

Hours Mon–Fri 9–5:30, Sat 9–6

Discount up to

60%

& Yes

Windsor

Scent To You

10 Peascod Street, Windsor, Berkshire, SL19 1DE
Tel: 01753 833693

Perfume & body lotion etc.

Hours Mon–Sat 9:30–5:30

Labels Armani, Lacroix, Charlie, Givenchy, Coco, Revlon

Discount
5%–60%

Windsor

Switchgear

20 St Leonard's Road, Windsor, Berkshire, SL4 3BU
Tel: 01753 867438

Merchandise is general wear with some evening outfits

Hours Mon–Sat 9:30–5

Labels Escade, F. Usher, B. Barclay, Jaeger

Discount
see text

Beaconsfield

Cache-Cache

10 Gregories Road, Beaconsfield, Buckinghamshire, HP9 1HQ
Tel: 01494 671727

Women's clothes

Hours Mon–Sat 10–5

Labels Yarrell, Max Mara, Costello

Discount
see text

Chalfont St Giles

The Changing Room

50 Hgh Streeet, Chalfont St Giles, Buckinghamshire, HP8 4QQ
Tel: 01494 875933

Ladieswear. Generally caters for the upper end of the market. Wonderful selection of hats

Hours Tue–Sat 10–5

Labels G. Weber, Basler, Costello, Armani

Discount

see text

Gerrards Cross

Revival Dress Agency

8 Station Approach, Gerrards Cross, Buckinghamshire, SL9 8PP
Tel: 01753 891130

Ladies clothes. Nearly new fashion items not more than 2 years old. Wide range from M & S to Yves St Laurent. All excellent condition at affordable prices. Half price sale January and July. Accept anytime. 50/50 commission

Hours Tue–Sat 10–5

Closed Bank Holidays

➡ Centre of Gerrards Cross next to Barclays Bank in Station Approach

Public Transport Gerrards Cross station

Labels Escada, Mondi, Burberry, Ralph Lauren, Jaeger, M & S, Next, Karen Millen

Discount 25%–50%

Parking Behind shop, ♿ Yes, **Group Tours** No, **Mail order** No, **Catalogue** No, ✗ Tea shop opposite, **Internet Sales** No

Great Missenden

Fumbies Antiques Clothing

66 The High Street, Great Missenden, Buckinghamshire, HP16 0AN
Tel: 01494 866404

Sells clothes from most periods and accessories

Hours Mon–Sat 9:30–5

Closed Thursday

Discount
see text

High Wycombe

Alexon Sale Shop

Unit 17, Chilterns Shopping Centre, Frogmore, High Wycombe, Buckinghamshire, HD13 5ES
Tel: 01494 464214

Women's clothes

Hours Mon–Sat 9–5:30

Labels Alexon, Eastex, Calico

Discount 40%–70%

London & South-East England

High Wycombe

Imps

35–39 Frogmoor, High Wycombe, Buckinghamshire
Tel: 01494 524924

Men's, women's and children's clothes, furniture,
household goods

Hours Mon–Sat 9–5

Discount
see text

Little Chalfont

Encore

Nightingales Corner, Little Chalfont, Buckinghamshire
Tel: 01494 764174

Good quality stylish but wearable ladies' clothes

Hours Mon–Sat 9:30–5:30

Discount
see text

Long Crendon

Hang-Ups

1A The Square, Long Crendon, near Thame,
Buckinghamshire, HP18 9AA
Tel: 01844 201237

Women's clothes

Hours Tues and Fri 9:30–5:30, Wed 5:30–8, Sat 10–5

Discount
see text

Marlow

Bumpsadaisy Maternity Style

33 West Street, Marlow, Buckinghamshire, SL7 2LS
Tel: 01628 478487

Large range of maternitywear to hire or buy

Hours Mon–Sat 10–5:30

Discount
see text

London & South-East England

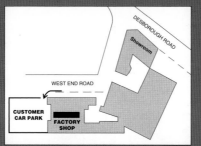
Milton Keynes

Matalan

Bilton Road, Bletchley, Milton Keynes, Buckinghamshire,
MK1 1HS
Tel: 01908 373735

Women's and children's clothes

Hours Mon–Fri 10–8, Sat 9–6, Sun 10–4

Discount up to
50%

Milton Keynes

Rohan Designs Plc

1–3 Knebworth Gate, Gifford Park, Milton Keynes,
Buckinghamshire, MK14 5QD
Tel: 01908 615407

Men's and women's clothes

Hours Mon–Sat 9:30–5:30

Discount
see text

Milton Keynes

World of Wood

7 Cornwall Place, Buckingham, Buckinghamshire,
MK18 1SB
Tel: 01280 822003 Fax: 01280 822003

Imported furniture from small cottage industries in Italy

Hours Mon–Sat 9–5:30

Closed Bank Holidays

➡ 4 or 5 shops from Budgens in a small precinct

Public Transport Bus

Discount

Parking Public car park, & Yes, Group Tours No,
Mail order No, Catalogue No, Internet Sales No

Old Amersham

Number Twenty

20 High Street, Old Amersham, Buckinghamshire, HP8 0DJ
Tel: 01494 432043

Women's clothes

Hours Tue–Sat 9:30–5:30

Labels Chanel, Cerruti, Mondi,
Max Mara

Discount

Olney

The Go Between

North Barn, 3 Bull Court, Market Squares, Olney,
Buckinghamshire, MK46 4EA
Tel: 01234 241193

Designer and High Street labels and accessories

Hours Tue–Sat 10–4:30

Labels Escade, Mondi, Farhi, B.
Barclay, Jaeger, M & S, Wallis

Discount

Brighton

Daisy Daisy

33 North Road, Brighton, East Sussex, BN1 1YB
Tel: 01273 689108

All the best designer clothes. Second-hand. Oilily, Jean
Barget, Miniman, IKKS. Also new traditional wooden toys
and beautiful dolls' houses for children. Unusual rattles,
comforters, shapes and mobiles

Hours Mon–Sat 10:30–5

Closed Christmas and New Year

➡ From Brighton station walk/drive down Queens Road.
Take 2nd turning on your left which is North Road. Daisy
Daisy is on the right

Public Transport Brighton mainline station

Labels Oilily, Jean Barget,
Miniman, IKKS, French
Connection, Osh Kosh, Next

Discount

& No, Group Tours No, Mail order Yes, Catalogue No,
Internet Sales No

London & South-East England

Honey

Merchants Quay, Brighton Marina, Brighton, East Sussex, BN2 5WA
Tel: 01278 818835

Women's clothes

Hours Mon–Sun 10–5:30

Discount up to

30%

Leading Labels Ltd

15 The Village Square, Brighton Marina, Brighton, East Sussex, BN2 5WA
Tel: 01273 683316 Fax: 01273 685509

A huge selection of quality mens and ladieswear over an extensive range of sizes. Top brand names and designer labels all at discounted prices

Hours Mon–Sun, various opening hours depending on site, Sun various

Closed Christmas Day

Labels Ben Sherman, Kangol, Whimsey, Kläss, Chilli Pepper, Roman Originals, Double Two

Discount

20%–75%

& No, **Group Tours** No, **Mail order** No, **Catalogue** No, **Internet Sales** No

The Factory Shop Ltd

Merchants Quay, Brighton Marina, Brighton, East Sussex, BN2 5UF
Tel: 01273 818590

Men's, ladies' and children's clothes, furniture, sportswear, houshold goods and sports equipment – a wide selection of goods

Hours Mon–Fri 10–5:30, Sat 10–6, Sun 10–4

Labels Wrangler, Nike, Adidas

Discount

30%–50%

Parking Yes, ✕ Refreshments on site

TK Maxx

36/37 North Street, Brighton, East Sussex, BN1 1EB
Tel: 01273 727483

Clothing for all the family

Hours Mon–Sat 9–6, Wed late until 8, Sun 11–5

Discount

see text

& Yes

Brighton

Tog 24

Merchants Quay, Brighton Marina, Brighton, East Sussex, BN2 5UF
Tel: 01273 818759

Specialist in outdoor clothing for all the family. Sports and sports equipment

Hours Mon–Sun 10–5:30

Discount up to

30%

Brighton

Tom Sayers Clothing Co

Merchants Quay, Brighton Marina, Brighton, East Sussex, BN2 5VA
Tel: 01273 818705

Men's clothes

Hours Mon–Sat 10–5:30, Sun 10–5

Discount

see text

Brighton

Toorak

Brighton Marina Village, Brighton, East Sussex, BN2 5UE

Mens and ladieswear. CK, Tommy, Timberland, Giorgio, Easy, Falmer at up to 75% below High Street

Hours Mon–Sun 10–6

Closed Christmas Day and Boxing Day

➡ In Brighton Marina Outlet Centre

Public Transport British Rail 1 mile

Discount

25%–75%

Parking 1500 Spaces, ♿ Yes, **Group Tours** Yes, **Mail order** Yes, **Catalogue** No, ✗ On site, **Internet Sales** No

Crowborough

Stock Exchange

Croft Road, Crowborough, East Sussex, TN6 1DL
Tel: 01892 662463

Sells designer clothes and accessories

Hours Mon–Sat 10–5

Closed Lunch 1–2 on Saturday

Labels Jaeger, Planet, Max Mara, Karen Miller, Condici

Discount

see text

Eastbourne

Cancer Research Campaign

172 Terminus Road, Eastbourne, East Sussex, BN21 3BB
Tel: 01323 739703

Bridalwear

Hours Mon–Fri 9–5, Sat 9:30–4:30, Sun 10–4

Discount

Eastbourne

Matalan

Unit 4, The Crumbies Retail Park, Pevensey Bay Road,
Eastbourne, East Sussex, BN23 6JH
Tel: 01323 470347

Fashion and homewares shop for all the family

Hours Telephone for opening hours

Discount up to
50%

Eastbourne

Napier

3 Courtland Road, Eastbourne, East Sussex, BN22 8SW
Tel: 01323 644511

Ladieswear. End of lines and limited editions of jewellery

Hours Mon–Sat 10–6, Sun 10–4

Discount

Parking Yes

Eastbourne

Revival Dress Agency

24 Grove Road, Eastbourne, East Sussex, BN21 4UP
Tel: 01323 649552

Excellent collection of chainstore and designer labels

Hours Mon–Sat 9–5:30

Discount

Labels Principles, Monsoon,
Wallis, Jaeger, Klein, Armani

see text

Hastings

Collins and Hayes Factory Shop

Menzies Road, Ponswood Industrial Estate, Hastings,
East Sussex
Tel: 01424 443834

One of the country's leading upholstery manufacturers;
half price sofas, chairs and fabrics. Stock clearance,
discontinued models, discounted fabrics, cancelled orders.
Stock is constantly changing; ex-display, end of lines, etc.

Hours Mon–Sat 9–5

See ad on page 22

Discount see text

Hove

Snips in Fashion

40 Church Road, Hove, East Sussex, BN3 2NF
Tel: 01273 729059

Women's clothes. Medium to better end. Mainly from
Germany, Italy and France

Hours Tue–Sat 9:30–5:30

Closed Christmas Day, Boxing Day, Good Friday

➡ 200 yards east from Hove town hall

Public Transport All main buses

Labels Olsey, Tru, Duo, Asper,
Michell, Kirstey, Doloras, Fink,
Hammerle

Discount 30%–50%

Parking Street, ♿ Yes, **Group Tours** No, **Mail order** No,
Catalogue No, **Internet Sales** No

Lewes

Roundabout

31 Cliffe High Street, Lewes, East Sussex, BN7 2DN
Tel: 01273 471325

Ladieswear. Good quality labels and a few accessories

Hours Mon–Sat 9:30–4:30

Closed Wednesday

Labels Jaeger, M & S, Principles,
Max Mara

Discount see text

Basildon

Choice Discount Stores Ltd

Unit 6A, Mayflower Retail Park, Gardiners Links, Basildon,
Essex, SS14 3AR
Tel: 01268 288331

Men's, women's and children's clothes

Hours Mon–Fri 9–6, Sat and Sun 11–5

See ad on page 75

Labels Next

Discount up to 50%

Basildon

Peter Newman Factory Shop

Pitsea Retail Park, Pitsea, Basildon, Essex, SS13 3BY
Tel: 01268 554344

Sportswear and footwear

Hours Mon–Sat 9–5:30, Sun 10–4

Labels Dr Martens, Clarks, Lotus, Equity, Hi-Tec

Discount up to 35%

Parking Yes

Basildon

The Factory Shop (Essex) Ltd

The Gloucesters, Luckyn Lane, Pipps Hill Industrial Estate, Basildon, Essex, SS14 3AY
Tel: 01268 520446 Fax: 01268 285274

Men's, ladies' and children's clothes, furniture, food, sportswear, electrical and household goods, toys, decorating, sports equipment, china and pets. 'Expect more, pay less'

Hours Mon–Sat 9–6, Sun 10:30–5

Closed Christmas and New Year

➡ A127

Public Transport Bus

Labels All

Discount see text

Parking Lots, ♿ Yes, **Group Tours** Yes, **Mail order** No, **Catalogue** No, ✗ On site, Cafés, **Internet Sales** No

Benfleet

Choice Discount Stores Ltd

14–20 Rectory Road, Hadleigh, Benfleet, Essex, SS7 2ND
Tel: 01702 555245

Men's, women's and children's clothes

Hours Mon–Thu 9–5:30

See ad on page 75

Labels Next

Discount up to

50%

Brentwood

Brandler Galleries

1 Coptfold Road, Brentwood, Essex, CM14 4BN
Tel: 01277 222269 Fax: 01277 222786
Email: art.british@dial.pipex.com
Web site: www.brandler-galleries.com

Understandable good art from Royal Academicians at 70% off of London prices

Hours Tue–Sat 10–5:30

➡ Just behind High Street, adjacent to multi-storey car park

Public Transport Brentwood rail station 400 yards. Brentwood High Street 300 yards

Labels Turner, Fedden, Tindle, Weight, Constable, Cuming, Stage, Howard

Discount

10%–70%

Parking 5 Spaces, & No, **Group Tours** No, **Mail order** Yes, **Catalogue** Yes, ✗ Pub, cafes – 200yds, **Internet Sales** Yes

Buckhurst Hill

Switchgear

160A Queens Road, Buckhurst Hill, Essex, IG9 5BD
Tel: 020 8505 3113

Women's nearly new clothing. Discounts on products at sale time

Hours Mon–Sat 10–5:00

Closed Wednesdays and lunchtime 1–2 daily

Public Transport Trains at bottom of road. Bus at top of road

Labels All brands

Discount

see text

Parking On road, & No, **Group Tours** No, **Mail order** No, **Catalogue** No, **Internet Sales** No

Chelmsford

Matalan

Unit 4, Riverside Retail Park, Victoria Road, Chelmsford, Essex, EM2 6LL
Tel: 01245 348787

Women's and children's clothes

Hours Mon–Fri 10–8, Sat 9.30–5.30, Sun 11–5

Discount up to

50%

Clacton-on-Sea

Leading Labels Ltd

Unit 12, Clacton Common Outlet Centre, Stevenson Road, Clacton-on-Sea, Essex, CO15 4TL
Tel: 01255 476260 Fax: 01255 434217

A huge selection of quality mens and ladieswear over an extensive range of sizes. Top brand names and designer labels all at discounted prices

Hours Mon–Sun, various opening hours depending on site, Sun various

Closed Christmas Day

Discount

Labels Ben Sherman, Kangol, Whimsey, Kläss, Chilli Pepper, Roman Originals, Double Two

20%–75%

& No, **Group Tours** No, **Mail order** No, **Catalogue** No, **Internet Sales** No

Clacton-on-Sea

Thorntons

Unit 42, Clacton Common, Factory Outlet Village, Clacton-on-Sea, Essex, CO16 9HB
Tel: 01255 220527

The factory outlet stores sell three different product categories: misshapes, discounted lines and standard lines. Misshapes are packed into assorted bags and offer a saving of between 35%–55%. Discount lines are offered at a discount of 25%–50%. Standard lines are also on sale at normal prices

Hours Opening times dependent upon individual factory outlet centre

Discount

Labels Thorntons

25%–55%

& No, **Group Tours** No, **Mail order** Yes, **Catalogue** Yes, ✕ Most outlet centres have food courts, **Internet Sales** Yes

Clacton-on-Sea

Choice Discount Stores Ltd

Clacton Common Factory Shopping Village, Stephenson Road West, Clacton-on-Sea, Essex, CO15 4TL

Men's, women's and children's clothes

See ad on page 75

Discount up to

Labels Next

50%

Grays

Choice Discount Stores Ltd

14–16 High Street, Grays, Essex, RM17 6LV
Tel: 01375 385780

Men's, women's and children's clothes

Hours Mon–Sat 9–5:30

See ad on page 75

Discount up to

Labels Next

50%

Great Chesterford

Swaine, Adeney, Brigg

Nursery Road, Great Chesterford, Essex, CB10 1QW
Tel: 01799 531522

Mens and ladieswear and household goods

Hours Mon–Sat 10–5, Thur late until 7

Discount
30%–50%

Parking Yes

Harlow

Sterlings Leathers

Unit A2, Seedbed Centre, Coldharbour Road, Annacles, Harlow, Essex, CM19 5AF
Tel: 01279 444449

Men's and ladies' clothing

Hours Mon–Fri 9–4, Sat 10–1

Discount
see text

Leigh-on-Sea

The Z Collection

120 Elm Road, Leigh-on-Sea, Essex, SS9 1SQ
Tel: 01702 480505

Garments for women which tend to be more dressy than casual

Hours Wed–Sat 9:30–1

Discount
see text

Rayleigh

The Falmer Factory Shop

24–26 Brook Road, Rayleigh Weir Industrial Estate, Rayleigh, Essex, S56 7XE
Tel: 01268 749207

Perfect and seconds jeans and T-shirts for all the family

Hours Mon–Fri 9–5:30, Sat 10–4

Labels Falmers

Discount
see text

Rochford

The Factory Shop (Essex) Ltd

1 Magnolia Way, Purdeys Industrial Estate, Rochford,
Essex, SS4 1ND
Tel: 01702 531153 Fax: 01702 531508

Men's, ladies' and children's clothes, furniture, food,
sportswear, electrical and household goods, toys,
decorating, sports equipment, china and pets. 'Expect
more, pay less'

Hours Mon–Sat 9–6, Sun 10.30–5

Public Transport Bus/train

Discount

see text

Parking Yes, & Yes, **Group Tours** Yes, **Mail order** No,
Catalogue No, ✗ Refreshments on site, **Internet Sales** No

Saffron Walden

Encore

2A Church Street, Saffron Walden, Essex
Tel: 01799 524812

Women's clothes

Hours Tues, Wed, Fri and Sat 10–4, Mon and Thur 10–1

Labels Escade, Mondi

Discount

see text

Saffron Walden

Labels For Less

The Cockpit, Emson Close, Saffron Walden, Essex,
CB10 1HF
Tel: 01799 523533

Men's and women's clothes and footwear

Hours Mon–Sat 10–5:30

Labels C. Klein, Lauren, Moschino,
Versace, YSL, Timberland, Armani

Discount

see text

Saffron Walden

Leather For Less

7 Market Row, Saffron Walden, Essex
Tel: 01799 516711

Women's clothes. Bags, shoes, belts, hats

Hours Mon–Sat 10–5:30

Discount

see text

Southend

Matalan

The Greyhound Retail Park, Sutton Park, Southend, Essex, SS2 5PY
Tel: 01702 466248

Fashion and homewares shop for all the family

Hours Telephone for opening hours

Discount up to
50%

Tiptree

The Factory Shop Ltd

The Cross Roads, Kelvedon Road, Tiptree, Essex, CO5 7VV
Tel: 01621 817662

Men's, ladies' and children's clothes, furniture, sportswear, houshold goods and sports equipment – a wide selection of goods

Hours Mon–Sat 9–5:30, Sun 10–4

Labels Wrangler, Nike, Adidas

Discount
30%–50%

Parking Yes, ✕ Refreshments on site

West Thurrock

Matalan

Unit 4B, The Turnel Estate, Western Avenue, Lakeside Retail Park, West Thurrock, Essex, RM16 1HH
Tel: 01708 864350

Women's and children's clothes

Hours Mon–Fri 10–8, Sat 9.30–5.30, Sun 10–6

Discount up to
50%

Wickford

Choice Discount Stores Ltd

10–11 Ladygate Centre, High Street, Wickford, Essex, SS12 9AK
Tel: 01268 764893

Men's, women's and children's clothes

Hours Mon–Sat 9–5:30

See ad on page 75

Labels Next

Discount up to
50%

Wickham Bishops

The Go-Between

Wickham Hall, Langford Road, Wickham Bishops, Essex, CM8 3JQ
Tel: 01621 891049

Designer clothes for ladies, also ski gear for the whole family

Hours Tues and Thur 10–3 or by appointment

Labels B. Barclay, Jaeger, N. Farhi

Discount **see text**

Andover

James Meade Ltd

48 Charlton Road, Andover, Hampshire, SP10 3JL
Fax: 01264 363200

Mail order clothing for men and women

Hours Mon–Fri 9–5:30, Sat 10–4

Closed Bank Holidays

➜ Near railway station

Public Transport Train

Discount **see text**

Parking 50 spaces, ♿ Yes, **Group Tours** No, **Mail order** Yes, **Catalogue** Yes, **Internet Sales** No

MasterCard, Switch, Visa, Delta, Diners Club International, American Express

Fareham

Grandford Carpet Mills

Unit 11, Bridge Industries, Broadcut, Fareham, Hampshire
Tel: 0500 717124

Carpets with huge savings of up to half shop prices. Rubber underlay and accessories supplied. We manufacture on the premises and sell direct at wholesale prices. Your own colour specially made in 80/20 twist. Minimum 50sq yards

Hours Telephone for opening hours

See ad on page 31

Discount **see text**

Fleet

Alexon Sale Shop

Hart Shopping Centre, Fleet, Hampshire
Tel: 01252 815055

Women's clothes

Hours Mon–Sat 9–5:30

Labels Alexon, Eastex, Calico

Discount **40%–70%**

New Milton

The Catalogue Shop

49 Old Milton Road, New Milton, Hampshire
Tel: 01425 629697

Men's, ladies' and children's clothes, furniture and
household goods, sports equipment. Returns, damaged
and worn goods, as well as clearance and end of lines
from mail order catalogues

Hours Mon–Sat 9–5, Sun 10–5

See ad on page 31

Discount up to

50%

Portsmouth

Gieves & Hawkes

22 The Hard, Portsmouth, Hampshire, PO1 3DY
Tel: 023 9282 6648

Mens and ladieswear

Hours Mon–Fri 9:30–6, Sat 9–5

See ad on page 31

Labels Yarell, Daks, Austin Reed

Discount

60%–70%

Portsmouth

Matalan

Station Road, Portsmouth, Hampshire, PO1 1BE
Tel: 023 9285 1967

Fashion and homewares shop for all the family

Hours Telephone for opening hours

Discount up to

50%

Ringwood

Pret a Porter

Shop One, 18–20 High Street, Ringwood, Hampshire,
BH24 1AF
Tel: 01425 476090

Nearly-new ladies' clothes

Hours Mon–Sat 9–4

Labels Escade, Eastex, Alexon

Discount

see text

Romsey

The Catalogue Shop

6 Church Street, Romsey, Hampshire, SO51 8BU
Tel: 01794 518522

Clothing for all the family

Hours Mon–Sat 9–5

See ad on page 31

Discount up to

50%

Southampton

TK Maxx

173–178 High Street, Southampton, Hampshire, SO14 2BY
Tel: 023 8063 1600

men's clothes, women's clothes, children's clothes, Accessories

Hours Mon–Fri 9–5:30, Thur late until 7, Sat 9–6, Sun 11–5

Discount up to

60%

& Yes

Southampton

Tog 24

Canute Pavilion, Ocean Village, Southampton, Hampshire, SO14 3JS
Tel: 023 8033 783

Specialist outdoor clothing for all the family and sports equipment

Hours Mon–Sun 9:45–5:45

Discount up to

30%

Stockbridge

Curtain Up

Stonefield Park, Martins Lane, Chilbolton, Stockbridge, Hampshire, SO20 6BL
Tel: 01794 341893 Fax: 01794 341893

Stocked at a fraction of their original cost are all sizes from grand curtains with swags and tails or pelmets to small cottage sizes, in names such as Colefax & Fowler, Percheron, Designers Guild, Bakers, Sandersons and Laura Ashley. Stock changes constantly and there is an alteration and make-up service. Also stocked are bedspreads, cushions, cloths, lamps and tie backs

Hours Mon–Thu 2 pm–5, Sat 10–1

Closed Christmas to New Year inclusive

➜ From Stockbridge take A30 in direction of Sutton Scotney. After 'Leckford Hutt' pub turn left. Then half mile on left

Discount

see
text

Parking 20 Spaces, & No, **Group Tours** No, **Mail order** No, **Catalogue** No, ✗ Tea-room and pubs in Stockbridge, **Internet Sales** No

Winchester

The Clothes Line

171 High Street, Winchester, Hampshire, SO23 9BQ
Tel: 01962 868892

Designer and High Street labels and accessories

Hours Mon–Sat 10–4

Closed Wednesday

➜ Situated near King Alfred's Statue

Labels YSL, Laurel, Next, L. Ashley, F. Usher

Discount

see text

Barnet

Catalogue Bargain Shop

101–107 High Street, Barnet, Hertfordshire, EN5 5UZ
Tel: 020 8364 9654

Men's, women's and children's clothes, furniture, sportswear, electrical and household goods, toys, sports equipment

Hours Mon–Sat 9–5:30, Sun 10–4

Labels Kays

Discount

see text

Berkhamsted

Cameo

150 High Street, Berkhamsted, Hertfordshire, HP4 3AT
Tel: 01442 865791

Sells children's and ladies' nearly-new clothes and accessories

Hours Mon–Fri 9:30–5:15, Sat 9.30–5

Labels Osh Kosh, Oilily, Benetton, Gap, Next, Mondi

Discount

see text

for leisure...

www.WestOneWeb.com

...great

expectations

Borehamwood

A & D Hope

Evelyn House, 3 Elstree Way, Borehamwood,
Hertfordshire, WD6 1RN
Tel: 020 8953 7278

All leather products for the whole family

Hours Mon–Fri 9–5

Closed Lunch 1–2 daily

Discount

Borehamwood

Rubert of London Limited

Unit 7, Stirling Industrial Centre, Stirling Way,
Borehamwood, Hertfordshire
Tel: 020 8207 2620

Women's clothes

Hours Mon–Fri 10–4

Discount

20%–40%

Hatfield

Bella Ricco Shoes

Galleria Outlet Centre, Comet Way, Hatfield,
Hertfordshire, AL10 0XR
Tel: 01707 266662

Sells shoes, jewellery and handbags to men, women and
children

Hours Mon–Fri 10–8, Sat 10–6, Sun 11–5

Discount

see text

Hatfield

Burtons

Galleria Outlet Centre, Comet Way, Hatfield,
Hertfordshire, AL10 0XR
Tel: 01707 251688

Men's clothes

Hours Mon–Fri 10–8, Sat 10–6, Sun 11–5

Labels Burton

Discount

see text

Hatfield

Choice Discount Stores Ltd

Galleria Outlet Centre, Comet Way, Hatfield,
Hertfordshire
Tel: 01707 278301

Men's, women's and children's clothes

Hours Mon–Fri 10–8, Sat 10–6, Sun 11–5

See ad on page 75

Labels Next

Discount up to

50%

Hatfield

Discount Dressing

Galleria Outlet Centre, Comet Way, Hatfield,
Hertfordshire, AL10 0XR
Tel: 01707 259925

Aladdin's cave of designer bargains for ladies

Hours Mon–Fri 10–8, Sat 10–6, Sun 11–5

Discount

50%–90%

Hatfield

Dorothy Perkins

Galleria Outlet Centre, Comet Way, Hatfield,
Hertfordshire, AL10 0XR
Tel: 01707 263640

Women's clothes

Hours Mon–Fri 10–8, Sat 10–6, Sun 11–5

Labels Dorothy Perkins

Discount

see text

Hatfield

Ecco

Galleria Outlet Centre, Comet Way, Hatfield,
Hertfordshire, AL10 0XR
Tel: 01707 258399

Shoes. For a catalogue telephone 0800 387368

Hours Mon–Fri 10–8, Sat 10–6, Sun 11–5

Discount up to
25%

Catalogue Yes

London & South-East England

Hatfield

Feet Street

Galleria Outlet Centre, Comet Way, Hatfield,
Hertfordshire, AL10 0XS
Tel: 01707 258653

Shoes for all the family

Hours Mon–Fri 10–8, Sat 10–6, Sun 11–5

Labels Loake, Gabor, Rockport,
Barkers, Bally, Trickers

Discount

see text

Hatfield

First Impressions

Unit 3, Galleria Outlet Centre, Hatfield, Hertfordshire,
AL10 0XR
Tel: 01707 268755

Clothes for all the family

Hours Mon–Fri 10–8, Sat 10–6, Sun 11–5

Discount up to **50%**

Hatfield

Jeffrey Rogers

Galleria Outlet Centre, Comet Way, Hatfield,
Hertfordshire, AL10 0XR
Tel: 01707 258144

Women's clothes. Emphasis on young street style

Hours Mon–Fri 10–8, Sat 10–6, Sun 11–5

Discount **25%–75%**

Hatfield

Land's End Direct Merchants

Galleria Outlet Centre, Upper Level, Comet Way, Hatfield,
Hertfordshire, AL10 0XR
Tel: 01707 264161

Men's, women's and children's clothes, furniture,
sportswear, electrical and household goods, sports
equipment. US mail order company which sells everything
you require

Hours Mon–Fri 10–8, Sat 10–6, Sun 11–5

Discount **25%–85%**

Catalogue Yes

Hatfield

Millano

Galleria Outlet Centre, Comet Way, Hatfield,
Hertfordshire, AL10 0XR
Tel: 01707 259199

Clothes for all the family

Hours Mon–Fri 10–8, Sat 10–6, Sun 11–5

Discount up to
30%

Hatfield

Pilot

Galleria Outlet Centre, Comet Way, Hatfield,
Hertfordshire, AL10 0XR
Tel: 01707 258030

Mainly younger style clothes for women

Hours Mon–Fri 10–8, Sat 10–6, Sun 11–5

Discount
see text

Hatfield

RS Shoes

Galleria Outlet Centre, Comet Way, Hatfield,
Hertfordshire, AL10 0XR
Tel: 01707 258021

Shoes for all the family

Hours Mon–Fri 10–8, Sat 10–6, Sun 11–5

Labels Dr Martens, Levi's, LSCO,
Kickers, Wrangler

Discount
see text

Hatfield

TK Maxx

Galleria Outlet Centre, Comet Way, Hatfield,
Hertfordshire, AL10 0XR
Tel: 01707 260066

Men's, ladies' and children's clothes

Hours Mon–Fri 10–8, Sat 10–6, Sun 11–5

Discount up to
60%

& Yes

MasterCard SWITCH VISA DELTA Diners Club International AMERICAN EXPRESS

London & South-East England

Hertfordshire

Hatfield

Tog 24

Galleria Centre, Comet Way, Hatfield, Hertfordshire
Tel: 01707 258088

Specialist in outdoor clothing for all the family. Sportswear and sports equipment

Hours Mon–Fri 10–8, Sat 10–6, Sun 11–5

Discount up to

30%

Hatfield

Tom Sayers Clothing Co

The Galleria Outlet Centre, Comet Way, Hatfield, Hertfordshire, AL10 0XR
Tel: 01707 257729

Men's clothes

Hours Mon–Fri 10–8, Sat 10–6, Sun 10–5

Discount

see text

Hatfield

Walker & Hall

Galleria Outlet Centre, Comet Way, Hatfield, Hertfordshire, AL10 0XS
Tel: 01707 270121

Sells Raymond Weil watches and many more

Hours Mon–Fri 10–8, Sat 10–6, Sun 11–5

Labels Longines, Gucci, Tag Heuer, Lacroix

Discount

see text

Hemel Hempstead

Aquascutum

Cleveland Road, Maylands Wood Estate, Hemel Hempstead, Hertfordshire, HP2 7EY
Tel: 01442 248333

Mens and ladieswear

Hours Mon–Sat 10–4

Discount up to

60%

Hertford

Lawther's Factory and Sample Shop

21 St Andrew's Street, Hertford, Hertfordshire
Tel: 01992 504038

Women's clothes

Hours Mon–Sat 10–5

Labels Monsoon, Azar, Domingo, Moonlight

Discount

see text

Letchworth

K Shoes

13 Commerce Way, Letchworth, Hertfordshire, SG6 3DN
Tel: 01462 243251

Shoes for all the family

Hours Mon–Sat 9–5:30

Labels La Gear, Clarks, Fila, Slazenger, Weider, Puma, Hi-Tec, K Shoes, Nike

Discount
see text

Royston

Clothing World

Orchard Road, Royston, Hertfordshire, SG8 5HA
Tel: 01763 249941

Clothing for all the family, sportswear and household goods

Hours Mon, Wed, Sat 9–5:30, Thur, Fri, Sun 9–5

Discount
30%–50%

Royston

The Shoe Shed

Orchard Road, Royston, Hertfordshire, SG8 5HA
Tel: 01763 241933

Shoes

Hours Mon, Wed and Sat 9–5:30, Thur and Fri 9–6, Sun 10–4

Discount up to
30%

St Albans

Just Between Us

29 Hillside Road, St Albans, Hertfordshire, AL1 3QW
Tel: 01727 811172

Enormous selection of women's eveningwear to hire

Hours By appointment only

Discount

Stevenage

Matalan

Unit B, Danestreet, Stevenage, Hertfordshire, SG1 1NB
Tel: 01438 312433

Fashion and homewares shop for all the family

Hours Mon–Fri 10–8, Sat 9–6, Sun 11–5

Discount up to

50%

Ware

Recollections

48 Church Street, Ware, Hertfordshire, SG12 9EW

Second-hand/new bridal gowns and new veils/head-dresses to purchase or hire. Bridesmaids' dresses. Men's and boys' formal dress hire. Wedding gowns made to your own design plus alteration service

Hours Tue–Sat 10–4

Closed Christmas and New Year

➜ Turning off the middle of the High Street

Public Transport Ware train station or buses

Discount

Labels Benjamin Roberts, Mon Cheri, Hilary Morgan, Mori Lee, Peter Posh, Berkertex, Joanne Hall

♿ No, **Group Tours** No, **Mail order** No, **Catalogue** No, ✗ Several restaurants and bar food, **Internet Sales** No

Watford

Cara

Garston, Watford, Hertfordshire, WD2 6PZ
Tel: 01923 670853

Home-based business selling a range of designer labels

Hours By appointment only

Discount

Labels Mondi, Escade, Max Mara, Jaeger, Windsmoor

London & South-East England

Watford

Choice Discount Stores Ltd

44–46 High Street, Watford, Hertfordshire, WD1 2BR
Tel: 01923 233255

Men's, women's and children's clothes

Hours Mon–Sat 9–5:30

See ad on page xxx

Labels Next

Discount up to

50%

Watford

Glasers Factory Shop

Rembrandt House, Whippendell Road, Watford, Hertfordshire, WD1 7QN
Tel: 01923 234067

Women's clothes

Hours Tues and Thur 10–4

Discount

25%–75%

Watford

Scent To You

Unit 142A, Harlequin Centre, Watford, Hertfordshire, WD1 2TL
Tel: 01923 225712

Perfume and body lotion etc.

Hours Mon–Sat 9:30–5:30

Labels Armani, Lacroix, Charlie, Givenchy, Coco, Revlon

Discount

5%–60%

Cowes

Artigiano

49 High Street, Cowes, Isle of Wight, PO41 0US

Ladieswear. Sells clearance from mail order

Hours Mon–Sun, April to end October only

Discount

see text

Cowes

Cameo of Cowes

16 Bath Road, The Parade, Cowes, Isle of Wight,
PO31 7QW
Tel: 01983 297907

Men's and ladies' clothes. Buy and sell unclaimed lost
property from British Airways, Royal Mail, London
Transport and Police departments

Hours Mon–Sun 10–5

Discount

Yarmouth

Chessell Pottery (Chessell Enterprises)

Chessell, Yarmouth, Isle of Wight, PO41 0UF
Tel: 01983 531248 Fax: 01983 531210
Email: chessell-pottery@isle-of-wight.uk.com
Web site: http://isle-of-wight.uk.com/chessell

Fine decorative porcelain. Seconds

Hours Mon–Sat 9–5, Sun 10–5

Closed Christmas and New Year

Discount

&. Yes, **Group Tours** Yes, **Mail order** Yes, **Catalogue** Yes, ✗
Refreshments on site, **Internet Sales** Yes

Beckenham

Frock Follies

49 High Street, Beckenham, Kent, BR3 1DA
Tel: 020 8650 9283

From M & S to Armani – many designer labels –
specialising in new hats and sample ranges

Hours Mon–Sat 9:30–5:30

Closed Bank Holidays

Public Transport Bus stop outside or Beckenham Junction
station

Discount

see text

Parking None, &. No, **Group Tours** No, **Mail order** No,
Catalogue No, ✗ Wine bars and local coffee shops,
Internet Sales No

Beckenham

Hangers

53 Croydon Road, Beckenham, Kent, BR4 4AB
Tel: 020 8658 5386

All High Street store names plus designer range of nearly
new mens and ladieswear

Hours Mon–Sat 9:30–5:30

Closed Bank Holidays

Public Transport Close to Elmers End station, on 54 bus
route

Discount

&. Yes, **Group Tours** No, **Mail order** No, **Catalogue** No,
Internet Sales No

Bexley

The Dress Agency

5 Bourne Road, Bexley, Kent, DA5 1LG
Tel: 01322 523451

Designer and chainstore clothes and accessories

Hours Tue–Sat 10:30–5

Labels Richards, Rodier, B. Barclay

Discount

see text

Bexleyheath

All Change

228A Broadway, Bexleyheath, Kent, DA6 7AU
Tel: 020 8303 3094

Sells ladies' clothing as well as bridalwear and eveningwear

Hours Mon–Sat 9:15–4:30

Labels Next, Wallis, M & S, Planet

Discount

see text

Bromley

Outlet

75 High Street, Bromley, Kent

Top fashions. All labels. Designer brands. All at prices that are truly outrageous

See ad on page 53

Discount

see text

Canterbury

Bon Marche

47 Northgate, Canterbury, Kent, CT1 1BE
Tel: 01227 764823

Ladieswear. Across the board labels from M & S to YSL

Hours Mon–Sat 9:30–5:30

Discount

see text

Kent

London & South-East England

LEADING LABELS IN FASHIONS AND FURNISHINGS
WITH UP TO
70% DISCOUNT

DE BRADELEI MILL SHOP

Chapel Street, Belper,

Derbyshire

Tel: 01773 829830

Chevin Coffee Shop

DE BRADELEI WHARF

Cambridge Road, Dover,

Kent

Tel: 01304 226616

Waves Coffee Shop

BOTH STORES OPEN 7 DAYS A WEEK
Monday–Friday: 9.30–5.30
Saturday: 9.30–6.00   Sunday: 11.00–5.00

Canterbury

Phase Eight
11 Butchery Lane, Canterbury, Kent, CT1 2JR

Women's clothes

Hours Mon–Sat 9–5:30

Discount

Cranbrook

Bell House Fabrics
High Street, Cranbrook, Kent, TN17 3DN
Tel: 01580 712555

Soft furnishing fabrics

Hours Mon–Sat 9–5:30

Discount

Crayford

David Evans World of Silk

Bourne Road, Crayford, Kent, DA1 4BP
Tel: 01322 559401

Mens and ladieswear

Hours Mon–Fri 9:30–5, Sat 9:30–4

➜ A223, five minutes from the A2 to London and 15 minutes from J2 of M25

Discount up to **50%**

Parking Yes, **Group Tours** Yes, ✕ Refreshments on site

Dover

De Bradelei Wharf

Cambridge Road, Dover, Kent, CT17 9BY
Tel: 01304 226616 Fax: 01304 226636
Email: mail@dbmsdover.enterprise.com

Leading Designer and High Street labels with up to 70% discount, from: Womenswear – Windsmoor, Planet, Précis Petite, French Connection, Four Seasons, Jaeger Knitwear, Phase Eight, Joyce Ridings and many more. Menswear – French Connection, Great Plains, Wolsey, Regatta, Hagga and Robert Leonard's Menswear selling leading international labels. Leisure wear – shoes for men and women. China and glass from Waterford Wedgwood, Royal Doulton, Stuart Crystal, Cloverleaf, Staffordshire Tableware, Churchill, Hornsea and many more

Hours Mon–Fri 9:30–5:30, Sat 9:30–6, Sun 11–5 pm

Closed Christmas Day, New Year's Day, Easter Sunday

➜ From London A20 follow signs to hoverport, then follow signs to De Bradelei Wharf (just off sea front)

Public Transport Bus and train

See ad on page 45

Labels Windsmoor, Planet, Précis Petite, Four Seasons, Phase Eight, French Connection, Liz Claiborne

Discount **20%–70%**

Parking 400 Spaces, ♿ Yes, **Group Tours** Yes, **Mail order** No, **Catalogue** No, ✕ On site coffee shop **Internet Sales** No

MasterCard, Switch, VISA, Delta

Faversham

Catalogue Bargain Shop

19A Preston Street, Faversham, Kent, ME13 8NX
Tel: 01795 591203

Men's, women's and children's clothes, furniture, sportswear, electrical and household goods, toys, sports equipment

Hours Mon–Sat 9–5:30, Sun 10–4

Labels Kays

Discount **see text**

Headcorn

The Factory Shop Ltd

The Formans Centre, High Street, Headcorn, Kent, TN27 9NE
Tel: 01622 891651

Men's, ladies' and children's clothes, furniture, sportswear, houshold goods and sports equipment – a wide selection of goods

Hours Mon–Sat 9–5:30, Thur and Fri late until 7, Sun 11–5

Labels Wrangler, Nike, Adidas

Discount **30%–50%**

Parking Yes, ✕ Refreshments on site

Herne Bay

Peter Newman Factory Shop

Unit 1B, Eddington Business Park, Thanet Way, Herne Bay, Kent, CT6 5TT
Tel: 01227 741112

Footwear

Hours Mon–Sat 9–5, Sun 10–4

Labels Dr Martens, Clarks, Lotus, Equity, Hi-Tec

Discount up to
35%

Parking Yes

Hythe

Reflections

7–9 Marine Walk Street, Hythe, Kent, CT21 5NW
Tel: 01303 262233

Sells designer and nearly-new outfits and hires out hats

Hours Mon–Sat 10–4

Closed Wednesday

Discount
see text

Maidstone

Clothesline

58 Union Street, Maidstone, Kent, ME14 1ED
Tel: 01622 758439

Women's clothes

Hours Tue–Sat 9:30–5

Labels Mondi, Jaeger, Yarrell, Escade, F. Usher

Discount
see text

Maidstone

Matalan

Unit A, The Broadway Shopping Centre, Maidstone, Kent, ME16 8PS
Tel: 01622 675153

Fashion and homewares shop for all the family

Hours Mon–Fri 10–8, Sat 9–6, Sun 11–5

Discount up to
50%

Margate

Peter Newman Factory Shop

154 North Down Road, Cliftonville, Margate, Kent,
CT9 2QN
Tel: 01843 298022

Footwear

Hours Mon–Sat 9–5:30

Labels Dr Martens, Clarks, Hi-Tec,
Lotus

Discount up to
35%

Parking Yes

Ramsgate

Alexon Sale Shop

64 The High Street, Ramsgate, Kent, CT11 9RS
Tel: 01843 589860

Women's clothes. Last year's stock

Hours Mon–Sat 9–5:30

Labels Alexon, Eastex, Calico,
Dash

Discount
40%–70%

Sevenoaks

Déjà Vu

Old Seal House, 19 Church Street, Seal, Nr. Sevenoaks,
Kent, TN15 0DA
Tel: 01732 762155

Designer and middle-market ladies' almost new clothes.
Max. age 2–3 years old or less. Small selection children's
2–8 years. Ski wear in season – not boots. Jewellery and
accessories

Hours Tue–Sat 10–4:30

Closed Christmas and Bank Holidays

➡ Just off A25 at Seal, near Sevenoaks. Short parking
'Yeoman' pub

Public Transport A25 Seal

Labels Paul Costelloe, Bianca,
Karen Millen, Betty Barclay,
Jaeger, Guy Laroche, Max Mara

Discount
30%–70%

& No, **Group Tours** No, **Mail order** No, **Catalogue** No, ✕
Coffee, lunches at 'Yeoman' pub, **Internet Sales** No

Sittingbourne

Michelsons

Staplehurst Road, Sittingbourne, Kent, ME10 2NH
Tel: 01795 426821

Largest tie manufacturers

Hours Fri 9–12

Labels Rifat Ozbek, Missoni,
Coppersheat, Dolce Gabbana,
Blundell, Isney, Sonia Rykiel

Discount up to
30%

Tunbridge Wells

Panache

90–92 High Street, Tunbridge Wells, Kent, TN1 1YF
Tel: 01892 522883

Women's clothes. Panache has been established for many years in the High Street. Customers come from as far afield as Cornwall to buy and sell

Hours Mon–Sat 10–5

Closed All Bank Holidays

➡ Panache is situated in the historic old High Street at the south end, next door to Cafe Uno and opposite Pizza Express

Discount
50%–80%

Labels Chanel, Joseph, Max Maria, Jasper Conran, Escada, D & G, Jaeger, Basler, Yarrel

♿ Yes, **Group Tours** No, **Mail order** No, **Catalogue** No, ✗ Refreshments on site, **Internet Sales** No

Tunbridge Wells

The Italian Wardrobe

2–4 Castle Street, Tunbridge Wells, Kent, TN1 1XJ
Tel: 01892 514143 Fax: 01892 514143

We stock eveningwear, suits, jeans and casualwear all with up to 15% off normal retail prices

Hours Mon–Sat 10–5

Closed Christmas Day, Boxing Day, New Year's Day

➡ From Tunbridge Wells station turn right into High Street. Castle Street is the first cobbled street on the right

Public Transport Tunbridge Wells station.

Discount
50%–75%

Labels Marella, Max Mara, Armani, Moschino, Sportmax, Iceburg, Valentino, around 50 more

♿ No, **Group Tours** No, **Mail order** No, **Catalogue** No, ✗ Lots of small cafes nearby., **Internet Sales** No

London

Designer Sales UK

London
Tel: 020 7226 7437

Men's and women's clothes

Hours Telephone

Discount
80%–90%

Labels Osh Kosh, Oilily, Gap, Next, Mondi

Bayswater, Kensington and Knightsbridge

American Classics

404 King's Road, London, SW10 0LJ
Tel: 020 7351 5229

Sells vintage clothes from '50s, '60s, '70s for men and women

Hours Mon–Sat 10–6:30, Sun 12–5

Discount

Labels Ralph Lauren, Levi's

Bayswater, Kensington and Knightsbridge

Bertie Golightly (UK) Ltd

48 Beauchamp Place, Near Harrods, London, SW3 1NX
Tel: 020 7584 7270 Fax: 020 7584 7270

Women's clothes. Hermes, Chanel, YSL, Christian Dior, Ungaro, Valentino, Akris, Prada, Gucci, Louis Vuitton, Jean Muir, Bruce Oldfield, I.S.E., Loewe, Thomas Starzewski, Armani, Massoni, Lacroix, Escada and many more, plus accessories. Eveningwear a speciality

Hours Mon–Sat 10–6

Closed Bank Holidays

➜ Knightsbridge tube, past Harrods, 3 streets

Public Transport Knightsbridge tube. Selection of buses to Sloane Street, Knightsbridge

See ad on page 51

Discount

20%–30%

Labels As above

Parking Parking meters, ♿ No, **Group Tours** Yes, **Mail order** No, **Catalogue** No, ✗ Plenty, **Internet Sales** Yes

---

Bayswater, Kensington and Knightsbridge

Catherine Grosvenor Designs

3 Elystan Street, Chelsea Green, London, SW3 3NT
Tel: 020 7584 2112

Men's, women's and children' s designer knitwear at competitive prices; made-to-measure service

Hours Mon–Fri 10–5:30, Sat 10–5

Discount

see text

Bayswater, Kensington and Knightsbridge

Chiceria and Chiceria Casa

93 Wandsworth Bridge Road, Fulham, London, SW6 4SW
Tel: 020 7371 0697

New and nearly-new designer clothes and accessories. Also range of quality household goods and soft furnishings

Hours Mon–Fri 11–7, Sat 10–5

Discount

Labels Chiceria Casa

see text

Bayswater, Kensington and Knightsbridge

Designer Bargains

29 Kensington Church Street, Kensington, London, W8 4LL
Tel: 020 7795 6777

Women's clothes. Top labels

Hours Mon–Sat 10–6:30

Labels Armani, Escada, Chanel, Dolce, Gucci, Versace

Discount

see text

Bayswater, Kensington and Knightsbridge

Hang Ups

366 Fulham Road, London, SW10 9UU
Tel: 020 7351 0047

High fashion designer labels, plus vintage clothes for women

Hours Mon–Fri 11–6:45, Sat 10.30–6

Labels Escade, Chanel, Azzedine, Aliai, Ghost, Gaultier

Discount

see text

Bayswater, Kensington and Knightsbridge

Joseph Clearance Shop

53 Kings Road, London, SW3 1QN
Tel: 020 7730 7562

Women's clothes. Clearance and end-of-season lines

Hours Mon–Fri 10:30–6:30, Wed 12–5, Sat open until 7

Labels Joseph, Gucci, Helmut Lang

Discount up to

70%

London & South-East England London

Bayswater, Kensington and Knightsbridge

La Scala

35, 37, 39 Elystan Street, London, SW3 3NT
Tel: 020 7589 2784

Men's, women's and children's clothes

Hours Mon–Sat 10–5:30

Labels Armani, Valentino, Boss

Discount

see text

Bayswater, Kensington and Knightsbridge

Levy and Friend

47 Sloane Avenue, off King's Road, London, SW3 3DH
Tel: 020 7589 9741

Women's designer clothes and accessories

Hours Tue–Sat 11–5

Labels Valentino, Escade, Ferragamo

Discount

see text

Bayswater, Kensington and Knightsbridge

Lunn Antiques Ltd

86 New King's Road, Parsons Green, London, SW6 4LU
Tel: 020 7736 4638

Largest stockist of antique and modern linen

Hours Mon–Sat 10–6

Discount
see text

Bayswater, Kensington and Knightsbridge

Notting Hill Housing Trust

309 Fulham Road, London, SW10 9QH
Tel: 020 7352 2986

Men's and women's clothes. Charity shop featuring top designers

Hours Mon–Sat 10–6, Sun 12–4

Labels Mondi, Versace

Discount
see text

OUTRAGEOUS
PRICES TO SCREAM ABOUT!
TOP FASHIONS • LOADSALABELS • DESIGNER BRANDS
ALL AT PRICES THAT ARE TRULY OUTRAGEOUS

160 OXFORD STREET, LONDON • 273 WALWORTH ROAD, LONDON • UNIT 160 MEADOWHALL, SHEFFIELD • 75 HIGH STREET, BROMLEY, KENT • 5 KENSINGTON CHURCH STREET, LONDON • 104 KENSINGTON HIGH STREET, LONDON • 83-85 BROMPTON ROAD, KNIGHTSBRIDGE • 22 SLOANE STREET, LONDON • 113 NORTH END, CROYDON • 18 RYE LANE, PECKHAM • 173 HIGH STREET, HOUNSLOW • 3A GEORGE STREET, RICHMOND, SURREY

OUTLET

London & South-East England

Bayswater, Kensington and Knightsbridge

Outlet

104 Kensington High Street, London

Top fashions. All labels. Designer brands. All at prices that are truly outrageous

See ad on page 53

Discount
see text

Bayswater, Kensington and Knightsbridge

Outlet

5 Kensington Church Street, London

Top fashions. All labels. Designer brands. All at prices that are truly outrageous

See ad on page 53

Discount
see text

Bayswater, Kensington and Knightsbridge

Outlet

83–85 Brompton Road, Knightsbridge, London

Top fashions. All labels. Designer brands. All at prices that are truly outrageous

See ad on page 53

Discount
see text

Bayswater, Kensington and Knightsbridge

Pamela's

16 Beauchamp Place, London, SW3 1MQ
Tel: 020 7589 6852

Selection of French and Italian designer labels for women

Hours Mon–Sat 10–5

Labels Chanel, Valentino, Jaeger

Discount
see text

London & South-East England

Pandora

16–22 Cheval Place, London, SW7 1ES
Tel: 020 7589 5289

Women's clothes and accessories

Hours Mon–Sat 9–6, Open most Bank Holidays

Discount

Labels Armani, Chanel, Ghost, Escade, Valentino

20%–30%

Philip of King's Road

191 King's Road, London, SW3 5ED
Tel: 020 7352 4332

Men's and ladies' clothes, sportswear and sports equipment. Specialists in American clothing

Hours Mon–Fri 10–6:30, Sat 10–7

Discount

Labels Levi's

see text

Salou

6 Cheval Place, London, SW7 1ES
Tel: 020 7581 2380

Women's clothes. Two-storey shop sells evening wear and separates downstairs

Hours Mon–Sat 10–5

Discount

Labels Chanel, Armani, Valentino, Moschino

see text

Sign of the Times

17 Elystan Street, London, SW3 3NT
Tel: 020 7589 4774

Women's clothes

Hours Mon–Sat 10–6, Wed late until 7.30

Discount

Labels Chanel, Escade, R. Lauren, YSL, J. Muir, G. Armani

see text

Bayswater, Kensington and Knightsbridge

Steinberg & Tolkein

193 King's Road, London, SW3 5EB
Tel: 020 7376 3660

Men's clothes and jewellery

Hours Mon–Sat 10:30–7, Sun 12–6.30

Discount

Bayswater, Kensington and Knightsbridge

Sunglass Hut International

Kings Walk Mall, 122 Kings Road, London, SW3
Tel: 020 7225 3150

Quality sunglasses

Hours Mon–Sat 10:30–6:30, Sun 12–6

Labels Ray-Ban, Oakley, Bolle,
Armani, Sungear, Georgio Armani

Discount

Bayswater, Kensington and Knightsbridge

The Corridor

309A King's Road, London, SW3
Tel: 020 7351 0772

Small personalised boutique for women

Labels Chanel, Valentino,
R. Lauren

Discount

Bayswater, Kensington and Knightsbridge

The Designer Store

289 King's Road, London, SW3 5EN
Tel: 020 7351 0880

Italian, German and French designer labels for women

Hours Mon–Sat 10:30–6:30, Sun 12–5

Discount

see text

London & South-East England

The Dress Box

8–10 Cheval Place, London, SW7 1ES
Tel: 020 7589 2240

Men's and women's clothing

Hours Mon–Fri 10–6, Sat 10.30–6

Labels YSL, Chanel, Gucci, Valentino

Discount

see text

The Dresser

10 Porchester Place, London, W2 2BS
Tel: 020 7724 7212

Second-hand designer clothes for men and women

Hours Mon–Sat 11–5:30

Labels Armani, YSL, P Smith

Discount

see text

The Make-Up Centre

26 Bute Street, London, SW7 3EX
Tel: 020 7584 2188

Make-up

Hours Mon–Fri 10–6:30, Sat 10–5:30

Discount

see text

The Wedding Shop

171 Fulham Road, London, SW3 6JW
Tel: 020 7838 0171

Wedding dresses

Hours Mon–Fri 9:30–6, Sat by appointment only

Labels Jasper, Armani

Discount up to

60%

Bayswater, Kensington and Knightsbridge

Twentieth Century Rox

614 Fulham Road, London, SW6 5RP
Tel: 020 7731 3242

Women's clothes

Hours Mon, Wed, Thur 10-7, Tues, Fri, Sat 10–6

Discount

Bayswater, Kensington and Knightsbridge

Vidal Sassoon Staff Training

Whiteleys of Bayswater, 151 Queensway, London, W2 4SB
Tel: 020 7318 5205

Hairdressing. Please make an appointment

Hours Mon–Sat 10–3

Discount

see text

Bloomsbury and City

Adam Richwood

5 Garden Walk, Shoreditch, London, EC2A 3EQ
Tel: 020 7729 0976 Fax: 020 7729 7296
Email: adamrichwood@bigfoot.com

A full range of period furniture from open bookcases of any size to bureaux, desks, chests, TV and Hi-Fi cabinets in a variety of woods. Commissions undertaken

Hours Mon–Fri 7–4

Closed Weekends and national holidays

➡ Garden Walk is situated off Great Eastern Street, 10 minutes walk from Liverpool Street mainline station or 5 minutes walk from Old Street tube station

Public Transport Old Street tube. Liverpool Street station

Discount up to

50%

Parking 8 Spaces, &. No, **Group Tours** No, **Mail order** No, **Catalogue** No, ✗ Yes, **Internet Sales** No

---

Bloomsbury and City

Angels and Bermans

119 Shaftesbury Avenue, London, WC2H 8AE
Tel: 020 7836 5678

Costumier to the public. Men's and women's clothes for hire

Hours Mon–Fri 9–5:30

Discount

London & South-East England

Bloomsbury and City

Annies

10 Camden Passage, Islington, London, N1 8DU
Tel: 020 7359 0796

Women's clothes, late Victorian times to the forties

Hours Mon, Tues, Thur, Fri 11–6 and Wed and Sat 9–6

Discount

see text

Bloomsbury and City

Blackout II

51 Endell Street, Covent Garden, London, WC2
Tel: 020 7240 5006

Specialist in '60s & '70s gear for men and women

Hours Mon–Fri 11–7, Sat 11.30–6.30

Discount

see text

Bloomsbury and City

Bumpsadaisy Maternity Style

43 Covent Garden Market, Covent Garden, London, WC2E 8HA
Tel: 020 7379 9831

Maternity wear

Hours Mon–Sat 10–6, Thur late until 7.30

Discount

see text

Bloomsbury and City

Butterfield 8

4 Ravey Street, London, EC2 4QP
Tel: 020 7739 3026

Period fancy dress for men and women

Hours Mon, Thur, Fri 11–6

Discount

see text

Bloomsbury and City

Butterfly

28 Old Bailey, London, EC4M 7HS
Tel: 020 7489 8288

Mainly size 10–12 designer clothes for women

Hours Wed–Fri 11:30–4, Tues 11–6:30

Labels Dusk, Caroline Roumer, Diana Gee, Frank Usher, August Silk

Discount
see text

Bloomsbury and City

Cenci

31 Monmouth Street, London, WC2 HDD
Tel: 020 7836 1400

Shop selling vintage clothes from '40s–'70s for men and women

Hours Mon–Fri 10:30–7, Sat 10.30–6:30

Discount
see text

Bloomsbury and City

City Clothing

1–5 Bread Street, Cheapside, London, EC4
Tel: 020 7248 1809

Moss Bros group that hires and sells morning suits, suits, shirts, wedding suits, dinner suits, overcoats and ties for men

Hours Mon–Fri 9–6

Discount up to

50%

Bloomsbury and City

G Thornfield

321 Grays Inn Road, London, WC1X 8PX
Tel: 020 7837 2771 Fax: 020 7278 2515
Email: dday@dircon.co.uk

Full framing service. Made to measure and clip frames also available. Large print and poster range. Also large wallpaper specialist. We mix all the Dulux range of 1700 colours and have in-store advice service. Established for over 40 years

Hours Mon–Fri 10–6, Sat –2

Closed All public holidays

➜ Directly opposite Kings Cross station, at the beginning of Grays Inn Road, just next to Scala club. Lots of side street parking

Public Transport Kings Cross station, many buses stop just outside

Labels Dulux, Sanderson, Coles, Harlequin, Vymura, Doshi

Discount
20%–50%

Parking 3 Spaces, ♿ No, **Group Tours** No, **Mail order** Yes, **Catalogue** No, ✗ Both sides – cafés, bars, **Internet Sales** Yes

Bloomsbury and City

Lipsmans Hire Department

22 Charing Cross Road, London, WC2
Tel: 020 7240 2310

Hires, and sells ex-hire outfits to men

Hours Mon–Fri 10–6, Sat 10–5

Discount
see text

Bloomsbury and City

Lunn Antiques Ltd

22 Cucumber Alley, Thomas Neal's, Shorts Garden,
Covent Garden, London, WC2 9LD
Tel: 020 7379 1974

Largest stockist of antique and modern linen

Hours Mon–Sat 10:30–6:30

Discount
see text

Bloomsbury and City

Mansfield/Cache d'Or

174 Old Street, London, EC1
Tel: 020 7253 6031

Women's clothes. Telephone for automatic invitation

Hours By invitation

Discount
see text

Bloomsbury and City

Moss Bros

27 King Street, Covent Garden, London, WC2E 8JD
Tel: 020 7240 4567

Own-label ex-hire department for men

Hours Mon–Fri 9–5:30, Sat 9–7

Discount
see text

Bloomsbury and City

Screenface

48 Monmouth Street, London, WC2
Tel: 020 7836 3955

Make-up

Hours Mon–Sat 11–7, Sun 12.30–6

Discount

Bloomsbury and City

Studio 201

201 Kings Road, London, SW3
Tel: 020 7376 3672

Women's clothes, handbags and accessories. Mostly Italian designer labels

Hours Mon–Sat 10:30–6:30, Sun 12–5

Labels Max Mara

Discount

Bloomsbury and City

The Designer Warehouse Sale for Women and Men

Roger Dack Ltd, Studio 2, Shepperton House, 83 Shepperton Road, London
Tel: 020 7704 1064 Fax: 020 7704 1379
Email: dwslondon@aol.com
Web site: www.dwslondon.co.uk

The Designer Warehouse Sales stock 80+ contemporary labels, direct from designers, at around two thirds off retail prices. Established designers: Nicole Farhi, John Rocha, Ally Capellino, Jasper Conran, Browns, Workers For Freedom, Jill Sander, Paul Smith. Samples, one-offs for the catwalk and current collections make up rails of clothing displayed in four studios. Communal changing rooms. Two fabric sales offer sample lengths and end of rolls from over 40 of England's top designers

Hours Specific dates and times – details on request

➜ Situated at The Worx, 45 Balfe Street, London N1 9EF

Public Transport Kings Cross tube

See ad on page 63

Discount

Labels Nicole Farhi, Paul Smith, Betty Jackson, Ghost, Jasper Conran, John Rocha, Donna Karan

25%–80%

Parking Meters, ♿ Yes, **Group Tours** No, **Mail order** No, **Catalogue** No, ✕ Kings Cross station, **Internet Sales** No

Bloomsbury and City

The Frock Shop

47 Bushfield Street, Spitalfields, London, E1 6AA
Tel: 020 7247 4222

Dress agency dealing with city women

Hours Tues, Thur, Fri 11–6.30, Wed 1–5:30

Labels Gucci, Prada, M Blahnik

Discount

The Designer Warehouse Sales for Men and Women

The biggest and best of all the designer sales, the 13 annual Designer Warehouse Sales are held in vast photographic studios in North London. Over 80 internationally renowned designer labels at greatly reduced prices.

> **The Independent Newspaper said:**
>
> *'These are a fashion insider's secret, every fashion fan's dream. A huge warehouse full of designer confections.'*

Women's wear	Men's wear	Fabric
11–13 February	18–20 February	2–4 March
7–9 April	14–16 April	
16–18 June	23–25 June	
22–24 September	29 Sept – 1 Oct	12–14 October
1–3 December	8–10 December	

The Worx, 45 Balfe Street, London N1 9EF

Opening times: Fri 10 am – 8 pm, Sat 10 am – 6 pm, Sun 11 am – 5 pm. Entrance £2

For futher information and registering on the Mailing List:
Tel: 020 7704 1064

Bloomsbury and City

The Loft

35 Monmouth Street, Covent Garden, London, WC2H 9DD,
Tel: 020 7240 3807
Email: mark.woolf@virgin.net and theloft2001@bigfoot.com

Most of our items have only been used on catwalks or film sets, but are sold at approx. one third of original price. We also buy designer clothes from the public who have items they no longer wear

Hours Mon–Sat 11–6, Sun 12 noon–5

Closed Christmas Day, Boxing Day and New Year's Day

➜ Go down Neal Street opposite Covent Garden tube station. Turn left up Shorts Gardens to Seven Dials roundabout. Turn right up Monmouth Street

Public Transport Covent Garden

Discount see text

Labels Prada, Paul Smith, Gucci, Joseph, Nicole Farhi, Versace, V. Westwood, Dolce & Gabbana

♿ Yes, **Group Tours** No, **Mail order** Yes, **Catalogue** No,
✗ Various places within Covent Garden, **Internet Sales** No

London & South-East England London

Bloomsbury and City

Stockhouse

101–105 Goswell Road, London, EC1V 7ER
Tel: 020 7253 5761/2 Fax: 020 7251 1680
Email: stockhouse@compuserve.com

Men's clothes. Suppliers to the trade now offering to supply direct to the public at heavily discounted prices. Full VAT returned for exports outside EEC. Clearing lines available

Hours Mon–Fri 9–5, Wed and Thur late until 6, Sun 9–2

Closed Bank Holidays

➡ Nearest tube station Barbican. Nearest main line stations Kings Cross and Euston

Public Transport Buses pass door

See ad on page 65

Discount

Labels Mario Barutti, Pierre Balmain, Xen, Ben Sherman, James Barry, Aldo Bernadi, Hom

Parking Few, & Yes, **Group Tours** Yes, **Mail order** No, **Catalogue** No, ✗ Pub, coffee house near, **Internet Sales** Yes

Bloomsbury and City

Wallers

21–24 Newport Court, Charing Cross Road, London, WC2H 7JS
Tel: 020 7437 1665 Fax: 020 7437 2057

Specialising in men's jackets, coats and casuals. Also dresswear. Famous brands at discounted prices. Large and small sizes a speciality

Hours Mon–Fri 9–5:30, Sat 9–4:30

Closed Christmas Day

➡ 50 yards from Leicester Square tube, just off Charing Cross Road

Public Transport Leicester Square

Discount

Labels Odermark, Maddison, Austin Reed, Savile Row

& No, **Group Tours** No, **Mail order** Yes, **Catalogue** Yes, **Internet Sales** No

Central London

Bertie Wooster

284 Fulham Road, London, SW10 9EW
Tel: 020 7352 5662

Second-hand and new clothes for men and luggage at low prices

Hours Mon, Wed and Fri 10–6, Tues and Thur 10–7, Sat 10–5

Discount
see text

Central London

Browns Labels for Less

50 and 62 South Molton Street, London, W1Y 1DA
Tel: 020 7409 7142

Men's and women's clothing

Hours Mon–Sat 10–6, Thur late until 7

Labels Rifat Ozbek, Missoni, Copperwheat, Dolce Gabbana, Blundell, Issey, Sonia Rykiel

Discount 50%–80%

Central London

Butterfly

28A Ponsonby Place, London, SW1
Tel: 020 7821 1983

Mainly size 10–12 women's designer clothes

Hours Wed–Fri 12–6:30, Thur late until 7:30

Labels Dusk, Caroline Roumer,
Diana Gee, Frank Usher, August
Silk

Discount
see text

Central London

Cassis

21 Upper Tachbrook Street, off Warwick Way, Pimlico,
London, SW1V 1SN

Designer label and good-quality clothes for women

Hours Tue–Sat 10–6, Thur late until 7

Labels Nicole Farhi, Joseph,
Moschino, Versace, Liberty, Jaeger,
Max Mara, Alexon, Valentino

Discount
see text

Central London

Catwalk Nearly-New Designer Clothes

52 Blandford Street, London, W1H 3HD
Tel: 020 7935 1052

Nearly-new designer clothes and accessories for women

Hours Mon 12:30–6, Tues, Wed and Fri 11:15–6, Thur 11:15–7, Sat 11:15–5

Labels Chanel, Gucci, Ghost, Armani

Discount

Central London

Cerruti 1881

23 Old Bond Street, London, W1
Tel: 020 7491 1881

Women's clothes. Telephone or write to get on to mailing list for an invitation to showrooms

Discount

see text

Central London

Cornucopia

12 Upper Tachbrook Street, London, SW1
Tel: 020 7828 5752

Specialises in glamorous evening wear for women

Hours Mon–Sat 11–6

Discount

see text

Central London

Discount Dressing

58 Baker Street, London, W1
Tel: 020 7486 7230

Women's clothes. German, Italian and French designer labels at 50–90% below normal outlets

Hours Mon–Sun 10–6

Discount

50%–90%

London & South-East England

Central London

Feminella Blouses

26 Eastcastle Street, London, W1
Tel: 020 7636 7991

Women's clothes. Telephone or write for an invitation

Hours Telephone or write

Discount
see text

Central London

FOFO Club

23 Old Bond Street, London, W1X 3DA
Tel: 020 7499 5132

Men's and women's clothes. Membership only

Hours By invitation

Discount
see text

Central London

Frank Usher

7 Noel Street, London, W1
Tel: 020 7287 0800

Women's clothes. Telephone or write for mailing list

Hours By invitation only

Discount
see text

for road maps...

www.WestOneWeb.com

...great offers

Central London

Gertrude Fashions

84 Wilton Road, Victoria, London, SW1V 1DL
Tel: 020 7834 6933 Fax: 01932 860 867

Women's clothes. Samples of Italian, German and French labels

Hours Mon–Sat 10–5:50

Closed Christmas from 24th–28th December and New Year's Day

➡ Come out of Victoria Station. Walk 200 yards down Wilton Road. Just by the traffic lights

Public Transport Victoria station

Labels Basler, Marcona, Ara, Weill, Gina, Flick,

Discount
25%–75%

& Yes, **Group Tours** Yes, **Mail order** No, **Catalogue** No, ✕ Cafes nearby, **Internet Sales** No

Central London

L'Homme Designer Exchange

50 Blandford Street, London, W1H 3HD
Tel: 020 7224 3266 Fax: 020 7224 3268

Men's clothes at a fraction of the retail price. Prada, Gucci, Yohgi, Comme, Gaultier, Hermes, Versace, Armani, Dolce Gabbana suits, jackets, club wear, casual, formal. Ties, shoes, accessories as well. Stock changes daily

Hours Mon–Fri 11–6, Thur late until 7, Sat 11–5, Sun 11–5

Closed Christmas Day, New Year, Bank Holidays

➡ Nearest tube – Baker Street. 4 roads down from Marylebone Road. 4 roads up from Oxford Street (Selfridges) 5–10 minutes walk

Public Transport Baker Street, Bond Street tubes

Labels Prada, Armani, Gucci, Dolce Gabbana, Versace, Gaultier, Miyake

Discount
30%–70%

& No, **Group Tours** No, **Mail order** No, **Catalogue** No, **Internet Sales** No

Central London

Oakville

Fifth Floor, 32–36 Great Portland Street, London, W1
Tel: 020 7580 3686

Women's clothes. Telephone for an invitation

Hours By invitation

Discount
see text

Central London

One Night Stand

44 Pimlico Road, London, SW1W 8LP
Tel: 020 7730 8708

Women's clothes

Hours Mon–Fri 10–6:30, Sat 10–5. Appointments preferred

Discount

London & South-East England

Central London

Outlet

160 Oxford Street, London

Top fashions. All labels. Designer brands. All at prices that are truly outrageous

See ad on page 53

Discount

Central London

Outlet

22 Sloane Street, London

Top fashions. All labels. Designer brands. All at prices that are truly outrageous

See ad on page 53

Discount

see text

Central London

Oxfam Origin

26 Ganton Street, London, W1
Tel: 020 7437 7338

Men's and women's clothes. Sells Retro and High Street clothing

Hours Mon–Sat 11–6

Discount

see text

Labels Levi's

Central London

Paul Smith Sale Shop

23 Avery Row, London, W1
Tel: 020 7493 1287

Menswear. Seconds, end of lines and wide selection of accessories

Hours Mon–Sat 10–6, Thur late until 7

Discount

40%–75%

Labels R Newbold

Central London

Proibito

52 South Molton Street, London, W1
Tel: 020 7491 3244

Women's clothes

Hours Mon–Sun 10–7

Labels Moschino, Fendi, Gianfranco
Ferre, Armani, Versace, Christian
Lacroix, Iceberg, Dolce Gabbana

Discount

Central London

Sally Hair & Beauty Supplies

81 Shaftesbury Avenue, London, W1V 7AD

Huge range of hair products, hair styling and beauty
supplies

Hours Mon–Sat 9–6, Sun 11–3

Discount

Central London

The Exchange Dress Agency

30 Elizabeth Street, Belgravia, London, SW1
Tel: 020 7730 3334

Women's cothes. All profits go to charity;
all top designers

Hours Mon–Sat 10–4, Thur late until 7

Discount

Central London

Vidal Sassoon School of Hairdressing

56 Davies Mews, London, W1Y 1AS
Tel: 020 7318 5205

Hairdressing. Please make an appointment

Hours Mon–Fri 10–3

Discount

London & South-East England

Real Nappy Association

PO Box 3704, London, SE26 4RX
Tel: 020 8299 4519
Web site: www.realnappy.com

For a FREE parents info pack send a large s.a.e. with 2 stamps on it

Discount

London North and East

Alexon Sale Shop

Shopping City, Wood Green, London, N22
Tel: 020 8889 9560

Alexon and Eastex from previous seasons for women

Hours Mon–Sat 9–5:30

Labels Alexon, Eastex

Discount

 10%–70%

London North & East

Baby Direct Discount Warehouse

8 Cromwell Centre, 10 River Road, Barking, London
Tel: 020 8507 0572 Fax: 020 8591 5539

Pram warehouse

Hours Mon–Sat 9–5, Sun 10–2

Public Transport Barking station

Labels Mamas & Papas, Silver Cross, McClaren

Discount

Parking Yes, ﹠ No, **Group Tours** No, **Mail order** Yes, **Catalogue** Yes, **Internet Sales** No

London North and East

Benny Dee (City) Ltd

112–114 Kilburn High Road, London, NW6 4HY
Tel: 020 7624 2995

Men's, women's and children's clothes and household goods. End of lines and bankrupt stock

Hours Mon–Sat 9–6, Sun 10–4

Labels Zorbit, Baby Togs, Mothercare, Grasshopper, Baby Gap, M & S

Discount

see text

London & South-East England

London

London North and East

Benny Dee (City) Ltd

136–138 Walthamstow High Street, London, E17 1JS
Tel: 020 8520 4637

Men's, women's and children's clothes and household goods. End of lines and bankrupt stock

Hours Mon–Sat 9–6

Labels Zorbit, Baby Togs, Mothercare, Grasshopper, Baby Gap, M&S

Discount

London North and East

Benny Dee (City) Ltd

4–6 High Road, Wood Green, London, N22 6BX
Tel: 020 8881 8101

Men's, women's and children's clothes and household goods. End of lines and bankrupt stock

Hours Mon–Sat 9–6, Sun 10–4

Labels Zorbit, Baby Togs, Mothercare, Grasshopper, Baby Gap, M & S

Discount

London North and East

Benny Dee (City) Ltd

74–80 Middlesex Street, London, E1
Tel: 020 7377 9067

Men's, women's and children's clothes and household goods. End of lines or bankrupt stock with labels out

Hours Mon–Fri 10–4, Sat 9–4

Labels Zorbit, Baby Togs, Berlei, Mothercare, Grasshopper, Gossard, Baby Gap, M&S, Warner

Discount

London North and East

Burberrys

29–53 Chatham Place, Hackney, London, E9 6LP
Tel: 020 8985 3344

Men's, women's and children's clothes

Hours Mon–Fri 11–6, Sat 9–3:30, Sun 11–5

Discount

see text

Change of Heart

59B–59C Park Road, London, N8 8DP
Tel: 020 8341 1575 Fax: 020 8341 1835
Email: maryley@globalnet.com

Clothes for all the family and accessories. Interiors, cushions, vases, candlesticks

Hours Mon–Sat 10–6, Sun 10–4

Closed Christmas and New Year

➔ Finsbury Park tube, bus

Discount

Labels Nicole Farhi, Prada, Ghost, Armani, Max Mara, Oasis, Whistles, Joseph, Jigsaw

40%–75%

& Yes, **Group Tours** No, **Mail order** No, **Catalogue** No, ✗ Banners restaurant and others, **Internet Sales** No

Choice Discount Stores Ltd

26–28 High Street, Barkingside, Ilford, London, IG6 2DD
Tel: 020 8551 2125

Men's, women's and children's clothes

Hours Mon–Sat 9–5:30, Sun 10–4

See ad on page 75

Discount up to

Labels Next

50%

Clothes Direct

48B Hendon Lane, Finchley, London, N3 1TT
Tel: 020 8889 9560

Warehouse selling Italian brand-name clothes for men at discount prices

Hours Mon–Fri 9–7, Sat mail order only

Discount

see text

London & South-East England

London North and East

Cobwebs

60 Islington Park Street, London, N1
Tel: 020 7359 8090

Small shop selling secondhand clothes in very English style for men and women

Hours Tue–Sat 11–5

Discount

London North and East

Dash Sale Shop

Wood Green Shopping Centre, London, N22 6YQ
Tel: 020 8889 9560

Women's clothes. Alexon and Eastex ends of range and seconds; Dash

Hours Mon–Fri 9–5:30, Sat 9–6

Labels Dash, Alexon, Eastex

Discount up to

50%

London North and East

Discount Dressing

16 Sussex Ring, Woodside Park, London, N12
Tel: 020 8343 8343

German, Italian and French designer labels for women

Hours Mon–Sun 10–6

Discount

50%–90%

London North and East

Dress Circle

2 Leverton Place, London, NW5 2PL
Tel: 020 7284 3967

Nearly-new clothing for adults and children

Hours Mon–Sat 10–6

Discount

London & South-East England

London North and East

46 Church Road, Leyton, London, E10 5JP
Tel: 020 8539 6872

Shoes imported from Italy and Spain

Hours Mon–Sat 10–4

Discount

London North and East

The Broadway, Muswell Hill, London
Tel: 020 8883 9122

High Street shop selling Principles, Top Shop, French
Connection and Oasis for women

Hours Mon–Sat 9:30–6, Sun 1–3

Labels Principles, Top Shop, Oasis,
French Connection

Discount

London North and East

18 The Grangeway, Grange Park, London, N21 2HG
Tel: 020 8360 3447

Ladieswear. Labels and accessories

Hours Tue–Sat 9:30–5

Labels Escade, Principles, Next,
Monsoon

Discount

London North and East

Hubbinet Reproductions

Unit 7, Hubbinet Industrial Estate, Eastern Avenue West,
Romford, London, RM7 7NV
Tel: 01708 762 212 Fax: 01708 766 511

Makers of quality traditional and reproduction furniture
in hand finished mahogany and yew wood veneer.
Bookcases, library bookcases, dining sets, desks, bureaux,
TV, hi-fi and video units, occasional tables. Advice on
furnishings. Factory seconds and export rejects at up to
50% off.

Hours Mon–Fri 9–5, Sat 10–4, Sun telephone
for information

See ad on page 77

Discount

see
text

Hubbinet Reproductions

Makers of quality traditional & reproduction furniture in hand finished mahogany and yew wood veneer. Over 100 models of bookcases (from £80), library bookcases (from £500), dining sets (from £600), desks, bureaux, TV, hi-fi and video units (from £200), occasional tables. Advice on furnishings.
'Factory seconds and export rejects at up to 50% off. Modify & colour to customers' requirements. January, April, Nov sales.'

Open: Mon–Fri 9–5; Sat 10–4; Sun 'phone for information

Hubbinet Reproductions, Unit 7, Hubbinet Ind. Estate,
Eastern Avenue West, Romford RM7 7NV
Tel: (01708) 762 212   Fax: (01708) 766 511

London North and East

I Kinn

80 George Lane, South Woodford, London, E18 1JJ
Tel: 020 8989 2927

Classic women's clothes as sold in stores such as House of Fraser, but at half retail price

Hours Mon–Fri 10–5:30, Sat 10–5, Sun 10:30–1

Closed Christmas Day, Boxing Day, Good Friday, Easter Monday

➔ 50 yards from South Woodford underground, bottom end of George Lane

Public Transport South Woodford underground (Central line)

	Discount from
Labels Stock varies from week to week	**50%**

Parking Many, ♿ No, **Group Tours** No, **Mail order** No, **Catalogue** No, **Internet Sales** No

London North and East

Losners Dress Hire

232 Stamford Hill, London, N16 6TT
Tel: 020 8800 7466

Wedding outfits to hire and buy

Hours Mon, Tues, Fri and Sat 9–5:30, Wed 9–7, Thur 9–5

	Discount
	see text

London & South-East England

Morrys

22 North Mall, Edmonton, London, N9 0EL
Tel: 020 8807 6747

Men's, ladies' and children's clothes, furniture,
sportswear, electrical and household goods, toys,
decorating and sports equipment. Liquidation stock

Hours Mon–Sat 8:30–5

Discount

Nicole Farhi Outlet Shop

75–83 Fairfield Road, Bow, London, E3 2QR
Tel: 020 8980 25681

Samples and seconds from previous season. Merchandise
from Nicole Farhi and French Connection for men and
women

Hours Tues, Wed, Sat 10–3, Thur and Fri 11–6.30

Labels Nicole Farhi, French
Connection

Discount

Sheila Warren-Hill

The Garden Flat, 63 Shepherds Hill, Highgate, London,
N6 5RE
Tel: 020 8348 8282

Second-hand designer clothes for women

Hours By appointment only

Labels Conran, YSL, Escade,
Chanel, Tomasz

Discount

The Costume Studio

Montgomery House, 159–161 Balls Pond Road, Islington,
London, N1 4BG
Tel: 020 7275 9614 Fax: 020 7837 6576
Email: costume.studio@easynet.co.uk

Manufacture and hire of costumes for TV films etc.

Hours Mon–Sat 9:30 am–6

Closed Sundays and Bank Holidays

➜ On main Balls Pond Road close to Essex road and
Southgate Road

Public Transport Highbury and Islington tube. Buses 30,
38, 277

Discount

Parking 4 Spaces, ♿ No, **Group Tours** No, **Mail order** Yes,
Catalogue Yes, ✕ Local café, **Internet Sales** Yes

London & South-East England

The Designer Source

610 Lancaster Road, London, W11 1QG
Tel: 020 7243 2396

Men's and ladies' clothes and accessories

Hours Mon–Sat 10–6

Discount

Labels R Ozbek, P Smith, Galliano, P Campbell

see text

TK Maxx

The Exchange, Ilford, London, 020 8514

Clothing for all the family

Hours Mon–Fri 9:30–6, Wed late until 8, Sat 9–6, Sun 11–5

Discount

see text

& Yes

USA Fashion

117 Fonthill Road, London, N4 3HH
Tel: 020 7272 3992

Women's clothes, sizes from 14 upwards. American designers

Hours Mon–Fri 9:30–5:30, Sat 9:30–4:30

Discount

see text

Valrose

610 Chigwell Road, Woodford Bridge, London, IG5 8AA
Tel: 020 8506 1667

Second-hand dress agency for ladies and children

Hours Tue–Sat 9:30–5

Discount

Labels Escade, Valentino, C. Klein, L. Ashley

see text

London & South-East England

London North and East

Windsmoor Warehouse

Windsmoor House, 83 Lawrence Road, Tottenham,
London, N15 4EP
Tel: 020 8800 8022

Men's and women's clothes. Telephone for mailing list

Hours Mailing lists

Discount up to

75%

Catalogue Yes

London North and West

Anything Goes

293 West End Lane, London, NW6
Tel: 020 7794 2565

Ladieswear. Upmarket labels and classic styles

Hours Tue–Fri 10–6, Sat 10–5:30, Mon 11–6

Discount

Labels Valentino, Chanel, Mondi,
Escade, Max Mara

see text

London North and West

Caroline Charles

9 St John's Wood High Street, London, NW8
Tel: 020 7483 0080

End of season outfits, samples and one-offs from Caroline
Charles for women

Hours Mon–Sat 10–5:30

Discount up to

Labels Caroline Charles

30%

London North and West

Charles Tyrwhitt Shirts

Unit 13, Silver Road, London, W12 7RR
Tel: 020 8735 1000

Jermyn Street shirts for men and women

Hours Mon–Fri 9–9, Sat 10–4

Discount

Labels Jermyn Street

see text

Catalogue Yes

London & South-East England

London North and West

Choice Discount Stores Ltd

67 Golders Green Road, Golders Green, London, NW11 8EL
Tel: 020 8458 8247

Ladies and menswear from Next and Next directory

Hours Tue–Sat 9–6, Sun 11–4

See ad on page 75

Labels Next

Discount up to
50%

London North and West

Damart

63–67 High Street, Hounslow, London
Tel: 020 8570 6796

Men's, women's and children's merchandise and underwear. Everything you will need

Hours Mon–Sat 9:30–5

Discount
see text

London North and West

Designers for Less

203 Uxbridge Road, London, W13 9AA
Tel: 020 8579 5954

Women's clothes. Factory seconds, end of range, samples and previous season's stock; also dresswear hire department. Suits from Germany for men

Hours Mon–Sat 9–6:30

Labels Helmond, Wiclax, Meyer

Discount
see text

London North and West

Designers For Less

203 Uxbridge Road, Ealing, London, W13 9AA
Tel: 020 8579 5954 Fax: 020 8579 4463

Menswear shop dealing mainly in Designer clothes from Germany or Italy. Also featuring suits, trousers, shirts, shoes, ties etc. We aim to sell everything for half price or less, so a suit worth £300–£400 sells for £135

Hours Mon–Sat 9:30–6

➡ Train to Ealing Broadway. Bus E.8 outside station to shop door (5–6 stops). Shop situated at junction of Northfields Avenue and Uxbridge Road

Public Transport Ealing Broadway or Northfields station. E.8, 207 buses stop outside

Labels Baumler, Masterhand, Dior, Zegna, Boss

Discount
50%–65%

&. Yes, **Group Tours** No, **Mail order** No, **Catalogue** No, ✗ Lots of facilities nearby, **Internet Sales** No

London North and West

Designs

60 Rosslyn Hill, London, NW3 1ND
Tel: 020 7435 0100

Armani, Ralph Lauren, Prada, Gucci, Joseph, Nicole Farhi, Issey Miyake, Chanel, TSE, nearly new designer clothes and accessories for women and children

Hours Mon–Sat 10–5:45, Thur late until 6:45

Closed Christmas – 1 week; 3 weeks summer – last week July, first two weeks of August

➡ Hampstead tube (Northern line) – down Hampstead High Street – 7 mins walk – on left

Public Transport Hampstead tube (Northern line)

Discount

Labels Gucci, Nicole Farhi, Armani, Prada, Ralph Lauren, Donna Karan, Issey Miyake, Chanel, Escada

Parking Meters, & Yes, **Group Tours** Yes, **Mail order** No, **Catalogue** No, ✗ Lots of cafés, **Internet Sales** No

London North and West

Dynasty

12A Turnham Green Terrace, Chiswick, London, W4
Tel: 020 8995 3846

Good-quality secondhand clothes for women

Hours Mon–Sat 10:30–5

Discount

London North and West

Dynasty Man

12 Turnham Green Terrace, Chiswick, London, W4 1QP
Tel: 020 8994 4450

Menswear. Sells labels only

Hours Mon–Sat 10:30–5:30

Discount

Labels Jaeger, Boss, Yves St Laurent, Armani

London North and West

Exclusivo

24 Hampstead High Street, Hampstead, London, NW3 1QA
Tel: 020 71 43 18618 Fax: 020 71 43 18618

A long-established designer second-hand store specialising in clothing and accessories as well as new designer samples. Large selection of Chanel, Gucci and Prada, together with High Street fashion

Hours Mon–Sat 10:30–6, Sun 11:30–6

Closed Christmas, New Year

➡ A short walk from Hampstead tube station, opposite main post office in Hampstead

Public Transport Hampstead underground station

Discount

Labels Gucci, Prada, Chanel, Armani, Versace, Westwood, Calvin Klein, Ralph Lauren, Max Mara

& No, **Group Tours** No, **Mail order** No, **Catalogue** No, ✗ Refreshments on site, **Internet Sales** No

London & South-East England

London North and West

Factory Outlet

11 Ealing Broadway, Ealing, London, W5
Tel: 020 8567 9799

High Street shop selling Principles, Top Shop, French
Connection and Oasis for women

Hours Mon–Sat 10–7, Sun 11–5

Labels Principles, French
Connection, Top Shop, Oasis

Discount

 see text

London North and West

Ghost Ltd

263 Kensal Road, London, W10 5DB
Tel: 020 8960 3121

Women's clothes. Telephone for invitation to warehouse

Hours By invitation

Discount

see text

London North and West

Gold's Factory Outlet

108–114 Golders Green Road, London, NW11 8HB
Tel: 020 8905 5721

Men's pinstriped suits, women's suits, blouses, ball gowns

Hours Sun–Fri 10–6

Closed Saturday

Discount

see text

London North and West

Gordons Connections

92–100 High Street, Yewsley, West Drayton, London,
UB7 7DU
Tel: 01895 441846

Well-known High Street brands for men and women

Hours Tues, Thur and Sat 9–6, Fri 9–7

Labels M & S, Principles

Discount up to

70%

London North and West

Hangers

120 Pitshanger Lane, Ealing, London, W5 1QP
Tel: 020 8810 9363

Women's and children's clothes and accessories

Hours Mon–Sat 10–6

Closed Lunch 1–2 daily

Labels Next, Jacques, Escade

Discount see text

London North and West

Jade

22 Hampstead High Street, London, NW3 1QA
Tel: 020 7794 3889

Designer clothes for women; there is a small selection for men

Hours Mon–Sun 10–6:30

Discount see text

London North and West

Jake Clearance Shop

7 Distillery Row, London, W6 9SE
Tel: 020 8237 7006

Hours Fri 10–5

Discount up to 70%

& No, **Catalogue** Yes

London North and West

Joel & Son Fabrics

75–81 Church Street, London, NW8 8EU
Tel: 020 7724 6895

Bridal wear & fabrics

Hours Mon–Sat 8:30–5

Labels St Laurent, Cerruti, Versace

Discount see text

London North and West

John Partridge Outlet Store

9 Perrins Court, Hampstead, London, NW3
Tel: 020 7433 3299

Hardwearing outdoor clothes for men and women

Hours Sat–Sun 12–6

Discount

30%–70%

London North and West

Labels

146 Fleet Road, London, NW3 2QX
Tel: 020 7267 8521

Clothes, accessories, shoes, handbags. Comprehensive selection from mid-market up to Nicole Farhi

Hours Tue–Sat 10–6

Labels Nicole Farhi, Betty Barclay, French Connection, Escade, Gap, Ghost, M & S

Discount

see text

London North and West

Laurel Herman

18a Lambolle Place, London, NW3 4PG

Concept shopping provides you with an unparalleled experience. 99% of customers leave with at least one purchase and a smile – and return! An enormous range of wearable but often unusual Designer clothes – day/evening, work and leisure for all body shapes. Free consultancy and alterations in-house. 2000 regular customers mean that appointments must be made

Hours Mon–Sat 10–10, By appointment only

➡ 5 minutes from Swiss Cottage

Public Transport 5 minutes from Swiss Cottage (Jubilee/District lines) and Belsize Park (Northern line)

Labels All

Discount

30%–85%

& No, **Group Tours** No, **Mail order** No, **Catalogue** No,
✗ On site, and masses locally, **Internet Sales** No

London North and West

Lunn Antiques Ltd

Unit 8, Admiral Vernon Arcade, Portobello Road, London, W11

Largest stockist of antique and modern linen

Hours Sat 7:30–3:30

Discount

see text

London & South-East England

London North and West

Matalan

317 Edgware Road, Cricklewood Broadway, Cricklewood, London, NW2 6PH
Tel: 020 8450 5667

Wide range of products for all the family

Hours Mon–Fri 10–8, Sat 9–6, Sun 11–5

Discount up to
50%

London North and West

Mode

18 Golders Green Road, London, NW11 9PU
Tel: 020 8209 0003

Men's shirts, ties and socks

Hours Mon–Sat 9–6:30

Discount
see text

London North and West

Modern Age Vintage Clothing

65 Chalk Farm Road, London, NW1 8AN
Tel: 020 7482 3787

American secondhand clothing for men and women

Hours Mon–Fri 11–6, Sat and Sun 10–6

Discount
see text

London North and West

Next to Nothing

Unit 11, Arcadi Centre, Ealing Broadway, London, W5 2ND
Tel: 020 8567 2747

Men's, women's and children's clothes. Perfect surplus stock from Next stores and Next directory

Hours Mon–Sat 9:30–6

Labels Next
Discount up to
50%

London

London & South-East England

London North and West

Nightingales Factory Shop

Monterey Place, The Broadway, Mill Hill, London, NW7 3DF
Tel: 020 8906 4366

Smart but casual clothes for women from mail order

Hours Mon–Sat 10–4

Discount

London North and West

Not Quite New

159 Brent Street, Hendon, London, NW4 4DH
Tel: 020 8203 4691

Hours Mon–Fri 10–4:30, Sat 10–1

Closed Wed

Labels Basler, Louis Feraud, Valentino, Yarell, Mondi, Jaeger

Discount

see text

London North and West

Outlet

173 High Street, Hounslow, London

Top fashions. All labels. Designer brands. All at prices that are truly outrageous

See ad on page 53

Discount

see text

London North and West

Penguin Society

144 West End Lane, London, NW6 1SD
Tel: 020 7625 7778 Fax: 020 7794 6383

Serious Continental and British design label and couture fashion not more than 18 months old. Many new and sample 'one offs'. Budget ranges of office, day and evening wear. Deposits accepted

Hours Mon–Fri 11–7, Sat 11–5:30, May–Sept Sun 2–4

Closed Christmas Day, Boxing Day, Easter Monday

➔ Adjacent to Jubilee Line, West Hampstead, Thameslink, West Hampstead and North London Line, West Hampstead. Buses 328, 139 and C11 pass the door

Public Transport As above

Labels Westwood, Joseph, Ghost, N. Farhi, DKNY, Versace, Boss, Calugi, Jasper Conran

Discount 20%–90%

Parking None, ♿ Yes, **Group Tours** No, **Mail order** No, **Catalogue** No, ✗ Starbucks, Café Rouge, **Internet Sales** No

MasterCard VISA

London & South-East England

London

London North and West

Rockit

225 Camden High Street, London, NW1
Tel: 020 7267 3046

Men's and women's clothes. Range of '50s to '80s gear

Hours Mon–Fri 10:30–6:30, Sat and Sun 10–7

Discount

see text

London North and West

Screenface

20 and 24 Powis Terrace, London, W11 1JH
Tel: 020 7221 8289

Make-up

Hours Mon–Sat 9–6

Discount

see text

London North and West

Session

Garden Room, Syon Park, Brentford, London
Tel: 020 8994 4983
Email: cs@compuserve.com

Women's clothes. Telephone for information

Hours Telephone for an appointment

Discount

see text

London North and West

Soviet Carpet And Art Galleries

303–305 Cricklewood Broadway, London, NW2 6PG
Tel: 020 8452 2445 Fax: 020 8450 2642

Oriental rugs from all major countries (Persian, Turkish, etc.); Caucasian rugs and Bukhara – main suppliers in UK. Russian art – oil paintings, prints, ceramics at a fraction of art gallery prices. Thousands of items in stock

Hours Sun–Fri 10:30–5:30, Weekdays and evenings by appointment. Sun no appointment.

Closed Saturdays

➜ On the A5. Nearest side road – Temple Road. 1 mile from North Circular Road (A406), 5 miles from Oxford Street. Very easy parking

Public Transport Bus 16 from Central London. British Rail (Cricklewood stop) nearby

Discount

20%–80%

&. No, **Group Tours** Yes, **Mail order** No, **Catalogue** Yes,
✗ Many cafés in the area, **Internet Sales** No

The Childrens Warehouse

Unit 4, 44 Colville Road, London, W3 8BL
Tel: 020 8752 1166 Fax: 020 8752 1177

Fun, stylish, affordable clothes that make children look good and feel comfortable 24 hours a day. For babies and children up to 12 years

Hours Tue–Fri 9–5, Sat 9–2

Closed Christmas, New Year, Bank Holidays

➡ Colville Road runs off Bollo Lane, which runs between Gunnesbury Lane and Chiswick High Road

Public Transport Chiswick Park tube station. Acton Town tube station

Discount

Labels The Childrens Warehouse

25%–50%

Parking 20 Spaces, & Yes, **Group Tours** No, **Mail order** Yes, **Catalogue** Yes, **Internet Sales** Yes

The Curtain Fabric Factory Shop

236a North End Road, Fulham, London, W14 9NU
Tel: 0207 381 1777 Fax: 0207 381 8879
Email: cfpolytrad@pol.com

Wide range (1000 rolls) curtain and upholstery fabric. Prices are per metre

Hours Mon–Sat 9:30–5:30

Closed Bank Holidays

➡ Adjacent to junction of North End Road and Lillie Road, Fulham

Public Transport West Kensington or West Brompton Road tube station – 5 minutes walk

Discount

see text

Parking Pay and display, & Yes, **Group Tours** Yes, **Mail order** No, **Catalogue** No, **Internet Sales** No

The Gallery of Antique Costume & Textiles

2 Church Street, London, NW8 8ED
Tel: 020 7723 9981

Men's and ladies' clothes. Original costumes, from Victorian to 1940s

Hours Mon–Sat 10–5:30

Discount

see text

The Merchant of Europe

232 Portobello Road, London, W11
Tel: 020 7221 4203

Men's and ladies' period-style clothing 1920s to 1970s

Hours Mon–Sat 11–6:30

Discount

see text

London North and West

The Salvage Shop

34–40 Watling Avenue, Burnt Oak, London, HA8 0LR
Tel: 020 8952 4353

Men's, women's and children's clothes, furniture, food
sportswear, electrical and household goods, toys
decorating and sports equipment. Salvage stock
i.e. bankruptcy, insurance claims, fire, flood

Hours Mon–Sun 9–5:30

Discount
50%–75%

London North and West

Upstairs Downstairs

8 Malcom Court, Malcom Crescent, Hendon, London,
NW4 4PJ
Tel: 020 8202 7720

Women's clothes

Hours By appointment only

Labels Louis Feraud, Yarell,
Valentino, Escade

Discount
see text

London North and West

Virginia

98 Portland Road, Holland Park, London, W11 4LQ
Tel: 020 7727 9908

Women's clothes. Antique clothing from turn of this
century to 1940's plus accessories

Hours Mon–Sat 11–6

Discount
see text

London North and West

Wellingtons

1 Wellington Place, London, NW8 7PE
Tel: 020 7483 0688

Men's and women's clothes – designer and High Street
brands

Hours Mon–Sat 11–5

Labels Valentino, Chanel, Escade,
Armani, Boss, Kenzo, M & S,
Benetton

Discount

see text

London

London North and West

World of Jewellery Factory Outlet

Hanworth Trading Estate, Hampton Road West, Feltham, London, TW13 6DH
Tel: 020 8755 2638

High quality branded fashion and designer jewellery direct from the manufacturer at prices substantially lower than retail

Hours Mon–Fri 9–4:30

Closed Bank Holidays

➜ 10 minutes from Heathrow on the A312

See ad on page 91

Discount

see text

World of Jewellery Factory Outlet

High quality branded fashion and designer jewellery direct from the manufacturer at prices substantially lower than retail.

**Hanworth Trading Estate, Hampton Road West, Feltham, Middlesex TW13 6DH.
Tel: (020) 8755 2638**

Mon-Fri 9:00-4:30 (except Holidays)

10 mins from Heathrow, on the A312

London South and East

Be-Wise

5 Gloucester Parade, Blackfen Road, Sidcup, London, DA15 8PS
Tel: 020 8859 2658

Ladieswear. Middle market names

Hours Mon–Sat 10–5

Closed Thursday

Labels Principles, M & S, Next

Discount
see text

London South and East

Catalogue Bargain Shop

103–113 Rye Lane, Peckham, London, SE15 4ST
Tel: 020 7358 1308

Men's, women's and children's clothes, sportswear, furniture, electrical and household goods, toys and sports equipment. Catalogue bargain shop from mail order companies

Hours Mon–Sat 9–5:30, Sun 10:30–4:30

Discount
see text

London & South-East England

Chloe Bromley Fashions Ltd

21 Montpelier Vale, Blackheath Village, London, SE3 0TJ
Tel: 020 8318 4300

Women's clothes. Special outfits in sizes 8–22. Frank Usher and Joseph Ribkoff factory rejects

Hours Mon–Sat 9:30–6, Sun 11–4

Labels Frank Usher, Joseph Ribkoff

Discount
25%–75%

City Menswear

3–5 High Street, Croydon, London, CR0 1QA
Tel: 020 8686 5047

Men's clothing

Hours Mon–Sat 9–6, Thur open until 8, Sun 11–5

Labels YSL, Boss, Cardin, Dior

Discount up to
50%

Damart

45 Lewisham Centre, Lewisham, London
Tel: 020 8318 4274

Men's and women's merchandise and underwear. Everything you will need

Hours Mon–Sat 9:30–5

Discount
see text

Designer Nearly New

109 Sanderstead Road, South Croydon, London, CR0 0RJ
Tel: 020 8680 5734

Upmarket ladieswear

Hours Mon–Sat 10–5:30

Labels Escade, Laurel, YSL, Chanel

Discount
see text

London & South-East England

Emporium

330–332 Creek Road, Greenwich, London, SE10
Tel: 020 8305 1670

Sells classic clothing for men and women, hats a speciality

Hours Tue–Sun 10:30–6

Discount

see text

Maxfield Parrish

5 Congreve Street, London, SE17
Tel: 020 7252 5225

Women's clothes. Telephone for an invitation

Hours By invitation

Discount

see text

Outlet

113 North End, Croydon, London

Top fashions. All labels. Designer brands. All at prices that are truly outrageous

See ad on page 53

Discount

see text

for hotels...

www.WestOneWeb.com

...great locations

London South and East

Outlet

18 Rye Lane, Peckham, London

Top fashions. All labels. Designer brands. All at prices that are truly outrageous

See ad on page 53

Discount

see text

London South and East

Outlet

273 Walworth Road, London

Top fashions. All labels. Designer brands. All at prices that are truly outrageous

See ad on page 53

Discount
see text

London South and East

Rainbow

249 & 253 Archway Road, Highgate, London, N6 5BS
Tel: 020 8340 8003

New children's clothes, IKKS, Mandia, Osh Kosh, etc. Always discounted. Second-hand clothes, toys, baby equipment. All good makes a fraction of their original price. Enormous range

Hours Mon–Sat 10:30–5:30

Closed Christmas, New Year, Bank Holidays

➡ Close to Highgate tube and buses. Free parking in side streets, plus outside shops on Saturdays

Public Transport 2 minutes from Highgate tube. Buses outside shop

Discount

Labels Oilily, IKKS, Next, Please Mum, Gap, Hennes, DKNY, M & S, Adams

25%–50%

♿ Yes, **Group Tours** No, **Mail order** No, **Catalogue** No, ✗ Jacksons Lane community centre, **Internet Sales** No

London South and East

Rainbow

41 High Street, Orpington, London, BR6 0JE
Tel: 01689 898878

Nursery equipment. Special offers

Hours Mon–Sat 9:30–5:00

Closed Thursdays and all Bank Holidays

➡ On one-way system. Parking meters outside

Public Transport Bus route

Discount

Labels Chicco, Emmal Junga

see text

♿ No, **Group Tours** No, **Mail order** No, **Catalogue** No, **Internet Sales** No

London South and East

Snips in Fashion

234 High Street, Orpington, London, BR6 0LS
Tel: 01689 828288 Fax: 01689 876517

Ladies' medium to better end, mainly from Germany, Italy, France, some English

Hours Mon–Sat 9:30–5:30

Closed Christmas Day, Boxing Day, Good Friday

➡ 10 minutes J4 M25. 5 minutes Orpington railway station and many bus routes

Public Transport Buses and Orpington main-line station

Discount

Labels Olsen, Tru, Duo, Aspa, Michelle, Kirsten, Delores, Fink, Hammerle

30%–50%

Parking 4 Spaces, & Yes, **Group Tours** No, **Mail order** No, **Catalogue** No, ✕ Local cafes and rest'nts, **Internet Sales** No

London South and East

The Frock Exchange

7 Walden Parade, Walden Road, Chislehurst, London, BR7 5DW

High Street labels and accessories and bric-a-brac

Hours Mon–Sat 9:30–4:30

Closed Wednesday

➡ Less than one mile from Chislehurst High Street

Discount

Labels M & S, Mondi, Alexon, Escade

 see text

Parking Yes

London South and East

The Observatory

20 Greenwich Church Street, Greenwich, London, SE10 9BJ
Tel: 020 8305 1998

Men's and ladies' retrospective clothing shop

Hours Mon–Sun 10–6

Discount

see text

London South and East

TK Maxx

The Drummond Centre, Croydon, London, CR0 1TY
Tel: 020 8686 9753

Clothing for all the family

Hours Mon–Fri 9–6, Sat 9–9, Sun 11–5

Discount

see text

& Yes

London South and West

British Designers Sale for Men and Women

42 York Mansions, Prince Wales Drive, London, SW11 4BP
Tel: 020 7228 5314

Men's and women's clothes

Hours Mon–Fri 10–4

Discount

London South and West

Browsers of Richmond

36 Friars Stile Road, Richmond, London, TW10 6QW
Tel: 020 8332 0875

The largest dress agency in Surrey

Hours Mon–Sat 10–5:30

Discount

London South and West

Bucks Furniture Warehouse

125 Evelyn Street, Deptford, London, SE8 5RJ
Tel: 020 8692 4447 Fax: 020 8469 3136

Over 15,000 sq.ft. of top quality furniture. End of lines, ex-display models and slight seconds from leading retailers at fraction of the price. Delivery service available within M25. Huge range of upholstered and wooden furniture. Ex-display beds and 100's of new quality beds, bedsteads and mattresses in new bed showroom

Hours Mon–Fri 10–7:00, Sat 10–5, Sun 10–4

Closed Christmas Day and New Year's Day.

➜ From south end of Tower Bridge follow A200 to Deptford – Tooley Street, then Jamaica Road. Pass Southwark Park on left. At roundabout with signs to Rotherhithe Tunnel take 3rd exit – A200 Lower Road which becomes Evelyn Street. Go under footbridge, pass Shell petrol station on left – huge shop is 100 yards on left

Public Transport Surrey Quays underground station. Deptford station

See ad on page 97

Discount

40%–50%

Parking 25 spaces, ♿ Yes, **Group Tours** Yes, **Mail order** No, **Catalogue** No, ✗ McDonalds, KFC, pub, **Internet Sales** No

London South and West

Butterfly

3 Lower Richmond Road, Putney Bridge, London, SW15
Tel: 020 8788 8304

Mid- to upper-range nearly-new designer clothes for women

Hours Mon–Fri 10–6:30, Sat 10–5:30

Discount

Labels Armani, Rifat Ozbek, Chanel, Nicole Farhi, French Connection, Jigsaw, Hobbs

London South and West

Change of Habit

65 Abbeville Road, London, SW4 9JW
Tel: 020 8675 9475

Everyday clothes for everyday people, designer to
High Street

Hours Mon–Sat 10–5:30, Wed late until 6:30

Discount

see text

London South and West

Denner Cashmere

PO Box 8551, London, SW11 1ZP
Tel: 0870 1200055 Fax: 020 8874 5053
Email: dennercashmere@bizonline.co.uk
Web site: www.dennercashmere.co.uk

We are principally a mail order company with a
warehouse shop open one day a week from September
to July (not August). Designer cashmere and silk/cashmere
knitwear, pashmina shawls, silk shirts, silk pyjamas and
dressing gowns, scarves and wraps. All our own brand.
Children's sweatshirts

Hours Thur only 10–5

Closed August

➜ Off Wandsworth Bridge. Address: Bemco building, Jews
Row, London SW18 1TB

Public Transport Wandsworth Town rail station. Buses

Discount

Labels Denner cashmere

25%–50%

Parking 10 Spaces, & No, **Group Tours** No, **Mail order** Yes,
Catalogue Yes, ✗ McDonalds, food pub **Internet Sales** Yes

London South and West

Frocks

33 Westfields Avenue, Barnes, London, SW13 0AT
Tel: 020 8392 1123

Wide range of evening wear and accessories for women

Hours Mon–Fri 9–8, Sat by appointment

Discount

see text

London South and West

Georgiana Grimston

18 Edna Street, London, SW11 3DP
Tel: 020 7978 6161

Men's and women's clothes. Telephone for an appointment – to suit workaholics

Hours By appointment only

Discount

London South and West

In Wear Factory Outlet

100 Garratt Lane, Wandsworth, London, SW18 4DT
Tel: 020 8871 2155

In Wear for women and Matinique for men

Hours Mon–Sat 10–5:30, Sun 11–4

Discount

30%–70%

London South and West

Larger than Life

2 Mortlake Terrace, Mortlake Road, Kew, Richmond, London, TW9 3DT
Tel: 020 8332 7661

Hiring mid-range designerwear for sizes 18–28 plus

Hours Mon–Sat 10–6

Discount

London South and West

Louis Feraud

Regency House, Hortensia Road, London, SW10
Tel: 020 7351 3399

Women's clothes. Telephone or write for an invitation

Hours By invitation

Discount

see text

London & South-East England

Mums2Be

3 Mortlake Terrace, Mortlake Road, Kew, Richmond,
London, TW9 3DT
Tel: 020 8332 6506

Offers day and evening wear for mums-to-be

Discount
see
text

Norton & Townsend

71 Bondway, London, SW8 1SQ
Tel: 020 7735 4701

Men's clothes. A tailor will visit either your home or your
work place

Hours By appointment

Labels Dormeuil, Holland

Discount
see
text

Outlet

3A George Street, Richmond, London

Top fashions. All labels. Designer brands. All at prices that
are truly outrageous

See ad on page 53

Discount
see
text

Pzazz

153 Church Road, Barnes, London, SW13 9HR
Tel: 020 8748 1094

Women's clothes and accessories, featuring more of the
avant garde designers

Hours Mon–Sat 10–6:30

Labels YSL, Kenzo, Ungaro

Discount
see
text

London & South-East England London

London South and West

Royal National Theatre

Hire Department, Chichester House, 1–3 Brixton Road,
London, SW9 6DE
Tel: 020 7735 4774

Theatrical costumes for hire

Hours Mon–Fri 10–6, By appointment only

Discount
see text

London South and West

Second Edition

7 Westmead Corner, Carshalton, London, SM5 2NZ
Tel: 020 8643 8639

Nearly new designer labels including High Street names

Hours Tues, Thur and Sat 10–4

Discount
see text

London South and West

Sequel

181 Chessington Road, West Ewell, London, KT19 9XE
Tel: 020 8786 7552

Sells new and nearly-new womenswear

Hours Mon–Sat 10–5

Closed Wednesday

Labels Armani, Moschino, Escade, Mondi

Discount

see text

London South and West

Shipton & Heneage

117 Queenstown Road, London, SW8 3RH
Tel: 020 7738 8484

Traditional men's and ladies' shoes – loafers, half-brogues, oxfords, chelsea

Hours Mon–Fri 9–6, Sat mail order

Discount up to
40%

London South and West

The Changing Room

148 Arthur Road, Wimbledon Park, London, SW19 8AQ
Tel: 020 8947 1258

Women's clothes

Hours Tues and Wed 10–6, Thur and Fri 10–8, Sat 10–5

Discount

Labels M & S, Episode, YSL

Abingdon

Togs

36 Stert Street, Abingdon, Oxfordshire, OX14 3JP
Tel: 01235 524989

Women's clothes

Hours Mon–Sat 9:30–5:00

Closed Bank Holidays and Christmas

Public Transport Bus

Discount

Labels Falmer jeans

Parking No, & Yes, **Group Tours** No, **Mail order** No,
Catalogue No, **Internet Sales** No

Banbury

TK Maxx

Calthorpe Street, off High Street, Banbury, Oxfordshire
Tel: 01295 277022

Men's, women's and children's clothes and household
goods. American concept has everything under one roof
for all the family

Hours Mon–Wed 9–5:30, Thur late until 9, Fri and Sat 9–6,
Sun 10–4

Discount up to

60%

Parking Yes, & Yes

Banbury

Top Marks

60 Parsons Street, Banbury, Oxfordshire
Tel: 01295 270530

Sells seconds from leading chain stores for all the family

Hours Mon–Fri 9–5:30, Sat 9–5

Discount

Labels M & S, Debenhams,
Richards

London & South-East England Oxfordshire

Aquascutum
Bicester Outlet Shopping Village, Pingle Drive, Bicester,
Oxfordshire, OX6 7WD
Tel: 01869 325943

Men's and women's clothes. End of range, last season's
stock and cancelled export orders

Hours Mon–Sun 10–6

Discount
25%–50%

Benetton
Bicester Outlet Shopping Village, Pingle Drive, Bicester,
Oxfordshire, OX6 7WD
Tel: 01869 320030

Wide range of clothes for all the family

Hours Mon–Sun 10–6

➡ Junction 9 of M40

Discount
see text

Parking Yes

Big Dog
Bicester Outlet Shopping Village, Pingle Drive, Bicester,
Oxfordshire, OX6 7WD
Tel: 01869 323280

Californian casualwear for all the family

Hours Mon–Sun 10–6

Discount

see text

, **Mail order** Yes, **Catalogue** Yes, ✕ Refreshments on site

Burberrys Ltd
Bicester Outlet Shopping Village, Pingle Drive, Bicester,
Oxfordshire, OX6 7WD
Tel: 01869 323522

Men's and ladies' goods by Burberry and Thomas
Burberry

Hours Mon–Sun 10–6

➡ Junction 9 of M40

Discount

see text

Parking Yes, ✕ Refreshments on site

Bicester

Cerruti 1881–Femme Ltd

Bicester Outlet Shopping Village, Pingle Drive, Bicester,
Oxfordshire, OX6 7WD
Tel: 01869 325519

Stylish shop selling ladieswear in this designer village

Hours Mon–Sun 10–6

➡ Junction 9 of M40

Discount up to

60%

Parking Yes

Bicester

Clarks Factory Shop

Bicester Outlet Shopping Village, Pingle Drive, Bicester,
Oxfordshire, OX6 7WD
Tel: 01869 325646

Not only shoes, but a wide range of accessories and gifts
and sporting goods and luggage

Hours Mon–Sun 10–6

➡ Junction 9 of M40

Discount

Labels Clarks, Nike, La Gear, Fila,
Cica, Hi Tec, Puma, Dr Martens

see text

Parking Yes

Bicester

Converse Emea Ltd

Bicester Outlet Shopping Village, Pingle Drive, Bicester,
Oxfordshire, OX6 7WD
Tel: 01869 325070

Sportswear, athletic clothing: specialises in baseball,
action sports, athletic originals

Hours Mon–Sun 10–6

➡ Junction 9 of M40

Discount up to

25%

Parking Yes

Bicester

Hobbs

Bicester Outlet Shopping Village, Pingle Drive, Bicester,
Oxfordshire, OX6 7WD
Tel: 01869 325660

Range of clothes for women and large selection of shoes

Hours Mon–Sun 10–6

➡ Junction 9 of M40

Discount

30%–70%

Parking Yes, ✗ Refreshments on site

Bicester

Imps

52 Sheep Street, Bicester, Oxfordshire
Tel: 01869 243455

Household goods and clothes for all the family. High Street lines and chainstore seconds

Hours Mon–Sat 9–5

Discount

see text

Bicester

In Wear Factory Outlet

Bicester Outlet Shopping Village, Pingle Drive, Bicester, Oxfordshire, OX6 7WD
Tel: 01869 369415

Last season's end of lines and seconds for men and women

Hours Mon–Sun 10–6

➡ Junction 9 of M40

Discount

30%–70%

Bicester

Jaeger Factory Shop

Bicester Outlet Shopping Village, 35 Pingle Drive, Bicester, Oxfordshire, OX6 7WD
Tel: 01869 369220

Contemporary classics from Jaeger

Hours Mon–Sat 10–6, Sun 11–5

➡ Junction 9 of M40

Discount

see text

Labels Jaeger

Parking Yes

Bicester

Jane Shilton

Bicester Outlet Shopping Village, Pingle Drive, Bicester, Oxfordshire, OX6 7WD
Tel: 01869 325387

Wide range of merchandise and accessories for women

Hours Mon–Sun 10–6

➡ Junction 9 of M40

Discount from

30%

Parking Yes, ✕ Refreshments on site

London & South-East England

Bicester

Jeffrey Rogers

Bicester Outlet Shopping Village, Pingle Drive, Bicester,
Oxfordshire, OX6 7WD
Tel: 01869 323567

Fashion for young and trendy end of the market

Hours Mon–Sun 10–6

➡ Junction 9 of M40

Discount up to

75%

Parking Yes, ✕ Refreshments on site

Bicester

Joan & David

Bicester Outlet Shopping Village, Pingle Drive, Bicester,
Oxfordshire, OX6 7WD
Tel: 01869 323387

Men's and women's clothes. 60% footwear, 25% classic
clothing, 15% accessories

Hours Mon–Sun 10–6

➡ Junction 9 of M40

Discount up to

50%

Parking Yes, ✕ Refreshments on site

Bicester

John Partridge Outlet Store

Bicester Outlet Shopping Village, 32 Pingle Drive, Bicester,
Oxfordshire, OX6 7WD
Tel: 01869 325332

Specialises in hardwearing outdoor clothing for men and
women

Hours Mon–Sun 10–6

➡ Junction 9 of M40

Discount

30%–70%

Parking Yes

Bicester

Kurt Geiger

Bicester Outlet Shopping Village, Pingle Drive, Bicester,
Oxfordshire, OX6 7WD
Tel: 01869 325410

Ladies' clothes and shoes

Hours Mon–Sun 10–6

➡ Junction 9 of M40

Discount

Labels Bruno Magli, C. Jourdan,
Via Spiga, Van-Dal, K. Geiger,
Carvel

see text

Parking Yes, ✕ Refreshments on site

Bicester

Land's End Direct Merchants

Bicester Outlet Shopping Village, Pingle Drive, Bicester,
Oxfordshire, OX6 7WD
Tel: 01869 369624

US Mail order and sells warehouse overstocks for men
and women

Hours Mon–Sun 10–6

➜ Junction 9 of M40

Discount

25%–40%

Parking Yes, ✕ Refreshments on site

Bicester

Monsoon

Bicester Outlet Shopping Village, Pingle Drive, Bicester,
Oxfordshire, OX6 7WD
Tel: 01869 323200

Women's discontinued lines, including jewellery

Hours Mon–Sun 10–6

Public Transport Junction 9 of M40

Discount

see text

Parking Yes, ✕ Refreshments on site

Bicester

Nicole Farhi/French Connection

Bicester Outlet Shopping Village, Pingle Drive, Bicester,
Oxfordshire, OX6 7WD
Tel: 01869 323200

Previous season's merchandise samples and seconds for
women

Hours Mon–Sun 10–6

➜ Junction 9 of M40

Discount

see text

Labels N. Farhi, French
Connection

Parking Yes, ✕ Refreshments on site

Bicester

Ouiset

Bicester Outlet Shopping Village, Pingle Drive, Bicester,
Oxfordshire, OX6 7WD
Tel: 01869 242402

Clearance lines for women

Hours Mon–Sun 10–6

➜ Junction 9 of M40

Discount

30%–70%

Parking Yes, ✕ Refreshments on site

Pepe Jeans

Unit 2, Bicester Outlet Shopping Village, Pingle Drive,
Bicester, Oxfordshire, OX6 7WD
Tel: 01869 325378

Jeans and casual wear for all the family

Hours Mon–Sun 10–6

Labels Pepe

Discount

see text

Parking Yes, ✕ Refreshments on site

Polo Ralph Lauren Factory Store

Bicester Outlet Shopping Village, Pingle Drive, Bicester,
Oxfordshire, OX6 7WD
Tel: 01869 325200

Full range of clothes for all the family

Hours Mon–Sat 10–6, Sun 12–6

➡ Junction 9 of M40

Discount

35%–60%

Parking Yes, ✕ Refreshments on site

Principles

Bicester Outlet Shopping Village, Pingle Drive, Bicester,
Oxfordshire, OX6 7WD
Tel: 01869 325300

Clearance and end of lines for men and women

Hours Mon–Sun 10–6

➡ Junction 9 of M40

Discount from

50%

✕ Refreshments on site

Racing Green

Bicester Outlet Shopping Village, Pingle Drive, Bicester,
Oxfordshire, OX6 7WD
Tel: 01869 325484

Overstocks and clearance lines from mail order

Hours Mon–Sun 10–6

➡ Junction 9 of M40

Discount

30%–70%

Parking Yes, ✕ Refreshments on site

Bicester

Red/Green

Unit 47, Bicester Outlet Shopping Village, Pingle Drive,
Bicester, Oxfordshire, OX6 7WD
Tel: 01869 323324

Very stylish 'posh sailing' or leisurewear

Hours Mon–Sun 10–6

➡ Junction 9 of M40

Discount
30%–70%

Parking Yes, ✕ Refreshments on site

Bicester

The Designer Room

Bicester Outlet Shopping Village, Pingle Drive, Bicester,
Oxfordshire, OX6 7WD
Tel: 01869 320052

Ever-changing range of top designer clothes

Hours Mon–Sun 10–6

➡ Junction 9 of M40

Labels Escade, Laurel, Mondi, Zapa, Portara

Discount
25%–50%

Parking Yes, ✕ Refreshments on site

Bicester

The Suit Company

Bicester Outlet Shopping Village, Pingle Drive, Bicester,
Oxfordshire, OX6 7WD
Tel: 01869 324321

Range of menswear and accessories

Hours Mon–Sun 10–6

➡ Junction 9 of M40

Discount
see text

Parking Yes, ✕ Refreshments on site

Bicester

Tog 24

Bicester Outlet Shopping Village, Pingle Drive, Bicester,
Oxfordshire, OX6 7WD
Tel: 01869 323278

Specialises in outdoor clothing for men and women

Hours Mon–Sun 10–6

➡ Junction 9 of M40

Discount up to
30%

Parking Yes, ✕ Refreshments on site

Bicester

Triumph International Ltd

Bicester Outlet Shopping Village, Pingle Drive, Bicester,
Oxfordshire, OX6 7WD
Tel: 01869 329930

Swimwear and underwear for men

Hours Mon–Sun 10–6

➡ Junction 9 of M40

Discount

see text

Parking Yes, ✕ Refreshments on site

Bicester

Warners

Bicester Outlet Shopping Village, Pingle Drive, Bicester,
Oxfordshire, OX6 7WD
Tel: 01869 324401

Women's lingerie, bras, bodies and briefs

Hours Mon–Sun 10–6

➡ Junction 9 of M40

Discount up to

30%

Parking Yes, ✕ Refreshments on site

Bodicote

Hilary's Hat Hire

The Oven, 1 High Street, Bodicote, Oxfordshire, OX15 4BZ
Tel: 01295 263880

Full range of hats for hire for women

Hours Mon–Fri 9:30–7, By appointment

Discount

see text

Burford

Discount China

High Street, Burford, Oxfordshire, OX18 4QA
Tel: 01993 823452

China. Prices from £2 upwards. Products already
discounted

Hours Mon–Sun 10–5:00

Closed Christmas Day and New Year's Day

Public Transport Bus

Labels Non brands

Discount

see text

♿ Yes, **Group Tours** No, **Mail order** No, **Catalogue** No,
Internet Sales No

Chipping Norton

Top Marks

8 High Street, Chipping Norton, Oxfordshire
Tel: 01608 642653

Sells seconds from leading chain stores for all the family

Hours Mon–Fri 9–5:30, Sat 9–5

Discount

Labels M & S, Debenhams, Richards

 see text

Henley on Thames

Peruvian Connection

28 Hart Street, Henley on Thames, Oxfordshire
Tel: 01491 414446

Ladies and menswear. Last season's stock from Peruvian Connection

Hours Mon–Sat 9:30–5:30, Sun 12–5

Discount up to

30%

Henley on Thames

Scoop

77 Bell Street, Henley-on-Thames, Oxfordshire, RG9 2BD
Tel: 01491 572962

Nearly-new ladieswear from the top end of the market, and accessories

Hours Mon–Sat 10–5

Discount

Labels Escade, B Barclay, L Feraud

see text

Oxford

Isis Ceramics

The Old Toffee Factory, 120A Marlborough Road, Oxford, Oxfordshire, OX1 4LS
Tel: 01865 722729 Fax: 01865 727521
Email: isisceram@aol.com

Hand painted ceramics, blue and white Delftware. 20–25% discount on seconds. Flat ware, ornamental lamps

Hours Mon–Fri 10–4:00

Closed Bank Holidays

➜ Parallel to Abingdon Road, A4144. Left down Whitehouse Road then right

Public Transport Buses, park and ride

Discount

20%–25%

Parking None, ♿ No, **Group Tours** Yes, **Mail order** Yes, **Catalogue** Yes, **Internet Sales** No

Oxford

Matalan

Unit 5, The John Allen Centre, Cowley, Oxford,
Oxfordshire, OX4 3JP
Tel: 01865 747400

Discount store. Top brands for men, women and children,
including homeware at discount prices. Members only

Hours Mon–Fri 10–8:00, Sat 9–5:30, Sun 10–6

➡ Cowley shopping centre

Public Transport Bus

Labels Lee Cooper, Wrangler, top
brands discounts

Discount from

50%

& Yes, **Group Tours** No, **Mail order** No, **Catalogue** No,
Internet Sales No

Oxford

Revival Clothes Agency

60 St Clements, Oxford, Oxfordshire, OX4 1AH
Tel: 01865 251005

Wide range of women's wear, wedding dresses;
menswear

Hours Tue–Wed 10–4, Thur 10–7, Fri and Sat 10–5

Labels Monsoon, R. Joyce,
Armani, Next, Jaeger

Discount

see
text

Oxford

The Ballroom

5–6 The Plain, Oxford, Oxfordshire, OX4 1AS
Tel: 01865 241054

Bridalwear, ball gowns and formal wear to hire or buy.
Brides dresses are self made. Price range from £25 to £200
to hire and from £68 to £800 to buy. Telephone 01865
202303 for menswear

Discount
see
text

Oxford

The Pamela Howard Fashion Consultancy

Woodland, Bedwells Heath, Boars Hill, Oxford,
Oxfordshire, OX1 5JE
Tel: 01865 735735

New and nearly-new designer wear, accessories and shoes
for women

Hours By appointment

Discount
see
text

Thame

High Society

6/7 Cornmarket, Thame, Oxfordshire, OX9 3DX
Tel: 01844 212209

Designer women's eveningwear, cocktail dresses and ballgowns for hire and sale

Hours Mon–Fri 9:30–5:30, Sat 9.30–5

Discount
see text

Thame

Imps

40 Upper High Street, Thame, Oxfordshire, OX9 3AG
Tel: 01844 212985

Household goods and clothes for all the family. High Street lines and chainstore seconds

Hours Mon–Sat 9–5

Discount
see text

Thame

Togs

13 High Street, Thame, Oxfordshire, OX9 2BZ
Tel: 01844 215002

Women's clothes

Hours Mon–Sat 9:30–5:00

Closed Bank Holidays

Public Transport Bus

Discount
see text

Parking No, & Yes, **Group Tours** No, **Mail order** No, **Catalogue** No, **Internet Sales** No

Wantage

Good As New

21 Newbury Street, Wantage, Oxfordshire, OX12 8BU
Tel: 01235 769526

Ladies' designer wear and accessories

Hours Mon–Sat 9:30–4

Labels F. Usher, M & S, Armani, J. Allen, L. Ashley

Discount
see text

Witney

Early's of Witney

Witney Mill, Burford Road, Witney, Oxfordshire, OX8 5EB
Tel: 01993 703131 Fax: 01993 771513
Email: jane@earlysofwitney.demon.co.uk

Blankets and throws in 100% pure new wool (including Merino); cotton and acrylic. Clearance and 'not quite perfect' lines are available and offered at substantial discounts. Also stocked are coloroll bedlinen (20% discount minimum), kitchen textiles, basketware and towels. Group tours by arrangement

Hours Mon–Sat 10–5

Closed Christmas to New Year inclusive; Bank Holidays

➡ Take A4095 from Witney town centre – signed 'Minster Lovell'. Early's factory is approx 300m from junction on right hand side. Factory shop is located off the main car park at front of building

Public Transport Bus to Witney town centre; rail – Oxford

Discount

20%–70%

Labels Early's of Witney, Coloroll

Parking 10+ Spaces, & Yes, **Group Tours** Yes, **Mail order** No, **Catalogue** No, ✗ In Witney town centre, **Internet Sales** No

Witney

Imps

34 Market Square, Witney, Oxfordshire, OX8 5BA
Tel: 01993 779875

Household goods and clothes for all the family. High Street lines and chainstore seconds

Hours Mon–Sat 9–5:30

Discount

see text

Ashtead

The Dress Agency

5B Rectory Lane, Ashtead, Surrey, KT21 2BA
Tel: 01372 271677
Email: d.agency@virgin.net
Web site: http://business.virgin.net/d.agency

We stock an ever-changing range of nearly new outfits, suits, dresses, separates, etc. Best and largest selection of once-worn wedding dresses in the area. Specialist in evening wear hire from cocktail to the full ball gown

Hours Mon–Fri 9–5, Wed 9–3, Sat 9–4

Closed Normal Public Holidays

➡ Rectory Lane runs off 'The Street' (A24) in centre of Ashtead village. 'Leg of Mutton' pub is on corner. Ashtead is found on A24 between Epsom and Leatherhead. J9 on M25 is 5 mins away

Public Transport Buses from Epsom and Leatherhead. Ashtead station is 20 mins walk away in Lower Ashtead

Discount

40%–70%

Labels All labels

Parking 2 Spaces, & Yes, **Group Tours** No, **Mail order** No, **Catalogue** No, ✗ Tea-room and 2 pubs in High Street, **Internet Sales** No

Camberley

Changes

121 Deep Cut Bridge Road, Deep Cut, Camberley, Surrey, GU16 6SD
Tel: 01252 834487

Designer and High Street range of new and nearly-new ladieswear

Hours Tue–Sat 10–5

Discount

see text

Camberley

China Matching Replacements

29 Greenhill Road, Camberley, Surrey, GU15 1HE
Tel: 01276 64587 Fax: 01276 64587

Mail order/collection by prior arrangement. Discontinued English china. Tableware – Doulton, Wedgwood, Spode, Denby, Worcester, etc. Internet sales available soon

Hours Mon–Sat 9–1, 24 hours ans/fax

Public Transport 6 miles Camberley Station/town

Discount up to

Labels Wedgwood, Spode, Masons, Doulton, Worcester, Midwinter, Denby, Royal Albert, Adatis

5%

♿ No, **Group Tours** No, **Mail order** Yes, **Catalogue** No, **Internet Sales** No

Camberley

The Curtain Agency

231 London Road, Camberley, Surrey, GU15 3EY
Tel: 01276 671672 Fax: 01420 544604
Email: jackie-curtains@lineone.net

Quality second-hand curtains, decorative and antique lighting. New and antique poles, tie backs and curtain accessories. Cushions, rugs, bedspreads

Hours Mon–Sat 10–5

Closed Bank Holidays

Discount

see text

Parking None, ♿ Yes, **Group Tours** No, **Mail order** No, **Catalogue** No

Chertsey

The Fabric Factory

Church Walk, Windsor Road, Chertsey, Surrey, KT16 8AP
Tel: 01932 570028 Fax: 01932 570028
Email: fabric-f@netcomuk.co.uk

Famous brand furnishing fabrics, perfects and seconds. Includes top Designer furnishing fabrics – most at least 50% discount. Hundreds of metres at £6.95 metre (normal retail price £25–£65 metre). All prices in metres

Hours Mon–Sat 9–5:30

Closed Bank Holidays

➡ Junction 11 off M25. Follow signs to Chertsey town centre. Down walkway next to St Peter's Church in London Street

Public Transport Chertsey railway station. Bus stop 100 yards

Discount

Labels Crowson, Osborne & Little, Colefax & Fowler, Jane Churchill, Harlequin, Sanderson, Anna French,

10%–75%

Parking Street, ♿ Yes, **Group Tours** No, **Mail order** No, **Catalogue** No, ✗ Two tea-rooms in town, **Internet Sales** No

Cobham

Flair of Cobham

15 Church Street, Cobham, Surrey
Tel: 01932 865825

Nearly-new ladieswear

Hours Mon–Sat 9:30–5

Labels Jaeger, Charles

Discount

see text

Cobham

Phoenix

5 Church Street, Cobham, Surrey, KT11 3EG
Tel: 01932 862147

Middle to upmarket labels for women

Hours Mon–Sat 9:30–5

Labels Viyella, Max Mara, Escade

Discount
see text

Dorking

Dorking Exchange

78 South Street, Dorking, Surrey, RH4 2HD
Tel: 01306 876828

New and nearly-new menswear for hire

Hours Tue–Sat 9:30–5:30

Closed Monday

Discount
see text

East Oxted

Designer Nearly New

121 Station Road, East Oxted, Surrey, RH8 0QE
Tel: 01883 717604

Upmarket ladies' designs

Hours Mon–Sat 10–5:30

Labels Escade, Laurel, YSL, Chanel

Discount
see text

Englefield Green

Encore

22–23 Victoria Street, Englefield Green, Surrey, TW20 0QY
Tel: 01784 439475

Encore sells nearly new designer clothes at a third to a half of original price. Stock is constantly changing so feel free to telephone to check availability of particular designers and sizes. Previous bargains include Thierry Mugler Suit – originally £1000 sold for £275; Louis Feraud evening dress – originally £995 selling for £99

Hours Tue–Sat 10–5, Thur late until 7

➜ From J13 of M25 take A30 in direction of Camberley. At traffic lights by Royal Holloway College turn right, then take 3rd turning on right into Victoria Street

Discount

Labels Moschino, Lacroix, Ungaro, Versace, Mugler, Louis Feraud, Betty Barclay, Escada, Mondi

50%–75%

⅃ No, **Group Tours** No, **Mail order** No, **Catalogue** No, ✗ Tea rooms in pub opposite, **Internet Sales** No

Epsom Downs

Designer Fashion Sale

79 Grosvenor Road, Langley Vale, Epsom Downs, Surrey, KT18 6JF
Tel: 01372 278194

Ladies and menswear. All designer merchandise

Hours Invitation only

Discount

see text

Ewell

Riche

87 High Street, Ewell, Surrey, KT17 1RX
Tel: 020 8393 2256

Womn's clothes. Chanel, Gucci, Yves Saint Laurent, Escada, Max Mara, Mathilde are just a few of the Designer names in stock

Hours Mon–Sat 9:30–5 pm

Closed Christmas to New Year's Eve

➜ High Street corner of Reigate Road/High Street. A3 from London, follow signs to Epsom

Public Transport Train to West Ewell. Bus

Discount

Labels Gucci, Escada, Joseph, YSL, Max Mara, Mathilde

see text

Parking Many, ⅃ No, **Group Tours** No, **Mail order** No, **Catalogue** No, ✗ Opposite, **Internet Sales** No

Farnham

The Curtain Agency

103 West Street, Farnham, Surrey, GU9 7EN
Tel: 01252 714711 Fax: 01420 544604
Email: jackie-curtains@lineone.net

Quality second-hand curtains, decorative and antique lighting. New and antique poles, tie backs and curtain accessories. Cushions, rugs, bedspreads

Hours Mon–Sat 10–5

Closed Bank Holidays

Public Transport Farnham – Waterloo train

Discount

see text

Parking None, ⅃ Yes, **Group Tours** No, **Mail order** No, **Catalogue** No, **Internet Sales** No

Farnham

The Dress Circle

6 Woolmead Walk, Farnham, Surrey, GU9 7SH
Tel: 01252 716540

Designer and High Street labels and accessories

Hours Mon–Sat 9:30–4:30

Labels M & S, L. Ashley, Next, Benetton

Discount

Godalming

Alan Paine Knitwear Factory Shop

Scats Country Store Courtyard, Brighton Road, Godalming, Surrey, GU7 1NS
Tel: 01483 419962 Fax: 01483 419962

Luxury knitwear in cashmere, camel hair, lambswool, merino and cotton at factory prices. Various sales promotions throughout the year. Can offer further discounts ranging from 15%–30% depending on time of year. Smaller range for women

Hours Mon–Fri 9–5, Sat 9.30–4

Closed Sundays, Bank Holidays

➜ 100 yards from northern end of High Street in Brighton Road. Signposted Cranleigh, Dunsfold. Left at 2nd set of traffic lights on Flambard Way (High Street Bypass) if travelling from Guildford/London, or right if from Portsmouth/Milford. Factory Shop 50 yards on left hand side

Public Transport 100 yards from all bus services to Godalming. 10 minutes walk from train station – London to Portsmouth

Labels Alan Paine

Discount up to

Parking 50 Spaces, ⅊ Yes, **Group Tours** No, **Mail order** Yes, **Catalogue** No, ✗ Cafés and rest'nts close, **Internet Sales** No

Godalming

Kent & Curwen

8A Farncombe Street, Farncombe, Godalming, Surrey, GU7 3AY
Tel: 01483 426917

High quality menswear

Hours Fri–Sat 10–5

Discount

see text

Grayshott

Bumpsadaisy Maternity Style

Crossways Road, Grayshott, Surrey, GU26 6HG
Tel: 01428 608345

Large range of maternitywear to hire or buy

Hours Mon–Sat 9:30–5:30

Discount

see text

Guildford

Clothes Line

Kilnhanger, Farley Heath, Albury, near Guildford, Surrey, GU5 9EW
Tel: 01483 898855

Eveningwear hire from designers

Hours By appointment

Labels B. Sassoon, R. Klein

Discount

 see text

Hampton Court

The Sale Room

33 Bridge Road, Hampton Court, Surrey, KT8 9ER
Tel: 020 8224 8515

Women's clothes

Hours Mon–Sat 10–5:30

Labels Prisma, Marina, Rinaldi, John Paul, Marc Aurel

Discount

25%–50%

Horley

The Factory Shop Ltd

The Engine Shed, Consort Way East, Horley, Surrey, RH6 7AU
Tel: 01293 823883

Men's, ladies' and children's clothes, furniture, sportswear, household goods and sports equipment – a wide selection of goods

Hours Mon–Sat 9–5:30, Sun 10–4

Labels Wrangler, Nike, Adidas

Discount

30%–50%

Parking Yes, ✕ Refreshments on site

Kingston Hill

Angela Marber's Private Buy

Fivemarch, Coombe Park, Kingston Hill, Surrey, KT2 7JA
Tel: 020 8549 8453

Private Buy arranges for club members to purchase current and next season's top label samples and stock. Displayed in intimate showrooms you can buy amazing clothes ahead of season at half the cost. Also available at trade prices are household linens, fabrics, wallpapers – even holidays. Usually a recommendation only club. Some personal references may be required. Membership costs £60 per year, includes a regular newsletter detailing future showroom visits, restaurant reviews and member recommendations

Discount

see text

London & South-East England

Lower Ashtead

Flair of Ashtead

11 Craddocks Parade, Craddocks Avenue, Lower Ashtead, Surrey, KT21 1QL
Tel: 01932 865825/01372 277207

Nearly-new ladieswear, also hat hire

Hours Mon–Sat 9:30–5

Discount

Oxted

Chanterelle

95–99 Station Road East, Oxted, Surrey, RH8 0AX Fax: 01883 716800
Email: chanterelle@saqnet.co.uk

Products mainly for women, some items for men

Hours Mon–Sat 9:30–5:30, Sun 11–5, open Bank Holidays

Public Transport Bus

Labels Design Haus, Roman Originals

Discount

Parking Nearby, ♿ No, **Group Tours** Yes, **Mail order** No, **Catalogue** No, **Internet Sales** No

Redhill

Choice Discount Stores Ltd

1 Warwick Quadrant, London Road, Redhill, Surrey
Tel: 01737 772777

Men's, women's and children's clothes

Hours Mon–Sat 9–6, Sun 10–4

See ad on page 75

Labels Next

Discount up to

50%

Redhill

Suit City

15 Holmethorpe Avenue, Holmethorpe Industrial Estate, Redhill, Surrey, RH1 2NB
Tel: 0173 778 9963

Men's clothes

Hours Fri 11–3, Sat and Sun 10–4

Discount up to

65%

Sutton

TK Maxx

Times Square Shopping Centre, High Street, Sutton,
Surrey, SM1 1LF
Tel: 020 8770 7786

Clothing for all the family

Hours Mon–Fri 9–5:30, Thur late until 7, Sat 9–6, Sun 11–5

Discount

& Yes

Walton-on-Thames

Linda Armanani

21 Stanley Gardens, Walton-on-Thames, Surrey, KT12 4HB
Tel: 01932 224368

Women's knitwear. Made-to-measure cashmere

Hours Phone for appointment

Discount

West Byfleet

Special Occasions

1 Old Woking Road, West Byfleet, Surrey, KT14 6LW
Tel: 019323 54907

Evening dress and menswear for hire

Hours Mon–Sat 9:30–5:30, Sat evenings in August by
appointment

Discount

Weybridge

Ancora Dress Agency

74 Church Street, Weybridge, Surrey, KT13 8DL
Tel: 01932 855267

Middle to upper range ladieswear

Hours Mon–Fri 9:30–5:30, Wed and Sat 9:30–5

Discount

Labels Alexon, Monsoon, Wallis,
Mondi, Yarell

Woking

TK Maxx

The Peacocks Centre, Woking, Surrey
Tel: 01483 771660

Men's clothes, women's clothes, children's clothes

Hours Mon–Fri 9:30–5, Thur late until 9, Sat 9–6, Sun 1–3

Discount

see text

& Yes

Arundel

Always in Vogue

1 The Old Mill, River Road, Arundel, West Sussex,
BN18 9DH
Tel: 01903 883192
Email: knightwork@compuserve.com

Stocks both new and end of lines. Designer clothing at up to 50% off and pristine nearly new designerwear, much of it last year's stock and still with its original labels, at between quarter and half of the original price. Labels range from Alexon to Versace but no High Street

Hours Mon–Sat 10–5, 10–4 during winter

Closed Christmas, New Year's Day

➜ Behind the 'Swan Hotel' in historic Arundel

Public Transport Arundel train station

Labels German, Italian, English

Discount

 25%–50%

Parking 1 Space, & Yes, **Group Tours** No, **Mail order** No, **Catalogue** No, ✗ Local rest'nts, tea-rooms, **Internet Sales** No

Bognor Regis

The Shoe Shed

3 The Arcade, Bognor Regis, West Sussex, PO21 1LH
Tel: 01243 829600

Shoes

Hours Mon–Sat 9–5:30, Sun 10–4

Discount up to

30%

Burgess Hill

Jaeger Factory Shop

Unit B, 208–216 London Road, Burgess Hill, West Sussex,
RH15 9NF
Tel: 01444 333100

Men's and ladies' clothes

Hours Mon–Fri 10–6, Sat 9–6, Sun 11–5

Discount

 see text

Crawley Down

Bargain Boutique

Snow Hill, Crawley Down, West Sussex, RH10 3EE
Tel: 01342 712022

Caters mainly for women and children, but there is a limited selection of menswear

Hours Tue–Sat 9–1

Labels M & S, Next, BHS

Discount

see text

Haywards Heath

Browns

Sussex Road, Haywards Heath, West Sussex
Tel: 01444 458295

Clothes for women

Hours Mon–Sat 10–4:30

Labels Jaeger, Yarell, Weber

Discount
see text

Hickstead

Impulse

London Road, Hickstead, West Sussex, RH17 5RL
Tel: 01444 881255

Mostly men's clothing and a large selection of ladies' shoes

Hours Mon–Sat 10–5

Discount
see text

Hickstead Village

M & G Designer Fashions

Old London Road, Hickstead Village, Haywards Heath, West Sussex, RH17 5RL
Tel: 01444 881511 Fax: 01444 881511

We buy end of lines, discontinued lines, late deliveries, cancelled orders, etc. We promise at least 20% to 70% discount, plus we have a bargain corner where everything is £30 or under. We carry a vast selection of evening wear all year round

Hours Mon–Sat 10–5

Closed Between Christmas and New Year

Public Transport Haywards Heath railway station

Labels Discount house cannot advertise labels

Discount
20%–75%

Parking 20 Spaces, ♿ Yes, **Group Tours** Yes, **Mail order** No, **Catalogue** No, ✗ On site, others 10 mins, **Internet Sales** No

London & South-East England

Horsham

Browns

32 East Street, Horsham, West Sussex
Tel: 01403 259711

Women's clothes. We stock many different labels from M
& S, Country Casuals, Oasis, Monsoon, Next to Bianca,
Jaeger, Betty Barclay and to designers such as Calvin
Klein, Ralph Lauren, DKNY, Tommy Hilfiger. We accept
clothing for sale every day and never know what is
coming in. Wedding dresses £40–£600

Hours Mon–Sat 10–4:30, Early closing Thur – 4

Closed Usual Holidays plus Bank Holidays

➜ From Swan Walk shopping centre, walk across The
Carfax to the 'Kings Head' public house and hotel. Walk
up East Street and we are towards the top on the right
hand side

Public Transport Carfax, Horsham – around corner

Discount

see text

Parking Nearby, ⟵ Yes, **Group Tours** No, **Mail order** No,
Catalogue No, ✗ Lots of cafes and restaurants very close
by. Toilets nearby, **Internet Sales** No

Littlehampton

Ricara Factory Shop

River Road, Littlehampton, West Sussex, BN17 5BZ
Tel: 01903 723843

Sells mainly schoolwear, men's casualwear and sportswear

Hours Mon–Fri 9:30–5, Sat 9–5, Sun 10–4

Discount

see text

Shoreham-by-Sea

Claremont Garments

26 Dolphin Road, Shoreham-by-Sea, West Sussex,
BN43 6PS
Tel: 01273 461571

Mainly ladies' fashion, but also stocks a few men's
garments, also some childrenswear

Hours Mon–Sat 9–4:30

Discount up to

50%

Storrington

Diamonds Dress Agency

48 School Hill, Storrington, West Sussex, RH20 4NB
Tel: 01903 746824

Women's clothes

Hours Mon–Sat 10–5

Labels Valentino, Escade, Mondi

Discount

see text

Worthing

Panache

5 Stanford Square, Warwick Street, Worthing, West Sussex, BN11 3EZ
Tel: 01903 212503 Fax: 01903 233661

Women's clothes. Labels always in stock: Jaeger, Betty Barclay, Gerry Weber, Laura Ashley, etc.

Hours Mon–Sat 10–5

Closed Christmas Day, Boxing Day, New Year's Day

➤ From middle of Warwick Street, turn south into Stanford Square

Discount

50%–80%

& No, **Group Tours** Yes, **Mail order** No, **Catalogue** No, **Internet Sales** No

Worthing

Smarties

4 Stanford Square, Warwick Street, Worthing, West Sussex, BN11 3EZ
Tel: 01903 233661

Children's clothes. Smarties sells top quality nearly new children's clothing: from birth to 13 years old

Hours Mon–Sat 10–5

Closed Christmas Day, Boxing Day, New Year's Day

➤ From the centre of Warwick Street, turn south into Stanford Square

Discount

Labels Marese, Oilily, Osh Kosh, Laura Ashley, Babar, Little Darlings, M & S, Paul Smith, Baby Mini

50%–80%

& Yes, **Group Tours** No, **Mail order** No, **Catalogue** No, **Internet Sales** No

Worthing

Something Special

15 Ardsheal Road, Broadwater Green, Worthing, West Sussex, BN14 7RN
Tel: 01903 217317

Sells good-as-new clothes for women at discount prices. Also hires out bridesmaid dresses and eveningwear

Hours Mon–Sat 9:30–5

Discount

Labels M & S

see text

Worthing

The Designer Sale Shop

8 Stanford Square, Warwick Street, Worthing, West Sussex, BN11 3DJ
Tel: 01903 824456 Fax: 01903 233661

Women's clothes. Probably the best discount outlet south of the Thames. Marella suits from £40

Hours Tue–Sat 10–4

Closed Christmas Day, Boxing Day, New Year's Day

➤ From the centre of Warwick Street turn south into Stanford Square

Discount

Labels Max Mara, Marella, Valentino, Armani, I Blues, D & G, Cautta, Basler, Ara

50%–75%

& Yes, **Group Tours** No, **Mail order** No, **Catalogue** No, ✗ Refreshments on site, **Internet Sales** No

SPENCER'S

The British Golf Directory

Courses where you can turn up and play

This new Spencer's guide provides full details of golf courses the length and breadth of Britain. All are courses where you can turn up and play, from municipal courses to some of the grandest in the land. You don't need to be members or pay membership fees. Just the rate for the round.

Whether you are an old hand or one of the new wave of golf enthusiasts you will find Spencer's Directory an invaluable companion - for your home, for your car or for your holidays.

With full-colour throughout it's easy-to-use, highly practical and perfect for browsing.

Each entry has a full quarter-page, with a description of the course, and information on yardage, par, standard scratch score, directions and green fees. There's also a full-colour route-planning and map section - a feature of all Spencer's titles.

Format:	210x148mm
No. of pages:	112pp
ISBN:	1 900327 51 1
Price:	£4.99
Publication date:	April 2000

West One Publishing
Kestrel House, Duke's PLace
Marlow, Bucks SL7 2QH

tel: 01628 487722

www.WestOneWeb.com

South-West England and South Wales

Bath

Fox and Chave

Fox House, Faulkland, Bath, Avon, SBA3 5XD
Tel: 01373 834210

Largest Italian silk tie collection

Hours By appointment only

Discount up to 50%

Bath

The Collectable Costume

Fountain Antiques Centre, 3 Fountain Buildings,
Lawsdown Road, Bath, Avon, BA1 2QZ
Tel: 01225 428731

Antiques centre selling pre-fifties men's and women's costumes

Hours Mon–Sat 10–5, Wed 7.30–5

Discount see text

Bath

Tie-Store

12 Royal Crescent, Bath, Avon, BA1 2LR
Tel: 01225 480292 Fax: 01225 480297
Email: mail@tie-store.com
Web site: www.tie-store.com

Silk ties for just £5 inc. delivery

Closed Never

➜ www.tie-store.com

Labels Fox and Chave

Discount see text

& No, **Group Tours** No, **Mail order** No, **Catalogue** No,
Internet Sales Yes

Bristol

Courtaulds Bodywear Factory Shop

The Garden Factory, Signal Road,, Staple Hill, Bristol,
Avon, BS16 5PG
Tel: 0117 975 5599 Fax: 0117 956 7147

Men's, women's and chldren's clothes including ladies' underwear

Hours 1:15 pm–3:00

Public Transport Bus

Labels Courtaulds

Discount see text

Parking Lots, & No, **Group Tours** No, **Mail order** No,
Catalogue No, **Internet Sales** No

South-West England & South Wales

Factory Pine

501 Bath Road, Saltford, Bristol, Avon, BS18 3HQ
Tel: 01225 874355 Fax: 01225 874355

Pine furniture. No discounts

Hours Sun–Sun 9–5:00

Closed Christmas, New Year and Bank Holidays

Discount

Labels Own label

see text

Parking Public car park, & Yes, **Group Tours** No,
Mail order No, **Catalogue** No, **Internet Sales** No

Matalan

Station Road, Filton, Bristol, Avon, BS12 7JW
Tel: 0117 974 8000

Fashion and homewares giving unbeatable value to the whole family

Hours Mon–Fri 10–8, Sat 9–6, Sun 11–5

Discount

see text

Second to None

2 Somerset Square, Nailsea, Bristol, Avon, BS48 2EU
Tel: 01275 851333

Womens and chldrenswear. Prices from £1.99 upwards

Hours Mon–Sat 9–5:00

Closed Christmas and New Year

Public Transport Bus

Discount

Labels All major brands when available

see text

Parking High Street, & Yes, **Group Tours** No,
Mail order No, **Catalogue** No, **Internet Sales** No

Second to None

42A High Street, Keynsham, Bristol, Avon, BS31 1DX
Tel: 0117 986 8627

Womens and childrenswear. Prices from £1.99 upwards. Products already discounted

Hours Mon–Sat 9–5:00

Closed Christmas and New Year

Public Transport Bus

Discount

Labels All major brands when available

see text

& Yes, **Group Tours** No, **Mail order** No, **Catalogue** No,
Internet Sales No

Bristol

Second to None

61 Henleaze Road, Henleaze, Bristol, Avon, BS8 3AW
Tel: 0117 965 1365

Women's clothing. Prices from £1.99 upwards. Products already discounted

Hours Mon–Sat 9–5:00

Closed Christmas Day , Boxing Day and New Year

Public Transport Bus

Discount

Labels All major brands stocked when available, i.e. Wallis, Next, Dorothy Perkins, M & S

see text

Parking High Street, & Yes, **Group Tours** No, **Mail order** No, **Catalogue** No, **Internet Sales** No

Bristol

Second to None

792 Fishponds Road, Fishponds, Bristol, Avon, BS16 3TE
Tel: 0117 965 9852

Women's and children's clothing. Prices from £1.99 upwards

Hours Mon–Sat 9–5:00

Closed Christmas and New Year

Public Transport Bus

Discount

Labels All major brands when available

see text

Parking High Street, & Yes, **Group Tours** No, **Mail order** No, **Catalogue** No, **Internet Sales** No

Bristol

The Continental Wardrobe

13 Regent Street, Clifton Village, Bristol, Avon, B58 4HW
Tel: 01468 738116

Clothes for men and women. Unusual dress agency

Hours Tue–Sat 10–5:30

Discount

Labels B. Barclay, Jil Sander, G. Brett

see text

Bristol

TK Maxx

Third Floor, The Galleries, Bristol, Avon, BS1 3XE
Tel: 0117 930 4404

Men's, ladies' and children's clothing, furniture, sportswear, electrical and household goods, toys, decorating and sports equipment. American concept; stocks everything under one roof

Hours Mon–Sat 9–5:30, Thur late until 7, Sun 11–5

Discount up to

60%

Midsomer Norton

Dickies UK Ltd

Charlton Lane, Midsomer Norton, near Bath, Avon,
BA3 4BH
Tel: 01761 410732

Casual outdoor wear for men and women

Hours Mon–Sat 9–5, Sun 10–4

Discount

see text

Midsomer Norton

Second to None

Chesterfield House, Midsomer Norton, Bath, Avon,
BA3 2DD
Tel: 01761 415545

Women's and children's clothing. Prices from £1.99
upwards. Products already discounted.

Hours Mon–Sat 9–5:00

Closed Christmas and New Year

Public Transport Bus

Labels All major brands when available

Discount

see text

& Yes, **Group Tours** No, **Mail order** No, **Catalogue** No,
Internet Sales No

Worle

Clarks Shoes

Unit 2, Sainsburys Precinct, Queensway Shopping Centre,
Worle, Avon, BS22 0BT
Tel: 01934 521693

Shoes for all the family

Hours Mon, Thur and Sat 9–6, Fri 9–8, Sun 10:30–4:30

Labels Clarks, Crockers, K. Shoes,
Nike, La Gear, Fila, Cica, Puma,
Weider

Discount up to

30%

Ammanford

Alan Paine Knitwear Ltd

New Road, Ammanford, Carmarthenshire, SA18 3ET
Tel: 01296 592316

Knitwear for men and women

Hours Mon–Sat 10–4

Discount

see text

Ammanford

Corgi Hosiery

New Road, Ammanford, Carmarthenshire, SA18 3DR
Tel: 01269 59 2104 Fax: 01269 59 3220

Quality men's, ladies' and children's knitwear in luxury yarns. Cashmere, wool, silk and cotton. Designer range for special orders

Hours Mon–Sat 9–4

➡ From M4 J49, A483 to Ammanford. After 4.9 miles turn right at New Road Industrial Estate sign. Factory on left in 200 yards

Public Transport Panterfynnon train station, 5 mins walk

Discount up to

Labels Ralph Lauren, Tommy Hilfiger, Scotch House, Hermes of Paris, Balenciaga, Hackett

50%

♿ Yes, **Group Tours** Yes, **Mail order** No, **Catalogue** No,
✗ Plenty in town and surrounding area, **Internet Sales** Yes

Carmarthen

Stewart Seconds

14 Notts Square, Carmarthen, Carmarthenshire, SA31 3PQ
Tel: 01267 222294

Branded merchandise from major chainstores for all the family

Hours Mon–Sat 9–5:30

Discount

40%–70%

Llanelli

Stewart Seconds

52 Stepney Street, Llanelli, Carmarthenshire, SA15 3TR
Tel: 01554 776957

Branded merchandise from major chainstores for all the family

Hours Mon–Sat 9–5:30

Discount

40%–70%

Guernsey

Stonelake Ltd

5 Smith Street, St Peter Port, Guernsey, Channel Islands, GY1 2JN
Tel: 01481 720053 Fax: 01481 713808

Pharmacy and perfumes for women

Hours Mon–Sat 9–5:15

Discount

Labels YSL, Chanel, E. Taylor, Boss, Georgio, Paco Ra, Gucci, Safari

see text

Mail order Yes, **Catalogue** Yes

South-West England & South Wales

Guernsey

Summerland Factory Shop

North Esplanade, Guernsey, Channel Islands
Tel: 01481 701336

Ladies and menswear also footwear

Hours Mon–Sat 9–5:30

Labels Wolsey, Jockey, Baumler, Caron

Discount up to **50%**

Jersey

Summerland Factory Shop

Gorey Woollen Mill, Gorey, Jersey, Channel Islands
Tel: 01534 858024

Ladies and menswear also footwear

Hours Mon–Fri 9–5:30, Sat 9.30–4.30, Sun 10–5

Labels Wolsey, Jockey, Baumler, Caron

Discount up to **50%**

Jersey

Summerland Factory Shop

International House, The Parade, St. Helier, Jersey, Channel Islands
Tel: 01534 625698

Ladies and menswear also footwear

Hours Mon–Sat 9–5:30

Labels Wolsey, Jockey, Baumler, Caron

Discount up to **50%**

Jersey

Summerland Factory Shop

Rouge Bouillion, St Helier, Jersey, Channel Islands, JE2 3ZA
Tel: 01534 33511

Ladies and menswear also footwear

Hours Mon–Fri 9–5:30, Sat 9–4.30

Labels Wolsey, Jockey, Baumler, Caron

Discount up to **50%**

Summerland Factory Shop

St Aubins Woollen Mill, Jersey, Channel Islands
Tel: 01534 44504

Ladies and menswear also footwear

Hours Mon–Fri 9–5:30, Sat 9–4.30, Sun 10–4

Discount up to

Labels Wolsey, Jockey, Baumler, Caron

50%

Cameleon

74 New Street, St Helier, Jersey, Channel Islands, JE2 3TE
Tel: 01534 722438

Offers nearly-new and period fashion for men and women

Hours Tue–Sat 10–5

Closed Christmas. Open between Christmas and New Year

➜ 5 minutes walk from main shopping precinct up New Street

Public Transport Outside Hoppa bus.

Discount

Labels Chanel, DKNY, Escada, YSL, Betty Barclay, Jaeger, Next, M & S, etc.

see text

& No, **Group Tours** Yes, **Mail order** Yes, **Catalogue** No, ✗ Nearby food outlets, **Internet Sales** No

Cinderella's Wardrobe

10 Conway Street, St Helier, Jersey, Channel Islands, JE2 3NT
Tel: 01534 618545

Sells nearly-new and new designer outfits for ladies

Hours Mon–Sat 10–5:30

Discount

Labels Max Mara, R. Lauren, L. Feraud, Escade, Chanel

see text

The Frock Exchange

Cheapside, St Helier, Jersey, Channel Islands, JE2 3PG
Tel: 01534 68324

Women's clothes with labels ranging from High Street to middle market

Hours Mon–Sat 10–5

Discount

Labels Jaeger, J. Vert

see text

Falmouth

Trago Mill Ltd

Arwenack Street, Falmouth, Cornwall, TR11 3LF
Tel: 01326 315738

A vast outlet, sells virtually everything: men's, ladies' and children's clothing, furniture, food, sportswear, electrical and household goods, toys decorating and sports equipment

Hours Mon–Sat 9–5:30, Sun 10:30–4:30

Discount up to

Labels Doc Martens, Lee Cooper, Joe Bloggs, Pierre Cardin

50%

✕ Refreshments on site

Victoria Square, Roche, Cornwall
Tel. 01726 891092

Ladies' blouses, skirts, separates, lingerie and hosiery, men's shirts, ties and boxer shorts, all at discount prices

Opening hours:
Monday–Saturday 9.30–5.30
Sunday 10–5

Open Bank Holidays except Good Friday, Christmas Eve, Christmas Day and Boxing Day
Ample parking off road outside premises

Launceston

Selections

4 Race Hill, Launceston, Cornwall, PL15 9BB
Tel: 01566 775471

Men's and women's High Street and designer labels

Hours Mon–Sat 9:30–4:30

Discount

Labels Planet, Jacques, M & S, Wallis, Jaeger, Next

see text

Liskeard

Trago Mill Ltd

2 Watersfoot, Liskeard, Cornwall, PL14 6HY
Tel: 01579 320584

A vast outlet, sells virtually everything: men's, ladies' and children's clothing, furniture, food, sportswear, electrical and household goods, toys decorating and sports equipment

Hours Mon–Sat 9–5:30, Sun 10:30–4:30

Discount up to

Labels Doc Martens, Lee Cooper, Joe Bloggs, Pierre Cardin

50%

Roche

Silken Ladder

Victoria Square, near Roche, Cornwall, PL26 8LX
Tel: 01726 891092

Wide range of womens and menswear

Hours Mon–Sat 9:30–5:30, Sun 10–5

➤ Cornwall's main arterial road the A30, six miles west of Bodmin, six miles north of St Austell, next to BP station, opposite Victoria Business Park

See ad on page 135

Discount

see text

Barnstaple

Bairdwear Lingerie

Howard Avenue, Whiddon Valley, Barnstaple, Devon, EX32 8LA
Tel: 01271 321337

Lingerie for a well-known department store, seconds, overmakes

Hours Mon–Sat 9:30–4:30

Discount up to

20%

Barnstaple

LS & J Sussman Ltd

Riverside Road, Pottington Industrial Estate, Barnstaple, Devon
Tel: 01271 379305

A range of clothes and household goods for all the family

Hours Tue–Thu 9–4:45, Fri and Sat 9–2

Discount

see text

Parking Yes

Bovey Tracey

House of Marbles and Teign Valley Glass

The Old Pottery, Pottery Road, Bovey Tracey, Devon, TQ13 9DR
Tel: 01626 835358 Fax: 01626 835315
Email: uk@houseofmarbles.uk.com
Web site: www.houseofmarbles.uk.com

Group tours by appointment only

Hours Mon–Sun 9–5

Closed Christmas Day, Boxing Day, 1st–2nd January, plus one week early January for refurbishment

➤ Turn off the A38 at the Drum Bridges roundabout. Follow A382 to Bovey Tracey, then follow the brown tourist signs, Marker House of Marbles

Public Transport Bovey Tracey

Discount

see text

Parking 160 Spaces, & Yes, **Group Tours** Yes, **Mail order** Yes, **Catalogue** No, ✗ On site, **Internet Sales** No

South-West England & South Wales

Sheila Aldridge Baby Equipment Hire

Heatherton, Woodbury, Exeter, Devon
Tel: 01395 233057

Cots and highchairs, buggies, top range framed back-packs, door hung bouncers, Britax car seats, stair gates – pressure fit, breast pumps, travel cots. 10% discount to twins club 'Tamba' members

Hours Sun–Sat 8–8

Closed Christmas, New Year's Day

➡ On B3179 between Woodbury and Clyst St George

Discount

Labels Maclaren, Brevi, Tomy, Britax

see text

Parking 2 Spaces, & No, **Group Tours** No, **Mail order** No, **Catalogue** No, **Internet Sales** No

The Shoe Shed

Units 1 and 2, Rolle House, Rolle Street, Exmouth, Devon, EX8 2SM
Tel: 01395 223343

Vast range of all types of shoes for the family

Hours Mon–Sat 9–5:30, Sun 10–4

Discount up to

30%

Curtain Trader

187 High Street, Honiton, Devon, EX14 8LQ
Tel: 01404 45451

Designer and discontinued fabrics. New and second-hand curtains. Fabrics to order. Making up service. Pine furniture – reclaimed wood – made to your own design

Hours Tue–Sat 9:30–4:30, Thur 9:30–1

Closed Christmas Eve to 10th January

➡ At the western end of the High Street at the bottom of the hill

Public Transport Buses to High Street. Trains into Honiton station

Discount up to

Labels Jane Churchill, Designers Guild, Ramm, Texcraft, Corniche, Chatsworth, Listers, Fibre Naturelle

60%

Parking Street, & No, **Group Tours** No, **Mail order** No, **Catalogue** No, ✗ Many cafes and restaurants in the town, **Internet Sales** No

Trago Mill Ltd

Regional Shopping Centre, Newton Abbot, Devon, TQ12 6JD
Tel: 01626 821111

A vast outlet, sells virtually everything: men's, ladies' and children's clothing, furniture, food, sportswear, electrical and household goods, toys decorating and sports equipment

Hours Mon–Sat 9–5:30, Sun 10:30–4:30

Discount up to

Labels Doc Martens, Lee Cooper, Joe Bloggs, Pierre Cardin

50%

✗ Refreshments on site

South-West England & South Wales Devon

Paignton

Clarks Shoes

Shoe Value, 22 The Crossways, Hyde Road, Paignton, Devon, TQ4 5BL
Tel: 01803 553444

Shoes for all the family

Hours Mon–Sat 9–5:30

Labels Clarks, Crockers, K. Shoes, Nike, La Gear, Fila, Cica, Puma, Weider

Discount up to 30%

Paignton

The Frock Exchange

9 Seaway Road, Preston, Paignton, Devon, TQ3 2NX
Tel: 01803 522951

Cross section of clothes from designer labels

Hours Tue–Sat 10–4:30

Labels YSL, C. Dior, Hodges, Dunns

Discount see text

Plymouth

Matalan

Transitway, Crown Hill, Plymouth, Devon, PL5 3TW
Tel: 01752 772313

Fashion and homewares giving unbeatable value to the whole family

Hours Mon–Fri 10–8, Sat 9–6, Sun 11–5

Discount see text

Plymouth

TK Maxx

Yeo Building, 28 Royal Parade, Plymouth, Devon, PL1 1SA
Tel: 01752 255081

Men's, ladies' and children's clothing, furniture, sportswear, electrical and household goods, toys, decorating and sports equipment. American concept; stocks everything under one roof

Hours Mon–Fri 9–5:30, Thur late until 8, Sat 9–6, Sun 11–5

Discount up to 60%

Dorset

South-West England & South Wales

Tiverton

Origin

Station Road Industrial Estate, Bampton, near Tiverton, Devon, EX16 9NG
Tel: 01398 331704

Large range of womenswear for casual and evening

Hours Mon–Fri 9–2, Sat 9–1

➡ Town of Bampton on the edge of Exmoor

Discount up to 50%

Parking Yes, & Yes

Torquay

Windsmoor Sale Shop

Fleet Street, Torquay, Devon, TW2 5DJ
Tel: 01803 201081

Ladieswear. Previous season's stock and overmakes

Hours Mon–Sat 9–5:30

Labels Planet, Precis Petite

Discount up to 50%

Blandford Forum

Curtains Encore

62 Salisbury Street, Blandford Forum, Dorset, DT11 7PR
Tel: 01258 458871 Fax: 01258 455221
Email: susanencore@clara.net

We sell top quality second-hand and 'designer mistake' curtains. We also offer an alteration service and design advice

Hours Mon–Sat 9:30–1:30, By appointment

Closed Bank Holidays

➡ Right after Market Square, right at Fork shop on corner site, on right hand side. Parking on left hand side of road

Public Transport Buses from Salisbury, Dorchester, Shaftesbury, Poole

Labels Colefax & Fowler, Jab, Osborne & Little, Design archives, Jane Churchill

Discount see text

Parking 1 Space, & Yes, Group Tours Yes, Mail order No, Catalogue No, ✗ In town, Internet Sales No

Boscombe

Damart

Adeline Road, off Christchurch Road, Boscombe, Bournemouth, Dorset
Tel: 01202 301627

Underwear and merchandise

Hours Mon–Sat 9:30–5

Discount see text

page 139

South-West England & South Wales Dorset

Bournemouth

Ancora Dress Agency

275 Charminster Road, Bournemouth, Dorset, BH8 9QJ
Tel: 01202 523848

Ladieswear. Top designer labels

Hours Mon–Sat 10–5:30

Labels Armani, Escade, Charles

Discount

see text

Bournemouth

The Shoe Shed

Units 9 & 12, Quadrant Centre, Hinton Road,
Bournemouth, Dorset, BH1 2AD
Tel: 01202 292992

Shoes

Hours Mon–Sat 9–5:30, Sun 10–4

Discount up to

30%

Bournemouth

TK Maxx

Quadrant Arcade, Old Christchurch Road, Bournemouth,
Dorset, BH1 2BX
Tel: 01202 316367

Men's, ladies' and children's clothing, furniture,
sportswear, electrical and household goods, toys,
decorating and sports equipment. American concept;
stocks everything under one roof

Hours Mon–Fri 9–5:30, Thur late until 8, Sat 9–6, Sun 10–4

Discount up to

60%

Christchurch

The Catalogue Shop

3 Wick Lane, Christchurch, Dorset
Tel: 01202 480422

Men's, ladies' and children's clothes, furniture and
household goods, sports equipment. Returns, damaged
and worn goods, as well as clearance and end of lines
from mail order catalogues

Hours Mon–Sat 9–5, Sun 10–5

See ad on page 31

Discount up to

50%

Ferndown

Look Twice

400 Ringwood Road, Ferndown, Dorset, BH22 9AU
Tel: 01202 875070

A mixture of labels

Hours Mon–Sat 10–5

Labels M & S, Windsmoor, Bianca, Escade, Jacques, F. Usher

Discount

Highcliffe

Gemma Dress Agency

422 Lymington Road, Highcliffe, Christchurch, Dorset, BH23 5HE
Tel: 01425 276928

Almost new clothing and accessories – Jasper Conran, Costelloe, Max Mara, Joseph, Jaeger, Ozbek, Bianca, Ralph Lauren, Episode, Austin Reed, etc. Plus excellent children's range. Half-price sales in July and January

Hours Mon–Sat 10–5, Wed 10–1

Closed Christmas until January 7th

➡ On main Highcliffe Street. Last shop on left when driving from Bournemouth towards Lymington

Public Transport Bus stop outside

Labels As above – varies from week to week

Discount

Parking 3/4 Spaces, & No, **Group Tours** No, **Mail order** No, **Catalogue** No, ✗ Local cafe, wine bar, **Internet Sales** No

Highcliffe

The Catalogue Shop

401 Lymington Road, Highcliffe, Dorset, BH23 5HE
Tel: 01425 271202

Men's, ladies' and children's clothes, furniture and household goods, sports equipment. Returns, damaged and worn goods, as well as clearance and end of lines from mail order catalogues

Hours Mon–Sat 9–5, Sun 10–5

See ad on page 31

Discount up to

50%

Poole

Matalan

Unit 2/3, Turbary Retail Park, Ringwood road, Poole, Dorset, BH12 3JJ
Tel: 01202 590686

Fashion and homewares giving unbeatable value to the whole family

Hours Mon–Fri 10–8, Sat 9–6, Sun 11–5

Discount

South-West England & South Wales Dorset

Sherborne

Browsers

35 Cheap Street, Sherborne, Dorset, DT9 3PU
Tel: 01935 813326

Upmarket dress agency

Hours Mon–Sat 10–5

Labels Jaeger, Mondi, Valentino

Discount

Wareham

Revival

16A South Street, Wareham, Dorset
Tel: 01929 554443

Women's labels with a small selection of wedding dresses, shoes, belts and handbags

Hours Mon and Tues 10–4, Wed 10–1, Thur–Sat 10–5

Closed Lunch 12.30–1 daily

Labels Alexon, Mondi, B. Barclay, F. Usher

Discount

Wimborne

Lori's Boutique

Millstream Close, East Street, Wimborne, Dorset
Tel: 01202 889575

Top quality nearly new garments, hats, bags, belts – only in excellent condition. Seasonal

Hours Mon–Fri 10–5, Wed 10–1, Sat 10–4

Closed Christmas – New Year, Bank Holidays

➡ Over the bridge on the one-way system, just past 'The Rising Sun' public house. Next door to Cloisters restaurant

Public Transport Bus stop Wimborne Square

Labels Bianca, Gerry Weber, Jaeger, Mondi, Country Casuals, Monsoon, Frank Usher, TRU

Discount

Parking None, & Yes, **Group Tours** No, **Mail order** No, **Catalogue** No, ✗ Next door restaurant, pub 2 doors down, **Internet Sales** No

Bourton on the water

Discount China

High Street, Bourton on the Water, Gloucestershire, GL54 2AP
Tel: 01451 820662

China. Prices from £2.00 upwards. Products already discounted

Hours Mon–Sun 10–5:00

Closed Christmas Day and New Year's Day

➡ Next door to Edinburgh Woollen Mill

Public Transport Bus

Labels Non brands

Discount

Parking Public car park, & Yes, **Group Tours** No, **Mail order** No, **Catalogue** No, ✗ Many, **Internet Sales** No

Cheltenham

Ancilla

15 Leckhampton Road, Cheltenham, Gloucestershire,
GL53 0AZ
Tel: 01242 242799

Cheltenham's first dress agency established 25 years ago.
For every woman size 8–20. From M & S to Louis Feraud
including Jaeger, Planet, Next, Bianca, Basler, Paul
Costello and Principles

Hours Tue–Fri 10–5, Wed and Sat 10–1

Closed Monday all day. Wednesday and Saturday after-
noons.

➔ B4070 (Cheltenham/Cirencester) Leckhampton Road.
150 yards from roundabout and Robert Young florist

Public Transport Bus stop 60 yards

Discount

Labels Jaeger, Bianca, Principles,
Windsmoor, Paul Costello, M & S,
Next, Basler, Planet

see
text

Parking Several, & No, **Group Tours** No, **Mail order** No,
Catalogue No, ✗ 100 yards – 2 cafés and wine bar,
Internet Sales No

Cheltenham

Magpie

41 Lyfield Road West, Charlton Kings, Cheltenham,
Gloucestershire, GL53 AT2
Tel: 01242 573909

Dress agency with a good selection and handbags

Hours Mon–Fri 10–5, Sat 10–3

Discount

Labels Next, Planet

see
text

Cheltenham

Matalan

Unit A1/A2, Gallagher Retail Park, Tewkesbury Road,
Cheltenham, Gloucestershire, GL51 9RR
Tel: 01242 254001

Fashion and homewares giving unbeatable value to the
whole family

Hours Mon–Fri 10–8, Sat 9:30–5:30, Sun 10–6

Discount

see
text

Cheltenham

Stephanie

65 Great Norwood Street, Cheltenham, Gloucestershire,
GL50 2BQ
Tel: 01242 512639

High Street to Designer labels and accessories for women

Hours Tue–Sat 10–4:45

Discount

Labels M & S, Next, Wallis,
Monsoon, Max Mara, Marella,
Eastex

see
text

Cheltenham

Toad Hall: The Dress Agency

7 Rotunda Terrace, Montpellier, Cheltenham,
Gloucestershire, GL50 1SW
Tel: 01242 255214

Two floors, exclusively filled with designer names for
women

Hours Mon–Sat 9–5:30

Labels Escade, Armani, Chanel,
Givenchy

Discount
see text

Cheltenham

Woosters & Co

2 Bath Road, off High Street, Cheltenham, Gloucestershire
Tel: 01242 256855

Designer labels for men and women

Hours Mon–Sat 10–5

Labels Boss, P. Smith, Farhi,
Armani

Discount
see text

Cirencester

Gerald Anthony Fashions

1 West Way, off Cricklade Street, Cirencester,
Gloucestershire, GL7 1JA
Tel: 01285 656100

Chainstore clothes for ladies and men at reduced prices

Hours Mon–Sat 9–5

Discount
see text

Cirencester

Rags to Riches

7 Gosditch Street, Cirencester, Gloucestershire
Tel: 01285 656864

High Street and designer labels and accessories for
women

Hours Mon–Sat 10–5

Labels Max Mara, Costello, Farhi

Discount
see text

Gloucester

Catalogue Bargain Shop

4–6 Grosvenor House, Station Road, Gloucester,
Gloucestershire
Tel: 01452 308779

Merchandise from ex-catalogue stock including men's,
ladies' and children's clothes, furniture, food, sportswear,
electrical and household goods, toys, decorating and
sports equipment

Hours Mon–Sat 9–5:30, Sun 10:30–4:30

Labels M & S, Kays, G. Universal

Discount
see text

Gloucester

Damart

Lister Building, Station Road, Gloucester, Gloucestershire
Tel: 01452 526510

Underwear and merchandise

Hours Mon–Sat 9:30–5

Discount
see text

Gloucester

Primark

53 Eastgate Street, Gloucester, Gloucestershire, GL1 1NN
Tel: 01452 424174

Sells mens, womens and childrenswear

Hours Mon–Fri 9–5:30, Sat 9–6, Sun 10–4

Discount
see text

Gloucester

The Edinburgh Woollen Mill

Merchants Quay, Dockyard, Gloucester, Gloucestershire,
GL1 2EH
Tel: 01452 300983

Ladies and menswear. Overmakes and clearance stock are
sold off

Hours Mon–Sat 10–5:30, Sun 11–5, (Mon–Sat 10–5 in
winter)

➔ Follow signs for historic dockyard

Discount
see text

Lechlade

Revival

Burford Street, Lechlade, Gloucestershire, GL7 3AP
Tel: 01367 253803

Wedding outfits, everydaywear, eveningwear (mainly near Christmas), jackets, coats, shoes, handbags, hats, jewellery

Hours Tue–Sat 10–5

Closed Lunch 1–2 daily. About 10 days at Christmas

➡ On the A361 to Burford – situated in Lechlade next door to the newsagents

Public Transport Bus route to/from Swindon

Discount

Labels Escada, Betty Barclay, Parigi, Jaeger, Viyella, Windsmoor, Next, M & S, BHS

see text

Parking Unlimited, & No, **Group Tours** No, **Mail order** No, **Catalogue** No, ✕ 4 pubs, 2 cafes, **Internet Sales** No

Moreton-in-Marsh

Castaway

High Street, Moreton-in-Marsh, Gloucestershire, GL56 0AD
Tel: 01608 652683

Sells wide range of womenswear

Hours Mon–Sat 9:30–5:30

Discount

Labels Monsoon, L. Ashley, Mondi, C. Dior, Mulberry

see text

Moreton-in-Marsh

Top Marks

23 High Street, Moreton-in-Marsh, Gloucestershire, GL56 0AF
Tel: 01608 651272

Sells seconds for all the family

Hours Mon–Fri 9–5:30, Sat 9–5

Discount

Labels M & S, Richards, Debenhams

see text

Newent

Stock Exchange

14 Church Street, Newent, Gloucester, Gloucestershire
Tel: 01531 821681

Nearly new labels for men and women

Hours Mon–Sat 9–5, Wed 9–1

Closed Lunch 1–2 daily

Discount

Labels M & S, Mondi, L. Ashley, Next, Willis

see text

Stow-on-the-Wold

Sequels

Digbeth Street, Stow on the Wold, Gloucestershire,
GL54 1BN
Tel: 01451 870041

Designer women's clothes for day and evening from
M & S – YSL

Hours Mon–Sat 10–5

Closed Lunch 1–2 daily

Labels M & S, YSL

Discount

Stow-on-the-Wold

Glenmatch

2 Brewery Yard, Sheep Street, Stow-on-the-Wold,
Gloucestershire, GL54 1AA
Tel: 01451 870840

Luxury Scottish knitwear direct for men and women

Hours Mon–Sat 9:30–5:30

Discount

30%–40%

Stroud

The Factory Shop

Cashes Green Road Retail Park, off Westward Road,
Cainscross, Stroud, Gloucestershire, GL5 4JE
Tel: 01453 756655

A wide range of goods: men's, ladies' and children's
clothing, furniture, sportswear, electrical and household
goods, toys decorating and sports equipment

Hours Mon, Thur, Sat 9–5, Fri 9–6, Sun 10–4

Labels Nike, Adidas, Wrangler

Discount

30%–50%

Parking Yes, **Catalogue** Yes

Tewkesbury

County Clothes

50 High Street, Tewkesbury, Gloucestershire, GL20 5BH
Tel: 01684 850446

Mid to upmarket ladieswear and accessories

Hours Mon–Sat 9:30–5:15

Discount

30%–40%

Tewkesbury

Garb Clothing

124 High Street, Tewkesbury, Gloucestershire
Tel: 01684 273733

Chainstore overmakes and seconds for all the family

Hours Mon–Sat 9–5

Discount

Tewkesbury

Just Thoughts

56 Church Street, Tewkesbury, Gloucestershire, GL20 5RZ
Tel: 01684 293037

Wide selection of labels for women – middle to upmarket

Hours Tue–Fri 10–5, Sat 10–4

Closed Lunch 1.30–2 daily

Labels Escade, B. Barclay, Costello

Discount

Winchcombe

Just-in-Limited

2 Hailes Street, Winchcombe, Gloucestershire
Tel: 01242 603204

Quality fashions, seconds, continental designerwear and nearly-new clothes

Hours Mon–Sat 10–5:30, Sun 12–5

Discount

see text

Parking Yes

Saundersfoot

Stewart Seconds

Brewery Terrace, Saundersfoot, Pembrokeshire, SA69 9HG
Tel: 01834 812579

Branded merchandise from major chainstores for all the family

Hours Mon–Sat 9–5:30, Sun 10–5:30

Discount

40%–70%

South-West England & South Wales

Saundersfoot

Stewarts Seconds

The Strand, Saundersfoot, Pembrokeshire, SA69 9GE
Tel: 01834 812579

Branded merchandise from major chainstores for all the family

Hours Mon–Sun 9:30–5:30

Discount

40%–70%

Tenby

Stewart Seconds

The High Street, Tenby, Pembrokeshire, SA70 7EW
Tel: 01834 844621

Branded merchandise from major chainstores for all the family

Hours Mon–Sat 9:30–5:30, Sun 10–5:30

Discount

40%–70%

Bridgwater

Clarks Shoes

2 Eastover, Bridgwater, Somerset, TA6 5AB
Tel: 01278 452617

Shoes for all the family

Hours Mon–Sat 9–5:30

Discount up to

Labels Clarks, Crockers, K. Shoes, Nike, La Gear, Fila, Cica, Puma, Weider

30%

Burnham-on-Sea

Clarks Shoes

10A High Street, Burnham-on-Sea, Somerset, TA8 1NX
Tel: 01278 794668

Shoes for all the family

Hours Mon–Sat 9–5:30, Sun 11–5, Bank Holidays 10–5

Discount up to

Labels Clarks, Crockers, K. Shoes, Nike, La Gear, Fila, Cica, Puma, Weider

30%

Burnham-on-Sea

JPS Footwear Ltd

2 High Street, Burnham-on-Sea, Somerset, TA8 1NK
Tel: 01278 780141

Most of stock consists of shoes from warehouse clearance lines and end of lines

Hours Mon–Sat 9–5:30, Sun 11–6

Discount

Burnham-on-Sea

Second to None

85 High Street, Burnham-on-Sea, Somerset, TA8 1PE
Tel: 01278 787457

Women's and children's clothes. Prices from £1.99 upwards. Products already discounted

Hours Mon–Sat 9–5:00, Sun through the summer

Closed Christmas and New Year

Public Transport Bus

Discount

Labels All major labels stocked when available

Parking High Street, & Yes, **Group Tours** No, **Mail order** No, **Catalogue** No, **Internet Sales** No

Glastonbury

Morlands (Glastonbury)

Northover, Glastonbury, Somerset, BA6 9YA
Tel: 01458 835042

Men and women's sheepskin coats and slippers; ladies' boots and accessories

Hours Mon–Sat 9:30–5

➡ On A39 just north of Clarks Village

Discount

Minehead

Minehead Shoe Co Ltd

1 North Road, Minehead, Somerset, TA24 5QW
Tel: 01643 705591

Specialist in made-to-measure footwear, including golf and bowling shoes

Hours Mon–Thu 9–5, Fri 9–4, Sat 10–4

Discount

Mail order Yes, **Catalogue** Yes

South-West England & South Wales

Minehead

The Factory Shop

Mart Road, Minehead, Somerset, TA24 5BJ
Tel: 01643 705911

A wide range of goods: men's, ladies' and children's clothing, furniture, sportswear, electrical and household goods, toys decorating and sports equipment

Hours Mon–Sat 9:30–5:30, Sun 11–5

Labels Nike, Adidas, Wrangler

Discount 30%–50%

Parking Yes, **Catalogue** Yes

Shepton Mallet

Mulberry

The Old School House, Kilver Street, Shepton Mallet, Somerset, BA4 5NF
Tel: 01749 340583

Clothes and household goods for all the family. Everything under one roof

Hours Mon–Sat 10–6, Sun 11–5

➤ Situated on A37

Discount 30%–40%

& Yes, ✗ Refreshments on site

Shepton Mallet

The Doc Shop

Townsend Road, Shepton Mallet, Somerset
Tel: 01794 347081

Sells Doc Marten shoes and boots – seconds. Also clothing

Hours Mon–Fri 9–5:30, Sat 9–5, Sun 10–4

See ad on page 203

Labels Dr Marten

Discount see text

Somerton

Enigma

The Market Place, Somerton, Somerset, TA11 7NB
Tel: 01458 274393

Top quality labels from German and UK fashion houses for women

Hours Mon–Sat 10–5

➤ Four miles south of Clarks Village in Street

Discount see text

Somerton

Janes Dress Agency

The Triangle, Somerton, Somerset, TA11 6QJ
Tel: 01458 273711

High Street and Designer labels and accessories for women

Hours Mon–Fri 9:30–5, Sat 9:30–4:30

Discount

Labels Escade

see text

Street

Clarks Factory Shop

Unit 13, Clarks Village, Farm Road, Street, Somerset, BA16 0BB
Tel: 01458 843161

Specialises in discontinued and slight sub-standard shoes for all the family

Hours Mon–Sat 9–6

Discount up to

Labels Nike, La Gear, Clarks, Fila

30%

Street

Clarks Shoes

112–114 High Street, Street, Somerset, BA16 0EW
Tel: 01458 442055

Shoes for all the family

Hours Mon, Sat and Bank Holidays 9–5:30, Sun 11–5

Discount up to

Labels Clarks, Crockers, K. Shoes, Nike, La Gear, Fila, Cica, Puma, Weider

30%

Street

Clarks Village Factory Shopping

Farm Road, Street, Somerset, BA16 0DB
Tel: 01458 840064

Full range of shops selling men's, ladies' and children's clothing, furniture, food, sportswear, electrical and household goods, toys decorating, sports equipment and shoes

Hours Mon–Sat 9–6

See ad on page 153

Discount

see text

Parking Yes, ✕ Refreshments on site

Street

Dickies UK Ltd

121 High Street, Street, Somerset
Tel: 01458 841900

Casual outdoor wear

Hours Mon–Sat 9–5, Sun 10–4

Discount **see text**

Street

Ecco

82 High Street, Street, Somerset, BA16 0EN
Tel: 01458 443950

Shoes for all the family. Telephone for a catalogue 0800 387368

Hours Mon–Sat 9–5:30

Discount up to **25%**

, **Catalogue** Yes

Street

Jaeger

Unit 30, Clarks Village, Farm Road, Street, Somerset, BA16 0BB
Tel: 01458 447215

Ladies and menswear. Designer name only

Hours Mon–Sat 9–6, Sun 11–5

Labels Jaeger

Discount **see text**

Street

James Barry Menswear

Clarks Village, Farm Road, Street, Somerset, BA16
Tel: 01458 840478

All men's clothing and accessories

Hours Mon–Sat 9–6, Sun 11–5

Discount **see text**

South-West England & South Wales

Jane Shilton

Clarks Village, Farm Road, Street, Somerset, BA16 0BB
Tel: 01458 840504

Merchandise from past season's stock of women's clothes and accessories and household items

Hours Mon–Sat 10–6, Sun 11–5

Discount up to
30%

Jumpers

Clarks Village, Farm Road, Street, Somerset, BA16 0BB
Tel: 01458 840320

A wide range of sweaters for men and women

Hours Mon–Sat 9–6, Sun 11–5

Discount up to
50%

Laura Ashley 9

Clarks Village, Farm Road, Street, Somerset, BA16 0BB
Tel: 01458 840405

Fashion for women and home furnishings

Hours Mon–Sat 9–5:30, Sun 11–5

Discount
see text

Liz Claiborne UK

Clarks Village, Farm Road, Street, Somerset, BA16 0BB
Tel: 01458 840912

American designer Liz Claiborne's shop for women

Hours Mon–Sat 9–6, Sun 11–5

Discount up to
50%

Street

Monsoon

Clarks Village, Farm Road, Street, Somerset, BA16 0BB
Tel: 01458 840890

Clothing for men and women. Selling last year's stock and discontinued lines

Hours Mon–Sat 9–6, Sun 11–5

Discount

see text

Street

Thorntons

Unit 20 Clarks Village, Farm Road, Street, Somerset, BA16 0BB
Tel: 01458 841553

The factory outlet stores sell three different product categories: misshapes, discounted lines and standard lines. Misshapes are packed into assorted bags and offer a saving of between 35%–55%. Discount lines are offered at a discount of 25%–50%. Standard lines are also on sale at normal prices

Hours Opening times dependent upon individual factory outlet centre

Labels Thorntons

Discount

25%–55%

&. No, **Group Tours** No, **Mail order** Yes, **Catalogue** Yes,
✗ Most outlet centres have food courts, **Internet Sales** Yes

Street

Tog 24

Clarks Village, Street, Somerset, BA16 0ND
Tel: 01458 840468

Specialist outdoor clothing for men and women. Sportswear and sports equipment

Hours Mon–Sat 9–6, Sun 11–5

Discount up to

30%

Street

Tom Sayers Clothing Co

Clarks Village, Farm Road, Street, Somerset
Tel: 01458 448874

Sweaters for men

Hours Mon–Sat 9–6, Sun 11–5

Discount up to

30%

Street

Triumph International Ltd

Clarks Village, Street, Somerset, BA16 0BB
Tel: 01458 840700

Lingerie and swimwear for men and women

Hours Mon–Sat 9–5:30, Sun 11–5

Discount

see text

Street

Viyella

Clarks Village, Street, Somerset, BA16 0BB
Tel: 01458 448533

Wide range of ladieswear

Hours Mon–Sat 9–6, Sun 11–5

Discount up to

30%

Street

Whittard of Chelsea

Clarks Village, Farm Road, Street, Somerset, BA16 0BB
Tel: 01458 841 323 Fax: 01458 841 323
Web site: www.whittard.com

Quality range of tea and coffee. Exclusive and extensive china, textiles, glassware, kitchenware

Hours Mon–Sat 9–6, Sun 11–5

Closed Christmas and New Year

➡ Buses from Bristol, Wells, Glastonbury

Discount

Labels Whittard, Sia Parlane

30%–75%

& Yes, **Group Tours** Yes, **Mail order** Yes, **Catalogue** No,
✗ Free tasting., **Internet Sales** Yes

Street

Windsmoor Sale Shop

Clarks Village, Street, Somerset, BA16 0BB
Tel: 01458 840888

Previous seasons stock of women's clothes

Hours Mon–Sat 9–6, Sun 11–5

Discount up to

50%

Taunton

Absent Labels

51B St James Street, Taunton, Somerset, TA1 1JH
Tel: 01823 3330242

Chainstore clothes for men and women

Hours Mon–Fri 9:30–5:30, Sat 9–5:30

Labels M & S

Discount
see text

Wellington

Fox's Mill Shop

Tonedale Mills, Wellington, Somerset, TA21 0AW
Tel: 01823 662271

Sells wool and cashmere for men and women. You can buy the fabric and take it away, or the in-situ tailor will make up garments

Hours Tue–Sat 10–5

Discount
see text

Weston-super-Mare

Clothing World

North Worle District Centre, Queensway, Worle, Weston-super-Mare, Somerset
Tel: 01934 522065

Extensive range of casualwear for girls and boys as well as adults and a range of household items

Hours Mon–Thu 9–5:30, Fri 9–6:30, Sat 9–6

Discount
30%–50%

Yeovil

Absent Labels

Church House, Church Street, Yeovil, Somerset, BA20 1HE
Tel: 01935 78183

Chainstore clothes for men and women

Hours Mon–Thu 9:30–5, Fri, Sat 9–5

Labels M & S

Discount
see text

Bargoed

Bairdwear Lingerie

St Davids Industrial Estate, Pengam, Bargoed, Gwent,
South Wales, NP2 1SW
Tel: 01443 821430

Underwear for ladies

Hours Mon–Fri 9:30–4:30, Sat 9–1

Discount **see text**

Blackwood

Gossard Factory Shop

Penmaen Road, Pontllanfraith, Blackwood, South Wales,
NP2 2DL
Tel: 01495 221103

Women's underwear

Hours Mon–Sat 9:30–5:30

Labels Gossard, Berlei

Discount **25%–75%**

Parking Yes, & Yes

Bridgend

Catalogue Bargain Shop

Ffalds Road Shopping Centre, Pyle Cross, Pyle, Bridgend,
South Wales, CF33 6BH
Tel: 01656 746426

Merchandise from ex-catalogue stock including men's,
ladies' and children's clothes, furniture, food, sportswear,
electrical and household goods, toys, decorating and
sports equipment

Hours Mon–Sat 9–8, Sun 10:30–4:30

Labels Kays, G. Universal

Discount **see text**

Bridgend

Ecco

McArthur Glen Designer Outlet Wales, The Derwen,
Bridgend, South Wales, CF32 3SU
Tel: 01656 767200

Ladies', men's and children's shoes. Telephone 0800
387368 for catalogue

Hours Mon–Sat 10–6, Thur late until 8, Sun 11–5

Discount **see text**

Mail order Yes, **Catalogue** Yes

South-West England & South Wales   South Wales

Bridgend

Famous Footwear

McArthur Glen Designer Outlet Wales, The Derwen, Bridgend, South Wales

Shoes for all the family

Hours Mon–Sat 9–6

Discount up to

Labels Dolcis, Cartier, Saxone, Lotus, K Shoes, Ava, Ecco, Hush Puppies

50%

Bridgend

John Partridge Outlet Store

McArthur Glen Designer Outlet Wales, The Derwen, Bridgend, South Wales

Specialises in hardwearing outdoor clothes for men and women

Hours Mon–Sat 9–6

Discount

30%–70%

Bridgend

Levi's Big Factory Outlet

McArthur Glen Designer Outlet Wales, The Derwen, Bridgend, South Wales, CF32 9FU
Tel: 01656 767335

Clothes for all the family. Most of the stock is seconds or end of line

Hours Mon–Sat 10–6, Thur late until 8, Sun 11–5

Discount

see text

Bridgend

McArthur Glen Designer Outlet Wales

The Derwen, Bridgend, South Wales, CF32 9SU
Tel: 01656 665703 Fax: 01656 665711

Reebok, Calvin Klein, Tie Rack, Bed & Bath, Overland, Pepe, Famous Footwear, Nickelbys, The Suit Company, Kids Play Factory, Vans, Red/Green, Travel Accessories, Ecco, Jacques Vert, Warners, Nike, Roman Originals, Paco, Helly Hansen, Cotton Traders, Lee Cooper, Donnay, So Kids, Wedgwood, Next to Nothing, Claks, Knickerbox, Jaeger, Van Heusen, Karrimor, Benetton, Elle, Pilot, Chilli Pepper, Timberland, Carphone Warehouse, Big L and 2 children's play areas, Odeon 9 Screen Cinema. 90 stores

Hours Mon–Sat 10–6, Thur late until 8, Sun 11–5

➡ Junction 36 off M4, just off slip road.

Public Transport Bridgend train station. Buses every hour from town centre

See ads on page 43 and 161

Discount

30%–70%

Parking Yes, **Group Tours** Yes

Bridgend

Sofa Concepts

Brynmenyn Industrial Estate, Brynmenyn, Bridgend, South Wales, CF32 9TD
Tel: 01656 841014 Fax: 01656 849205
Email: sales@sofaconcepts.co.uk
Web site: www.sofaconcepts.co.uk

Range of over 10 models in choice of fabrics – construction guaranteed for 4 years – 21 day full-refund guarantee – sample service. Deliveries all over UK

Hours Mon–Sun 10–4

Closed Christmas closedown 23rd–25th December and 1st January

➡ Leave M4 at J36. Head towards Bryncethin. Left at lights in Bryncethin. First unit on left in industrial estate about 5 minutes from motorway

Public Transport Bus No.12, platform 5 from Bridgend. Approximately 15 minutes by taxi from Bridgend railway station.

Labels Sofa Concept

Discount
30%–50%

Parking 10 Spaces, & No, Group Tours Yes, Mail order Yes, Catalogue Yes, ✗ On site, Internet Sales Yes

Bridgend

Thorntons

Unit 69, Welsh Designer Factory, Bridgend, South Wales, CF32 9BU
Tel: 01656 657104

The factory outlet stores sell three different product categories: misshapes, discounted lines and standard lines. Misshapes are packed into assorted bags and offer a saving of between 35%–55%. Discount lines are offered at a discount of 25%–50%. Standard lines are also on sale at normal prices

Hours Opening times dependent upon individual factory outlet centre

Labels Thorntons

Discount
25%–55%

& No, Group Tours No, Mail order Yes, Catalogue Yes, ✗ Most centres have food courts, Internet Sales Yes

Bridgend

Tog 24

McArthur Glen Designer Outlet Wales, Bridgend, South Wales
Tel: 01656 767033

Specialist in outdoor clothing for men and women

Hours Mon–Fri 10–6, Thur late until 8, Sat 9–6, Sun 11–5

Discount up to
30%

Bridgend

Viyella

McArthur Glen Designer Outlet Wales, Pen-y-Car Lane, Bridgend, South Wales, CF32 9ST
Tel: 01656 648660

Wide range of ladieswear

Hours Mon–Fri 10–6, Thur late night until 8, Sat 9–6, Sun 11–5

Discount up to
30%

South-West England & South Wales

Caerphilly

Bairdwear Lingerie

Bedwas Business Park, Bedwas, Caerphilly, South Wales, NP1 6XH
Tel: 029 2086 4699

Underwear for women

Hours Mon–Sat 10–4

Discount

see text

Caerphilly

Stewart Seconds

4 Cardiff Road, Ytwyn, Caerphilly, South Wales, CF8 1JN
Tel: 029 2088 8054

Branded merchandise from major chainstores for all the family

Hours Mon–Sat 9:30–5:30

Discount

40%–70%

Caldicot

Bairdwear Lingerie

Unit 11, Symondscliff Way, Severn Bridge Industrial Estate, Caldicot, South Wales, NP6 4TH
Tel: 01291 421551

Underwear for women

Hours Mon–Sat 9:30–4:30

Discount

see text

Cardiff

Matalan

Unit 2, 382–384 Newport Road, Cardiff, South Wales,
Tel: 029 2049 1781

Fashion and homewares shop for all the family

Hours Mon–Fri 10–8, Sat 9–6, Sun 11–5

Discount

see text

Chepstow

Second to None

17 High Street, Chepstow, South Wales, NP6 5LG
Tel: 01291 622424

Clothes, accessories and housewares for all the family. Women's and children's clothes. Prices from £1.99 upwards

Hours Mon–Sat 9–5

Closed Christmas and New Year

Public Transport Bus

Discount up to

Labels Gossard, Zorbit, Berlei, all major brands when available

75%

&. Yes, **Group Tours** No, **Mail order** No, **Catalogue** No, **Internet Sales** No

Cowbridge

Changes Dress Agency

27A High Street, Cowbridge, South Glamorgan, South Wales, CF71 7AG
Tel: 01446 772184

Designer and high quality labels for women

Hours Tue–Sat 10–5

Discount

Labels Max Mara, C. Dior, Laurel, Escade, Jaeger, Mani

 see text

Cowbridge

Elle

41A High Street, Cowbridge, South Glamorgan, South Wales, CF71 7AG
Tel: 01446 772184

Lots of separates and office wear for women

Hours Mon–Sat 10:30–5:30

Discount

Labels J. Conran, Escade, Mondi, C. Dior, Armani

 see text

Cwmbran

Matalan

Unit 4B, Cwmbran Retail Park, Cwmbran Drive, Cwmbran, South Wales, NP44 3JQ
Tel: 01633 866944

Fashion and homewares shop for all the family

Hours Mon–Fri 10–8, Sat 9:30–5:30, Sun 10–6

Discount

see text

South-West England & South Wales

Ebbw Vale

Catalogue Bargain Shop

Bryn Ferth Road, Rhy-y-Blen, Ebbw Vale, South Wales, NP3 5YD
Tel: 01495 309297

Merchandise from ex-catalogue stock including men's, ladies' and children's clothes, furniture, food, sportswear, electrical and household goods, toys, decorating and sports equipment

Hours Mon–Sat 9–8, Sun 10–4

Labels Kays, G. Universal

Discount
see text

Ebbw Vale

Jane Shilton

Festival Park Shopping Centre, Victoria Road, Ebbw Vale, South Wales, NP3 6OH
Tel: 01495 302216

Last seasons collectons of ladies clothes and accessories

Hours Mon–Sat 10–6, Sun 11–5

Discount up to
30%

Ebbw Vale

John Partridge Outlet Store

Festival Park, Victoria, Ebbw Vale, Gwent, South Wales
Tel: 01495 352643

Specialises in hardwearing outdoor clothes

Hours Mon–Sat 10–6, Sun 11–5

Discount
30%–70%

for road maps...

www.WestOneWeb.com

...great offers

Ebbw Vale

Leading Labels Ltd

Festival Park Shopping Centre, Unit 29, Victoria Road,
Ebbw Vale, South Wales, NP3 6UF
Tel: 01495 305643(off) / 305674 (shop) Fax: 01495 306995

A huge selection of quality mens and ladieswear over an
extensive range of sizes. Top brand names and designer
labels all at discounted prices

Hours Mon–Sun, Various opening hours depending on
site, Sun various

Closed Christmas Day

Labels Ben Sherman, Kangol,
Whimsey, Kläss, Chilli Pepper,
Roman Originals, Double Two

Discount
20%–75%

& No, **Group Tours** No, **Mail order** No, **Catalogue** No,
Internet Sales No

Ebbw Vale

The Factory Shop Ltd

Festival Park Factory Outlet Shopping Village, Festival
Park, Victoria, Ebbw Vale, Gwent, South Wales, NP3 6UF
Tel: 01495 352533

Men's, women's and children's clothes, furniture,
sportswear, electrical and household goods, toys,
decorating and sports equipment. Wide range of
goods on sale

Hours Mon–Sat 10–6, Sun 10–4

Labels Adidas, Nike, Wrangler

Discount
30%–50%

Ebbw Vale

Thorntons

Unit 50, Festival Park, Factory Shopping Centre, Victoria,
Ebbw Vale, South Wales, NP3 6FP
Tel: 01495 305099

The factory outlet stores sell three different product categories: misshapes, discounted lines and standard lines.
Misshapes are packed into assorted bags and offer a saving of between 35%–55%. Discount lines are offered at a
discount of 25%–50%. Standard lines are also on sale at
normal prices

Hours Opening times dependent upon individual factory
outlet centre

Labels Thorntons

Discount
25%–55%

& No, **Group Tours** No, **Mail order** Yes, **Catalogue** Yes,
✗ Most centres have food courts, **Internet Sales** Yes

Ebbw Vale

Tog 24

Festival Park Outlet Centre, Victoria, Ebbw Vale, Gwent,
South Wales
Tel: 01495 301902

Specialist in outdoor clothing for men and women

Hours Mon–Sat 10–6, Sun 11–5

Discount up to
30%

South-West England & South Wales

Ebbw Vale

Tom Sayers Clothing Co

Festival Shopping Centre, Victoria Road, Ebbw Vale,
South Wales, NP3 6AU
Tel: 01495 301414

Men's sweaters

Hours Mon–Sat 10–6, Sun 11–5

Discount from
30%

Llantrisant

Matalan

Unit 8, Glamorgan Vale Retail Park, Llantrisant, South
Wales, CF7 8RP
Tel: 01443 224854

Fashion and homewares shop for all the family

Hours Mon–Fri 10–8, Sat 9–6, Sun 10–5

Discount
30%–50%

Merthyr Tydfil

Bairdwear Lingerie

Cyfartha Industrial Estate, Merthyr Tydfil, South Wales,
CF47 8PE
Tel: 01685 383837

Underwear for women

Hours Mon–Sat 10–4:30

Discount
see text

Merthyr Tydfil

Catalogue Bargain Shop

61 High Street, Merthyr Tydfil, South Wales, CF47 8DE
Tel: 01685 385653

Merchandise from ex-catalogue stock including men's,
ladies' and children's clothes, furniture, food, sportswear,
electrical and household goods, toys, decorating and
sports equipment

Hours Mon–Sat 9–5:30, Sun 10–4

Labels Kays, G. Universal

Discount
see text

Merthyr Tydfil

Pendor Factory Shop Ltd

Dowlais Industrial Estate, Merthyr Tydfil, South Wales, CF48 3TF
Tel: 01685 722681

Clothing for the whole family and sportswear and equipment, also electrical goods

Hours Mon–Fri 9:30–7, Sat 9:30–6, Sun 11–5

Discount

Labels Reebok, Nike, Adidas

30%–60%

Monmouth

Stewart Seconds

7–11 Monnow Street, Monmouth, South Wales
Tel: 01600 716926

Branded merchandise from major chainstores for all the family

Hours Mon–Sat 9:30–5:30

Discount

40%–70%

Monmouth

Togs

6 Monnow Street, Monmouth, South Wales, NP25 3EE
Tel: 01600 772629

Casualwear for women

Hours Mon–Sat 9:30–5:00

Closed Bank Holidays

Public Transport Bus

Discount

Labels Loom, Adini, Chilli Pepper

see text

Parking No, & Yes, **Group Tours** No, **Mail order** No, **Catalogue** No, **Internet Sales** No

Pontardawe

Bairdwear Lingerie

Church Street, Pontardawe, South Wales, SA8 4JB
Tel: 01792 830490

Underwear for women

Hours Mon–Fri 9–4, Sat 9–12 noon

Discount

see text

Pontypridd

Alexon Sale Shop

Cardiff Road, Hawthorn, Pontypridd, South Wales
Tel: 01443 480673

Last seasons stock of women's clothes

Hours Mon–Sat 10–5

Labels Alexon, Eastex, Calico

Discount **40%–70%**

Pontypridd

Catalogue Bargain Shop

5 High Street, Pontypridd, South Wales, CF37 1QJ

Merchandise from ex-catalogue stock including men's, ladies' and children's clothes, furniture, food, sportswear, electrical and household goods, toys, decorating and sports equipment

Hours Mon–Sat 9–5, Sun 10:30–4:30

Labels Kays, G. Universal

Discount **see text**

Pontypridd

Fabric World

Factory E6, Treforest Industrial Estate, Pontypridd, South Wales, CF37 5ST
Tel: 01443 842286 Fax: 01443 662929

Complete range of furnishing fabrics, including curtaining, upholstery, bedding, dress fabrics – fashion and basic, haberdashery, foam, cushions, tracks and poles, patterns. We run monthly promotions on products and periodic sales

Hours Mon–Sat 9–5, Thur late until 7, Sun 11–4

Closed Bank Holidays

➡ Off M4 to A470 Merthyr. Treforest Industrial Estate, turn off, follow dual carriageway approx. half mile, on left 'Pottery' pub, behind there

Public Transport Bus 100 metres away.

Labels Moygashel, Prestigious, SMD, Coates, Swish, Simplicity, Whiteheads, Gardisseite, Romo

Discount **10%–50%**

Parking 50 Spaces, ♿ Yes, **Group Tours** Yes, **Mail order** No, **Catalogue** No, ✗ Tesco's or pub food., **Internet Sales** No

Pontypridd

Stewart Seconds

79A Taff Street, Pontypridd, South Wales, CF37 4SU
Tel: 01443 402225

Branded merchandise from major chainstores for all the family

Hours Mon–Sat 9:30–5:30

Discount **40%–70%**

South-West England & South Wales South Wales

Bairdwear Lingerie

Sandfields Estate, Purcell Avenue, Sandfields, Port Talbot,
South Wales, SA12 7UF
Tel: 01639 895038

Underwear for women

Hours Mon–Thu 9:30–4, Fri 9–4, Sat 9–12 noon

Discount see text

Port Talbot

Catalogue Bargain Shop

31 Station Road, Port Talbot, South Wales, SA13 1NN
Tel: 01639 899419

Merchandise from ex-catalogue stock including men's,
ladies' and children's clothes, furniture, food, sportswear,
electrical and household goods, toys, decorating and
sports equipment

Hours Mon–Sat 9–5

Labels Kays, G. Universal

Discount see text

Pyle

Bairdwear Lingerie

Village Farm Industrial Estate, Pyle, South Wales,
CF33 6NU
Tel: 01656 742511

Underwear for women

Hours Mon–Sat 9:30–4:30

Discount see text

Rhondda

Burberry

Ynyswen Road, Treorchy, Rhondda, South Wales
Tel: 01443 772020

Good merchandise for all the family

Hours Mon–Thu 9–4

Discount see text

✕ Refreshments on site

Swansea

Catalogue Bargain Shop

229–230 High Street, Swansea, South Wales
Tel: 01792 456748

Merchandise from ex-catalogue stock including men's, ladies' and children's clothes, furniture, food, sportswear, electrical and household goods, toys, decorating and sports equipment

Hours Mon–Sat 9–8, Sun10:30–4:30

Labels Kays, G. Universal

Discount
see text

Swansea

Dewhurst Clothing Factory Shop

Unit 22, The Kingsway, Fforestfach Industrial Estate, Fforestfach, South Wales, SA5 4HY
Tel: 01792 584621

Selection of clothes for men, women and children

Hours Mon–Fri 9–3:30, Sat 9–5, Sun 11–5

Discount up to
50%

Swansea

Gainsborough

12 Swansea Road, Llangyfelach, Swansea, South Wales, SA5 7JD
Tel: 01792 790922 Fax: 01792 790922
Email: susan.gainsborough@virgin.net

Impeccable day, occasion and eveningwear resold at huge discounts. Over 1,000 items in stock. Day 2/3 pieces, dresses, tops, skirts, trousers, jackets, suits, casualwear, coats, evening dresses, evening separates, ball gowns, wedding outfits, hats and more. Average price £45

Hours Mon–Sat 10–5

Closed Christmas, New Year and Bank Holidays

➡ Leave M4 at J47 or 46, B4489. Gainsborough on village green near large gabled pub, 'Plough and Harrow'

Public Transport No. 36 from Quadrant Shopping Centre, Swansea, hourly.

Labels Frank Usher, Condici, Jacques Vert, Armani, Max Mara, Gerry Weber, Gina Bacconi, Mani

Discount

50%–80%

Parking 20 Spaces, ☟ Yes, Group Tours No, Mail order No, Catalogue No, ✗ Refreshments on site, and 'Plough and Harrow' on the green is very good; in nearby Morriston, Internet Sales No

Swansea

Matalan

Foundry Road, Morriston, Swansea, South Wales, SA6 8DU
Tel: 01792 792229

Fashion and homewares shop for all the family

Hours Mon–Fri 10–8, Sat 9:30–5:30, Sun 10–6

Discount
see text

South-West England & South Wales South Wales

Swansea

Stewart Seconds

228–230 Oxford Street, Swansea, South Wales
Tel: 01792 410906

Branded merchandise from major chainstores for all the family

Hours Mon–Sat 9:30–5:30

Discount

40%–70%

Usk

Peggy Sue Dress Agency

28 Bridge Street, Usk, Gwent, South Wales, NP5 1BG
Tel: 01291 673309

Popular labels

Hours Mon–Sat 10–5

Closed Wednesday

Discount

Labels Escade, Jacques Vert, Windsmoor, M & S

see text

Chippenham

Second to None

13 The Bridge, Chippenham, Wiltshire, SN15 1HA
Tel: 01249 656456

Women's and children's clothing. Prices from £1.99 upwards. Products already discounted

Hours Mon–Sat 9–5:00

Closed Christmas and New Year

Public Transport Bus

Discount

Labels All major brands when available

see text

Parking High Street, & Yes, **Group Tours** No, **Mail order** No, **Catalogue** No, **Internet Sales** No

Corsham

The Factory Shop Ltd

23–25 New Place, Corsham, Wiltshire, SN13 0HL
Tel: 01249 712160

A wide range of goods: men's, ladies' and children's clothing, furniture, sportswear, electrical and household goods, toys decorating and sports equipment

Hours Mon–Sat 9–5:30, Sun 10–4

Discount

Labels Nike, Adidas, Wrangler

30%–50%

Parking Yes, **Catalogue** Yes

South-West England & South Wales

Georgina von Etzdorf

The Avenue, Odstock, near Salisbury, Wiltshire
Tel: 01722 415969

Men's and women's clothes

Hours Mon–Sat 10–5:30

Closed Lunch 1–2 daily

Discount

see text

Goldi

53 Winchester Street, Salisbury, Wiltshire, SP1 1HL
Tel: 01722 421969

High quality, non-chainstores, designer

Hours Mon–Sat 10–5

Labels Escade, Max Mara, YSL, Dior, Valentino

Discount up to

50%

TK Maxx

Cross Keys Shopping Centre, Salisbury, Wiltshire
Tel: 01722 320644

Men's, ladies' and children's clothing, furniture, sportswear, electrical and household goods, toys, decorating and sports equipment. American concept; stocks everything under one roof

Hours Mon–Fri 9–5:30, Thur 9–8, Sat 9–6, Sun 11–5

Discount up to

60%

Burberrys Ltd

McArthur Glen Designer Outlet, Great Western, Churchward Village, Swindon, Wiltshire, SN2 2DY
Tel: 01793 507600

Burberry and Thomas Burberry goods for men and women

Hours Mon–Fri 10–6

➡ Junction 16 off M4

Discount

see text

South-West England & South Wales Wiltshire

Clarks Shoes

Units 1A and G13, West Swindon District Centre,
Swindon, Wiltshire, SN5 7DI
Tel: 01793 873662

Shoes for all the family

Hours Mon, Wed and Sat 9–6, Thur and Fri 10–4, Sun 10–5

Labels Clarks, Crockers, K. Shoes, Nike, La Gear, Fila, Cica, Puma, Weider

Discount up to **30%**

Daks Simpson

McArthur Glen Designer Outlet, Great Western,
Churchward Village, Swindon, Wiltshire, SN2 2DY
Tel: 01793 507600

Previous stocks of clothing for women and men

Hours Mon–Fri 10–6

→ Junction 16 off M4

Discount **see text**

Designer Room

McArthur Glen Designer Outlet, Great Western,
Churchward Village, Swindon, Wiltshire, SN2 2DZ
Tel: 01793 436941

Sells international designers clothes for women

Hours Mon–Fri 10–6, Thur 11–5, Sat 9–6

Labels Moschino, Armani, YSL, Cerruti, Gucci, L. Feraud

Discount **see text**

Dorothy Perkins

McArthur Glen Designer Outlet, Great Western,
Churchward Village, Swindon, Wiltshire, SN2 2DY
Tel: 01793 639796

Dorothy Perkins women's clothes, end of season lines

Hours Mon–Fri 10–6, Thur late until 8, Sat 9–6, Sun 11–5

Discount **see text**

Swindon

Ecco

McArthur Glen Designer Outlet, Great Western,
Churchward Village, Swindon, Wiltshire, SN2 2DZ
Tel: 01793 422240

All the family's shoes. Telephone 0800 387368 for catalogue

Hours Mon–Fri 10–6, Thur late until 8, Sat 9–6, Sun 11–5

Discount up to
25%

Catalogue Yes

Swindon

Hanro of Switzerland

McArthur Glen Designer Outlet, Great Western,
Churchward Village, Swindon, Wiltshire
Tel: 01793 480118

Luxury lingerie for men and women

Hours Mon–Fri 10–6, Thur late until 9, Sat 9–6, Sun 11–5

Labels Harrods, Harvey Nichols, Selfridges

Discount
35%–50%

Swindon

Jaeger

McArthur Glen Designer Outlet, Great Western, Kemble
Drive, Churchward Village, Swindon, Wiltshire, SN2 7AA
Tel: 01793 484660

Ladies and menswear. Designer name only

Hours Mon–Fri 10–6, Thur late until 8, Sat 9–6, Sun 11–5

Labels Jaeger

Discount
see text

Swindon

James Barry Menswear

McArthur Glen Designer Outlet, Great Western,
Churchward Village, Swindon, Wiltshire
Tel: 01793 655020

All men's clothing and accessories

Hours Mon–Fri 10–6, Thur late until 8, Sat 9–6, Sun 11–5

Discount
see text

South-West England & South Wales

Wiltshire

Swindon

Jane Shilton

McArthur Glen Designer Outlet, Great Western, Kemble Drive, Churchward Village, Swindon, Wiltshire, SN2 2DY
Tel: 01793 430356

Merchandise from past season's stock of women's clothes and accessories and household items

Hours Mon–Fri 10–6, Sat 9–6, Sun 11–5; open Bank Holidays

Discount up to

30%

Swindon

Joe Bloggs

McArthur Glen Designer Outlet, Great Western, Churchward Village, Swindon, Wiltshire, SN2 2DY
Tel: 01793 435543

Range of casual clothing for all the family

Hours Mon–Sat 10–6, Sun 11–5

Labels Joe Bloggs

Discount up to

30%

Swindon

Laura Ashley 9

McArthur Glen Designer Outlet, Great Western, Kemble Drive, Swindon, Wiltshire
Tel: 01793 511355

Fashion and home furnishings for all the family

Hours Mon–Fri 10–6, Sat 9–6, Sun 11–5

Discount

see text

Swindon

Levi's Big L Factory outlet

McArthur Glen Designer Outlet, Great Western, Churchward Village, Swindon, Wiltshire, SN2 2DZ
Tel: 01793 693339

Jeans and clothes for men and women – end of lines and seconds

Hours Mon–Fri 10–6, Thur late until 9, Sat 9–6, Sun 11–5 and Bank Holidays

Discount

see text

South-West England & South Wales

Matalan

Unit 2B, Mannington Retail Park, Wootton Bassett Road,
Swindon, Wiltshire, SN5 9NP
Tel: 01793 649500

Fashion and homewares giving unbeatable value to the
whole family

Hours Mon–Fri 10–8, Sat 9–6, Sun 10–4

Discount

see text

Mexx International

McArthur Glen Designer Outlet, Great Western,
Churchward Village, Swindon, Wiltshire, SN2 2DY
Tel: 01793 692205

High Street fashions which are heavily discounted

Hours Mon–Fri 10–6, Thur late until 8, Sat 9–6, Sun 11–5

Discount up to

50%

Old Dairy Saddlery

Greenway, Tockenham, Swindon, Wiltshire, SN4 7PY
Tel: 01793 849282

Large shop on farm selling outdoorwear, horse blankets,
country clothing, etc.

Hours Mon–Sat 10–5, Thur late until 8, Sun 10–1

Discount

see text

Ouiset

McArthur Glen Designer Outlet, Great Western, Kemble
Drive, Churchward Village, Swindon, Wiltshire, SN2 2TA
Tel: 01793 480535

Ladieswear – sells clearance lines

Hours Mon–Fri 10–6, Thur late until 9, Sat 9–6, Sun 11–5

Discount

30%–70%

South-West England & South Wales Wiltshire

Paco Life in Colour

Unit 107, McArthur Glen Designer Outlet, Great Western,
Kemble Drive, Churchward Village, Swindon, Wiltshire,
SN2 2DY
Tel: 01793 536936

Leisure, casual, knitwear and accessories mainly for
women and children

Hours Mon–Fri 10–6, Thur late until 8, Sat 9–6, Sun 11–5

Discount up to

30%

Pied A Terra Sale Shop

McArthur Glen Designer Outlet, Great Western, Kemble
Drive, Churchward Village, Swindon, Wiltshire, SN2 2DZ
Tel: 01793 695774

Shoes, clothing and accessories including high-fashion
wear

Hours Mon–Fri 10–6, Thur late until 9, Sat 9–6, Sun 11–5

Discount up to

50%

Principles

McArthur Glen Designer Outlet, Great Western,
Churchward Village, Swindon, Wiltshire, SN2 2DY
Tel: 01793 695774

End of season lines for women, men and children

Hours Mon–Fri 10–6, Thur late until 9, Sat 9–6, Sun 11–5

Discount

see text

The Designer Store

McArthur Glen Designer Outlet, Great Western,
Churchward Village, Swindon, Wiltshire, SN2 2DZ
Tel: 01793 486161

Sells British catwalk designer labels

Hours Mon–Fri 10–6, Sat 9–6, Sun 11–5

Labels Amanda Wakeley, Paddy
Campbell, N. Peal, R. Klein, C.
Paul, D. Fielden

Discount

see text

Swindon

The Dressing Room

Little Thatch, High Street, Wanborough, near Swindon,
Wiltshire, NS4 0AE
Tel: 01793 791450

New and nearly new labels for women

Hours Tue–Thu 9–1, or by appointment

Labels Costello

Discount

see text

Swindon

The Shoestring

5 Apsley House Arcade, Wootton Bassett, Swindon,
Wiltshire
Tel: 01793 850106

Sells clothes and accessories

Hours Sat 9–5

Discount

see text

Swindon

Thorntons

Unit 80, Great Western Outlet, Churchward Village,
Kemble Drive, Swindon, Wiltshire, SN2 7AA
Tel: 01793 692438

The factory outlet stores sell three different product
categories: misshapes, discounted lines and standard
lines. Misshapes are packed into assorted bags and offer
a saving of between 35%–55%. Discount lines are offered
at a discount of 25%–50%. Standard lines are also on sale
at normal prices

Hours Opening times dependent upon individual factory
outlet centre

Labels Thorntons

Discount

25%–55%

&. No, **Group Tours** No, **Mail order** Yes, **Catalogue** Yes,
✕ Most centres have food courts, **Internet Sales** Yes

Swindon

Tie Rack

McArthur Glen Designer Outlet, Great Western,
Churchward Village, Swindon, Wiltshire, SN2 2DY
Tel: 01793 531070

Tie Rack items, silk boxers, socks, scarves, waistcoats
for men

Discount

see text

South-West England & South Wales Wiltshire

Timberland

McArthur Glen Designer Outlet, Great Western, Churchward Village, Swindon, Wiltshire, SN2 2DY

Footwear, clothing and outdoor wear for men and women

Hours Mon–Fri 10–6, Thur late until 8, Sat 9–6, Sun 11–5

Discount up to
30%

Tog 24

McArthur Glen Designer Outlet, Great Western, Churchward Village, Swindon, Wiltshire, SN2 2DY
Tel: 01793 695966

Specialist outdoor clothingfor men and women. Sportswear and sports equipment

Hours Mon–Fri 10–6, Thur late until 9, Sat 9–6, Sun 11–5

Discount up to
30%

Tom Sayers Clothing Co

McArthur Glen Designer Outlet, Great Western, Churchward Village, Swindon, Wiltshire, SN2 1NJ
Tel: 01793 484212

Sweaters for men

Hours Mon–Fri 10–6, Sat 9–6, Sun 11–5

Discount up to
30%

Triumph International Ltd

McArthur Glen Designer Outlet, Great Western, Churchward Village, Swindon, Wiltshire, SN2 7AA
Tel: 01793 480892

Lingerie and swimwear for men and women

Hours Mon–Fri 10–6, Thur late until 8, Sat 9–6, Sun 11–5

Discount
see text

South-West England & South Wales

United Footwear

Horsham Crescent, Park South, Swindon, Wiltshire,
SN3 2LX
Tel: 01793 435238

Shoes for all the family, clothes and accessories

Hours Mon–Sat 9–5:30, Sun 10–4

Labels Clarks, K. Shoes, Elmdale

Discount

Viyella

McArthur Glen Designer Outlet, Great Western,
Churchward Village, Swindon, Wiltshire, SN2 7AR
Tel: 01793 484450

Wide range of ladieswear

Hours Mon–Sat 10–6, Thur late until 9, Sun 11–5

Discount

see text

Wear It Well

59 North Street, off Eastcott Hill, Oldtown, Swindon,
Wiltshire, SN1 3JY
Tel: 01793 695223

Two-storey shop selling High Street labels to men and
women

Hours Mon, Tue, Thur–Sat 10–4

Labels Armani, N. Farhi, Mulberry

Discount

see text

Windsmoor Sale Shop

McArthur Glen Designer Outlet, Great Western,
Churchward Village, Swindon, Wiltshire, SN2 2DZ
Tel: 01793 507600

Previous seasons stock of women's clothes

Hours Mon–Fri 10–6, Thur late until 8, Sat 9–6, Sun 11–5

Discount up to

50%

Trowbridge

The Factory Shop Ltd

36–37 Roundstone Street, Trowbridge, Wiltshire,
BA14 8DE
Tel: 01225 751399

A wide range of goods: men's, ladies' and children's
clothing, furniture, sportswear, electrical and household
goods, toys decorating and sports equipment

Hours Mon–Sat 9–5

Labels Nike, Adidas, Wrangler

Discount
30%–50%

Parking Yes, **Catalogue** Yes

Warminster

Dents

Fairfield Road, Warminster, Wiltshire, BA12 9DL
Tel: 01985 212291

Accessories, i.e. gloves, belts, handbags, etc.

Hours Tue–Sat 10–4

See ad on page 183

Discount up to
50%

Warminster

Encore

42 George Street, Warminster, Wiltshire, BA12 8QB
Tel: 01985 84600

Specialists in nearly new and designer clothes – casual,
leisure, formal, executive, evening. New hats in stock and
made to order

Hours Mon–Sat 9:30–5

Closed Bank Holidays

➜ Bath side of main High Street, down the hill from
Woolworths

Discount
see text

♿ Yes, **Group Tours** Yes, **Mail order** No, **Catalogue** No,
✗ 12 yards away, **Internet Sales** No

Warminster

The Factory Shop Ltd

24 Market Place, Warminster, Wiltshire, BA12 9AN
Tel: 01985 217532

A wide range of goods: men's, ladies' and children's
clothing, furniture, sportswear, electrical and household
goods, toys decorating and sports equipment

Hours Mon–Sat 9–5

Labels Nike, Adidas, Wrangler

Discount
30%–50%

Parking Yes, **Catalogue** Yes

Wilton

Karalynes

20 West Street, Wilton, Wiltshire, SP2 0DF
Tel: 01722 742802

Quality nearly new clothing for women of all ages, all sizes. From M & S to Gucci. 12-year reputation for quality and standard. Good turnover with new arrivals daily. Constant half-price rails. Children's play corner

Hours Tues, Thur, Sat 9.30–4

Closed Monday, Wednesday and Sunday. 2 weeks over Christmas and New Year

➡ Shop in main shopping area. Last shop at end of West Street near church entrance at side

Public Transport Bus stop across from shop

Discount

Labels Any label

25%–75%

Parking Street, & No, Group Tours No, Mail order No, Catalogue No, ✗ Teashop next door, Internet Sales No

Wilton

Leading Labels Ltd

The Wilton Shopping Village, Minster Street, Wilton, Salisbury, Wiltshire, SP2 0RS
Tel: 01722 741400 Fax: 01722 741490

A huge selection of quality mens and ladieswear over an extensive range of sizes. Top brand names and designer labels all at discounted prices

Hours Mon–Sun, Various opening hours depending on site, Sun various

Closed Christmas Day

Discount

Labels Ben Sherman, Kangol, Whimsey, Kläss, Chilli Pepper, Roman Originals, Double Two

20%–75%

& No, Group Tours No, Mail order No, Catalogue No, Internet Sales No

Wilton

Tom Sayers Clothing Co

Wilton Factory Shopping Village, King Street, Wilton, Salisbury, Wiltshire, SP2 0RS
Tel: 01722 741257

Sweaters for men

Hours Mon–Fri 9:30–7, Thur late until 8, Sat 9–6, Sun 11–5

Discount up to

30%

Central England and Mid Wales

Cambridge

Barneys Factory Outlet

38–42 Mill Road, Cambridge, Cambridgeshire, CB1 2AD
Tel: 01223 369596

Ladies' and mens' designer labels, mostly end of lines

Hours Mon–Sat 9–6, Sun 10–5

Labels C. Klein, R. Lauren, YSL, M. Polo

Discount up to

60%

Fenstanton

The Frock Exchange

7 High Street, Fenstanton, Cambridgeshire, PE18 9LQ
Tel: 01480 461187

East Anglia's first and probably best dress agency, specialising in designer names

Hours Tue–Sat 9–5

Closed Christmas, New Year and all Bank Holidays

➡ Just off A14 which connects A1 and M11 (20 minutes either way). Look for the clock tower

Public Transport Peterborough to Cambridge bus. St. Ives to Cambridge bus

Labels Louis Feraud, Betty Barclay, Valentino, Nicole Farhi, Escada, Ghost, all mid-price German labels

Discount

20%–50%

Parking 2 Spaces, & Yes, **Group Tours** No, **Mail order** No, Catalogue No, ✕ Pub, take-away bakery, **Internet Sales** No

Peterborough

Stage 2

Saville Road, Westwood, Peterborough, Cambridgeshire, PE3 7PR
Tel: 01733 263308 Fax: 01733 268127

Footwear and all catalogue stock from Freemans catalogue sold on at discount prices. Group tours by appointment

Hours Mon–Fri 10–8, Sat 9–6, Sun 10–4, Bank Holidays 10–4

➡ City centre and Sleaford. Signs to Westwood Industrial Estate

Public Transport Bus and train

Labels All brands, varied

Discount

see text

Parking Yes, & Yes, **Group Tours** Yes, **Mail order** No, Catalogue No, **Internet Sales** No

St Ives

Ramsey Paint Company

19B East Street, St Ives, Cambridgeshire
Tel: 01480 465002 Fax: 01480 465002

Decorators merchant, trade outlet. Goods at trade prices. Public welcome. 6000 colour range of all types of house and industrial paints and sundries. 100 wallpaper books

Hours Mon–Fri 8–5, Sat 9–12 noon

Closed All Bank Holidays

Public Transport St Ives

Labels Crown, Permoglaze, MacPhersons, Leyland, own brand

Discount

see text

& No, **Group Tours** No, **Mail order** No, **Catalogue** No, **Internet Sales** No

Aberystwyth

Seconds Out

58 Great Darkgate Street, Aberystwyth, Cardiganshire
Tel: 01970 611897

Clothes for all the family

Hours Mon–Fri 9–5, Sat 9–4

Discount

see text

Aberystwyth

Stewart Seconds

12 Pier Street, Aberystwyth, Cardiganshire, SY23 2LJ
Tel: 01970 611437

Branded merchandise from major chainstores for all the family

Hours Mon–Sat 9–5:30, Sun 11–5 (summer only)

Discount

40%–70%

Cardigan

Seconds Ahead

10 Pendre, Cardigan, Cardiganshire, SA43 1DT
Tel: 01239 612721

Seconds for men, women and children

Hours Mon–Fri 9:30–5:30, Sat 9–5:30

Discount

see text

Lampeter

Stewart Seconds

Harford Square, Lampeter, Cardiganshire, SA48 7HD
Tel: 01570 422205

Branded merchandise from major chainstores for all the family

Hours Mon–Sat 9:30–5:30

Discount

40%–70%

Newquay

Stewart Seconds

Glamore Terrace, Newquay, Cardiganshire, SA45 9PL
Tel: 01545 560740

Branded merchandise from major chainstores for all the family

Hours Mon–Sat 9:30–5:30, Sun 10–5:30

Discount

40%–70%

Alfreton

Thorntons

Unit 5, Designer Outlet Village, Mansfield Road, South Normanton, Alfreton, Derbyshire, DE55 2JW
Tel: 01773 545289

The factory outlet stores sell three different product categories: misshapes, discounted lines and standard lines. Misshapes are packed into assorted bags and offer a saving of between 35%–55%. Discount lines are offered at a discount of 25%–50%. Standard lines are also on sale at normal prices

Hours Opening times dependent upon individual factory outlet centre

Labels Thorntons

Discount

25%–55%

&. No, **Group Tours** No, **Mail order** Yes, **Catalogue** Yes, ✗ Most centres have food courts, **Internet Sales** Yes

Ambergate

End of the Line

32 Derby Road, Ambergate, Derbyshire, DE56 2GE
Tel: 01773 856082 Fax: 01773 856082

Furniture factory shop

Hours Telephone for information

Discount

see text

Belper

De Bradelei Mill Shop Ltd

De Bradelei House, Chapel Street, Belper, Derbyshire, DE56 1AR Tel: 01773 829830 Fax: 01773 829822
Email: mail@debradelei.enterprise-plc.com

Leading designer and High Street labels with up to 70% discount, from: Womenswear – Windsmoor, Planet, Précis Petite, French Connection, Four Seasons, Jaeger Knitwear, Phase Eight, Joyce Ridings and many more. Menswear – French Connection, Great Plains, Wolsey, Regatta, Haggar and Robert Leonard Menswear selling leading international labels. Shoes for men and women

Hours Mon–Fri 9:30–5:30, Sat 9:30–6, Sun 11–5

Closed Christmas Day, New Year's Day, Easter Sunday

➜ Just off the A6 at Safeway roundabout. From Derby – follow A6 to Belper, turn left at roundabout, past petrol station to car park on right. From Matlock – turn right at roundabout in Belper. From Heanor via A609 – go straight over roundabout

Public Transport Bus station – 2 minutes walk (opposite shop). Train station – 5 minutes walk. Taxis

See ad on page 45

Labels Windsmoor, Planet, Précis Petite, Four Seasons, Phase Eight, French Connection, Liz Claiborne

Discount

25%–70%

Parking 50 Spaces, &. Yes, **Group Tours** Yes, **Mail order** No, **Catalogue** No, ✗ On site coffee shop, **Internet Sales** No

Chesterfield

Yew Tree Ltd

Yew Tree Farm, Hardstoft, Pilsley, Chesterfield,
Derbyshire, S45 8AE
Tel: 01246 853614 Fax: 01246 859864
Email: EAdsetts@aol.com

The Garden Factory Shop open from April–September. A
very large range of beautiful Swedish wooden garden
furniture and accessories like planters and parasols all at
unbeatable prices. The Christmas Factory Shop is open
from October–December. A beautiful and very big range
of all kinds of Christmas decorations for indoors and out
– all at unbeatable prices

Hours Mon–Fri 1–5, Sat and Sun 10–5

See ad on page 189

Discount

Labels Decorations for indoors
and outdoors. The Garden Shop –
Swedish wooden garden furniture

Parking Yes

Derby

Derwent Crystal Ltd

Little Bridge Street, Derby, Derbyshire, DE1 3LE
Tel: 01332 360186 Fax: 01332 360186

Full range of crystal glassware, tableware and fancies.
Engraving for anniversaries etc. 10% discount for sports
clubs

Hours Mon–Sat 9–5

Closed Sundays and Bank Holidays

➜ A52 into Derby. Off at one-way system to Bridge Street

Discount

Labels Own

Parking On street, & Yes, **Group Tours** No, **Mail order** Yes,
Catalogue Yes, **Internet Sales** No

Derby

Langley Furniture

Delves Road, Heanor Gate Ind. Estate, Heanor, Derbyshire,
DE75 7SJ
Tel: 01773 765544 Fax: 01773 531322
Email: antonybaines@langleypine.freeserve.co.uk

Handmade, solid timber, traditional style pine furniture.
Full range includes bedroom, dining and kitchen furniture,
fitted bedrooms and kitchens, tables, chairs, dressers and a
complete made-to-measure and design service

Hours Mon–Sat 9–5, Sun 10:30–4

Closed Christmas Day, Boxing Day, New Year's Eve and
Day, Bank Holidays

➜ A608 Heanor to Derby Road, Heanor Gate Industrial
Estate is clearly signposted

Public Transport Bus stop on Derby Road. Train station at
Langley Mill

Discount

Parking 20 Spaces, & Yes, **Group Tours** No, **Mail order** Yes,
Catalogue Yes, ✗ On site, **Internet Sales** No

Glossop

Abris Outdoor Clothing

3 Wrens Nest, High Street West, Glossop, Derbyshire, SK13 8EX
Tel: 01457 863966 Fax: 01457 854712

Manufacturers of specialist high quality clothing for hill-walking and backpacking for all the family. Reps samples, ends of lines, factory specials all at reduced prices

Hours Tue–Thu 10–5, Fri and Sat 10–3

Closed Monday, Christmas and New Year, telephone about Bank Holidays

➡ On western end of town behind Telegraph petrol station

Public Transport 15 minutes walk from Glossop train station. Buses to Glossop from Manchester and Sheffield

Discount

see text

Parking Yes, & Yes, **Group Tours** Yes, **Mail order** Yes, **Catalogue** Yes, ✗ Numerous local cafés, **Internet Sales** No

Glossop

Glossop Factory Shop

Howard Town Mills, Glossop, Derbyshire, SK13 8LR
Tel: 01457 866039

Men's and women's well-known branded names. The majority of items are perfects sold at discount prices

Hours Mon–Sat 9–5:15, Bank Holidays 9–5:15

Closed Christmas Day and New Year's Day

➡ Close to centre of town, easy to find

Public Transport Easy walk from town centre. Trains to Glossop. Buses from Manchester stop in Henry Street, 2 minutes walk from shop

Discount

see text

Parking Yes, & Yes, **Group Tours** Yes, **Mail order** No, **Catalogue** No, ✗ Several places in town, **Internet Sales** No

Ilkeston

R S Designer Leisurewear Ltd

192–194 Norman Street, Cotmanhay, Ilkeston, Derbyshire, DE7 8NR
Tel: 01159 323865 Fax: 01159 301919
Email: rscmt@aol.com

Mens ladies and childrenswear, sportswear. Small shop offering personal service from a small manufacturing unit. All items for sale made on premises. Made to measure and alteration service

Hours Mon–Fri 9–3, Some Sats – ring to confirm

Closed All Bank Holidays – ring to confirm

➡ Follow signs to Heanor from Ilkeston.

Discount

Labels Own label, High Street overmakes

20%–50%

Parking On street, & No, **Group Tours** No, **Mail order** Yes, **Catalogue** Yes, **Internet Sales** No

Rowsley

Leading Labels Ltd

Unit 7/8, Peak Village Outlet Shopping Centre, Chatsworth Road, Rowsley, Derbyshire, DE4 2JE
Tel: 01629 735038 Fax: 01629 735489

A huge selection of quality mens and ladieswear over an extensive range of sizes. Top brand names and designer labels all at discounted prices

Hours Mon–Sun, Various opening hours depending on site, Sun various

Closed Christmas Day

Discount

Labels Ben Sherman, Kangol, Whimsey, Kläss, Chilli Pepper, Roman Originals, Double Two

20%–75%

& No, **Group Tours** No, **Mail order** No, **Catalogue** No, **Internet Sales** No

- **TOP DESIGNER BRANDS**
- **THEMED FOOD COURT**
- **CHILDREN'S PLAY AREAS**

OPEN 7 DAYS A WEEK

MON/TUES/WED/FRI 10am – 6pm

THUR 10am – 8pm / SAT 9am – 6pm / SUN 11am – 5pm

McARTHURGLEN OUTLET STORE DERBYSHIRE – JCT 28 M1. TEL: 01773 545000

Swadlincote

TDP Textiles Ltd

TDP House, Rawdon Road, Moira, Swadlincote,
Derbyshire, DE12 6DT
Tel: 01283 550400

Fashions for all the family, animated film/series
underwear and nightwear. T-shirts, jeans etc.The majority
of goods are manufactured under contract for major
chainstores and mail order companies. This is a new look
factory shop with a children's play area

Hours Mon–Sat 9:30–6, Sun 10–4. Open Bank Holidays

Closed Christmas and New Year

➡ From the traffic lights at the main crossroad in the
centre of Moira (where B5003 crosses B586); take B586
north for Swadlincote. Go under railway; drive to shop is
on the right after 100 yards. From Swadlincote/Woodville;
go south on B586 towards Moira; go left into factory (100
yards before the railway bridge). Entrance is clearly
marked

See ad on page 193

Discount

see text

Parking Yes, ⅋ Yes, **Group Tours** Yes

Barnt Green

Continental Exchange

48 Hewell Road, Barnt Green, Hereford and Worcester,
B45 8NF
Tel: 0121 447 7544

Evening wear, wedding outfits, ball gowns, hats

Hours Tue–Sat 10–5

Labels M & S, Chanel

Discount

see text

Evesham

Leading Labels Ltd

Unit 1, Evesham Country Park, Evesham, Hereford and
Worcester, WR11 4TP
Tel: 01386 47572 Fax: 01386 41263

A huge selection of quality mens and ladieswear over an
extensive range of sizes. Top brand names and designer
labels all at discounted prices

Hours Mon–Sun, Various opening hours depending on
site, Sun various

Closed Christmas Day

Discount

Labels Ben Sherman, Kangol,
Whimsey, Kläss, Chilli Pepper,
Roman Originals, Double Two

20%–75%

⅋ No, **Group Tours** No, **Mail order** No, **Catalogue** No,
Internet Sales No

Hereford

Chameleon Dress Agency

123 Eign Street, Hereford, Hereford and Worcester,
HR4 0RJ
Tel: 01432 353436

Wide range of clothes as well as a huge range of hats for
women

Hours Mon–Sat 10–5

➡ Sited near Sainsburys

Discount

Labels M & S, Alexon, C. Casuals,
Eastex, Yarrel, N. Farhi, Joseph, R.
Lauren

see text

Kidderminster

Top Drawer
The Old Malt House, Chaddesley Corbett, Hereford and Worcester, DY10 4FD
Tel: 01562 777808

Upmarket dress agency

Hours Tue–Fri 10–4, Sat 10–1

Labels A Wakeley, Bed de Lisi, Max Mara, B Jackson, P Costelloe, N Farhi

Discount **see text**

Leominster

E Walters Factory Shop
Station Road, Leominster, Hereford and Worcester, HR6 0RJ
Tel: 01568 616127

Largest trousers manufacturer, sells end of lines, cancelled orders; also golf wear, trainers

Hours Mon–Fri 9–5, Sat 9–4

Discount **30%–40%**

Central England & Mid Wales Hereford and Worcester

Malvern

Catalogue Bargain Shop

233 Worcester Road, Malvern Link, Malvern, Hereford
and Worcester, WR14 1SY
Tel: 01684 893062

Merchandise from ex-catalogue stock including men's,
ladies' and children's clothes, furniture, food, sportswear,
electrical and household goods, toys, decorating and
sports equipment

Hours Mon–Sat 9–5:30, Sun 10:30–4:30

Labels Kays, G. Universal

Discount

 see text

Malvern

Studio

11 Abbey Road, Malvern, Hereford and Worcester,
WR14 3ES
Tel: 01684 576253

Finest designer clothes from the continent for women

Hours Mon–Sat 9–5:30

Discount up to

50%

Pershore

The Factory Shop Ltd

New Road, Pershore, Hereford and Worcester, WR10 1BY
Tel: 01386 556467

Men's, women's and children's clothes, sportswear,
electrical and household goods, toys, decorating items
and sports equipment. Wide range of merchandise under
one roof

Hours Mon–Sat 9–5, Sun 10.30–4.30

Labels Adidas, Nike, Wrangler

Discount

30%–50%

Pershore

The House of Beautiful

13 Bridge Street, Pershore, Hereford and Worcester,
WR10 1AT

Agency jewellery, hats and handbags. Good as new and
new at discount prices

Hours Mon–Sat 10–4:30

Closed Thursdays and Bank Holidays

➡ Down from square where parking is

Public Transport Bus

Labels Basler, Chada, Lucia,
Jaeger, Alexon, Windsmoor

Discount

see text

& Yes, **Group Tours** No, **Mail order** No, **Catalogue** No,
Internet Sales No

Central England & Mid Wales

Pershore

The House of Beautiful Clothes

18 Bridge Street, Pershore, Hereford and Worcester,
WR10 1AT
Tel: 01386 552121

High-class, pristine condition and seasonal garments for women. Also hats, jewellery and handbags

Hours Mon–Sat 10–4:30

Closed Thursday

Discount

Labels Basler, Windsmoor, Jaeger, Eastex, J Vert, C Casuals

Ross-on-Wye

Ross Labels Ltd

Overross House, Ross-on-Wye, Hereford and Worcester,
HR9 7QJ
Tel: 01989 769000

Outfits for all the family

Hours Mon–Wed 9–5:30, Thur, Fri 9:30–5:30, Sat 9–5, Sun 10–5

Discount

Labels L. Cooper, Wolsey, Lyle & Scott

20%–50%

Ross-on-Wye

Designer Discount Club

Unit E, Ashburton Estate, Ross-on-Wye, Hereford and Worcester, HR9 7BW
Tel: 01989 564357

Women's clothes. Members only, with massive savings. Membership £5

Hours Mon–Fri 9:30–5, Sat 10–5

Discount up to

80%

Ross-on-Wye

Stewart Seconds

33 High Street, Ross-on-Wye, Hereford and Worcester,
HR9 5HD
Tel: 01989 762403

Clothing for men and women. Top-quality merchandise at highly competitive prices

Hours Mon–Sat 9:30–5:30

Discount

40%–70%

Central England & Mid Wales

Worcester

Bumpsadaisy Maternity Style
25 Friars Street, Worcester, Hereford and Worcester
Tel: 01905 28993

Specialists in maternity wear

Hours Mon–Sat 10–5:30

Discount

see text

Worcester

Catalogue Bargain Shop
15 Pump Street, Worcester, Hereford and Worcester, WR1 22X
Tel: 01905 617211

Merchandise from ex-catalogue stock including men's, ladies' and children's clothes, furniture, food, sportswear, electrical and household goods, toys, decorating and sports equipment

Hours Mon–Sat 9–5:30, Sun 10:30–4:30

Labels Kays, G. Universal

Discount

see text

Worcester

Catalogue Bargain Shop
West Bank, Berry Hill Industrial Estate, Droitwich, Worcester, Hereford and Worcester, WR9 9AP
Tel: 01905 779850

Merchandise from ex-catalogue stock including men's, ladies' and children's clothes, furniture, food, sportswear, electrical and household goods, toys, decorating and sports equipment

Hours Mon–Fri 9–8, Sat 9–5.30, Sun 10.30–4.30

Labels Kays, G. Universal

Discount

see text

Worcester

Designer Depot
Unit 5, Charles House, Charles Street, Worcester, Hereford and Worcester, WR1 2AQ
Tel: 01905 611568

Top quality branded fashions for women

Hours Mon–Sat 9–5:30

Discount up to

50%

Worcester

Exchange & Smart
45 New Street, Worcester, Hereford and Worcester,
WR1 2DL
Tel: 01905 611522

Women's excellent quality clothing, hats, bags and shoes

Hours Mon–Fri 10–4:30, Sat 10–5

Labels M & S, Max Mara, N Farhi, Mani, Monsoon, Windsmoor

Discount see text

Worcester

The Designer Agency
31 Pump Street, Worcester, Hereford and Worcester,
WR1 2QX
Tel: 01905 21414

A comprehensive selection of designer ladieswear

Hours Mon–Sat 10–4

Labels Armani, Jean Muir, Joseph Janard, Escade, Max Mara

Discount see text

Earl Shilton

The Factory Shoe Company
Hill Top Works, Earl Shilton, Leicester, Leicestershire,
LE9 9DT
Tel: 01455 823300 Fax: 01455 823300

Ladies' and men's quality leather sandals, shoes and boots at heavily discounted prices. Wrangler. Line dancing boots discounted

Hours Mon–Sat 10–5

Closed Wednesdays, Christmas, New Year, Bank Holidays

➡ Factory shop on A47 top of hill coming from Leicester into Earl Shilton on right hand side. Car park at rear and across road (public)

Public Transport Bus stop nearby coming from Leicester and Hinckley

Labels Wrangler, R.P. Ellens, Kit, Gringos, Cat Eyes, Firenze

Discount 50%–75%

& Yes, **Group Tours** No, **Mail order** No, **Catalogue** No, ✗ in village, **Internet Sales** No

Leicester

Appliance Centre
87 Lothair Road, Aylestone Park, Leicester, Leicestershire,
LE2 7QE
Tel: 0116 244 0150

Cookers, ovens, hobs, range cookers, washing machines, tumble-driers, fridges, freezers, dishwashers etc., etc. Top brands. Perfects and seconds, all with full guarantee, at heavily discounted prices

Hours Mon–Fri 7:45–5:30

Closed Christmas

➡ A426 south out of Leicester. Fork left at Toyota showroom along Saffron Lane. Turn 2nd right into Lothair Road. Factory shop approx. 200 yards on left

Labels Stoves, Tricity Bendix, Bosch, Siemens, AEG, ASKO

Discount 25%–40%

& Yes, **Group Tours** No, **Mail order** Yes, **Catalogue** No, ✗ Café within 200 yards. Chip shop within 300 yards., **Internet Sales** No

Leicester

Blunts

128–132 Gramby Street, Leicester, Leicestershire, LE1 1DL
Tel: 0116 255 5959

Well-known brand names of shoes for men and women

Hours Mon–Sat 8:30–6, Sun 10–4

Discount

Leicester

Creative Carpets Ltd

Unit 8 Mill Hill Ind. Estate, Quarry Lane, Enderby,
Leicestershire, LE9 5AU
Tel: 0116 2841455 Fax: 0116 2752550

Carpets (prices per square metre) manufactured on premises. All 80% wool, heavy domestic. Large colour selection available in plain dyed, heathers and berber flecks. Underlay and fitting service available. Genuine factory shop with savings of up to 50%. Seconds from £7.75 per square metre

Hours 9–3, Weekdays by appointment

Closed Christmas, New Year

➦ The factory is 5 mins from Fosse Park shopping centre and same distance from M1 exit 21 and M69. Follow signs Enderby/Narborough. Through Enderby, just past 'Plough' pub on left

Public Transport 5 minutes walk

See ad on page 199

Discount

Parking Unlimited, ♿ Yes, **Group Tours** No, **Mail order** Yes, **Catalogue** No, ✕ Local pubs across road, **Internet Sales** No

Leicester

Doc Shop

Bruce Way, Cambridge Road Industrial Estate, Whetstone, Leicester, Leicestershire
Tel: 0116 286 5958

The latest range of Dr. Martens footwear and accessories

Hours Contact for opening hours

See ad on page 203

Discount

Market Overton

The Table Place

Workshop Showroom, Thistleton Road Industrial Estate, Market Overton, Leicestershire, LE15 7PP
Tel: 0800 731 1687 Web site: www.table_place.co.uk

All furniture own label. Hand-finished and lifetime guarantee, exclusive hallmarks. Direct selling saves 20–25% off normal retail prices. Seconds and end of lines sometimes available – discount up to 40%. Telephone orders welcome. Disabled access to ground floor only. Group tours by appointment. Conducted tours – second Saturday every month

Hours Mon–Sat 10–4, Sun 11–4

Closed 25th–30th December, Bank Holiday Mondays

➦ Approximately 5 miles from A1/B668 junction. Take B668 to Cottesmore, turn right to Market Overton. From Oakham take B668 to Cottesmore, turn right to Market Overton

Public Transport Oakham railway station – approximately 6.5 miles by bus or taxi

See ad on page 199

Discount

20%–25%

Parking Plenty, ♿ Yes, **Group Tours** Yes, **Mail order** No, **Catalogue** Yes, ✕ Refreshments on site, **Internet Sales** No

Melton Mowbray

Beck Mill Factory Shop

33 Kings Road, Melton Mowbray, Leicestershire, LE13 1AF
Tel: 01664 501105 Fax: 01664 501104
Email: mail@dbmsmelton.enterprise.com

Men's and women's High Street fashions with up to 70% discount. Dannimac, Roman Originals, Alexara, Silken Ladder, Susan Jon, Double Two, Spicy, Blast. Menswear – Double Two, James Barrie, Wolsey, Ratcatcher, Dannimac

Hours Mon–Sat 10–5, Sun 10–4

Closed Christmas Day, New Year's Day, Easter Sunday

➡ Just north of town centre off Norman Way. In Kings Road go round S-bend; arched door to shop 50 yards on left. From Leicester – A607 towards Grantham. Pass Rover Garage on left, take second left next to pedestrian crossing into Kings Road

Public Transport Bus and train

Discount

20%–70%

 ♿ Yes, **Group Tours** Yes, **Mail order** No, **Catalogue** No,
✗ In town, **Internet Sales** No

Visit our genuine factory shop.
Carpets manufactured on the premises.
All carpets 80% wool. Heavy domestic
underlay and fitting service available

Every Saturday 9am to 3pm
Weekdays by appointment

Savings of up to 50%
Extensive colour choice available

CREATIVE CARPETS LTD
Unit 8, Mill Hill Industrial Estate
Quarry Lane, Enderby,
Leicester LE9 5AU

Telephone: 0116 284 1455
Fax: 0116 275 2550

Superb Quality ~ Exceptional Value

**Workshop
Showroom**

Thistleton Road
Industrial Estate
Market Overton
Rutland
LE15 7PP

Call Freephone
0800 731 1687

Shepshed

Charterhouse Retail Outlet

Charterhouse Holdings PLC, Charnwood Road, Shepshed, Leicestershire, LE12 9NN
Tel: 01509 50 50 50 Fax: 01509 50 73 73
Email: retail@charterhouse-holdings.co.uk
Web site: www.charterhouse-holdings.co.uk/retail

Familywear, fashionwear, top-brand sportswear, footwear, luggage, gifts and houseware and much, much more. All prices with seriously good savings. Group tours must be booked. A small brochure/leaflet is available. Infoline 01509 600 006

Hours Mon–Sat 10–5:30, Thur and Fri late until 8, Sun 11–5

Closed Christmas Day and Boxing Day

➡ Either M1 to J23, take A512 Ashby Road to Shepshed. At second set of lights turn into Charnwood Road; OR take A512 from Ashby towards M1 and turn left at first set of lights

Public Transport Bus service available from all local towns to Shepshed–Charnwood Road

See ad on page 201

	Discount
Labels Thousands of ex-chainstore and branded products	**25%–70%**

Parking 100+ spaces, & Yes, Group Tours Yes, Mail order No, Catalogue Yes, ✗ On site, pub opposite, Internet Sales No

Uppingham

Jillys Dress Agency

The Sondes Barns, Main Street, Rockingham, Nr Market Harborough, Leicestershire, LE16 8TG
Tel: 01536 770352

Designer dress agency and ladies' eveningwear and hat hire. (New gowns bought in regularly for hire section.) Occasion wear new and nearly new by Roland Joyce, Vivienne Lawrence, Fink etc., plus labels: Escada, Max Mara, Dejac etc. High street labels, Monsoon, Alexon, Planet, Jacques Vert. Gent's section Magee, Aquascutum, Christian Dior

Hours Mon–Sat 10:30–4

Closed Christmas, New Year and Bank Holidays

Public Transport Corby

	Discount
Labels Roland Joyce, Attire, as above	**25%–75%**

Parking 6 Spaces, & Yes, Group Tours Yes, Mail order No, Catalogue No, ✗ On site, also pub close, Internet Sales No

Grantham

Boundary Mill Stores, within Downtown Furniture Store

Gonerby Moor, A1, Grantham, Lincolnshire, NG32 2AB
Tel: 01476 591001

Clearance store for men and women from high street to designer

Hours Mon–Sat 9:30–5:30, Sun 11–5

➡ Within Downtown Furniture Store

	Discount
	30%–50%

Parking Yes, ✗ Refreshments on site

Grantham

Mansworld Department

Boundary Mill Stores, Gonerby Moor, Grantham, Lincolnshire, NG32 2AB
Tel: 01476 591001 Fax: 01476 591184

A huge selection of quality mens and ladieswear over an extensive range of sizes. Top brand names and designer labels all at discounted prices

Hours Mon–Sun, Various opening hours depending on site, Sun various

Closed Christmas Day

	Discount
Labels Ben Sherman, Kangol, Whimsey, Kläss, Chilli Pepper, Roman Originals, Double Two	**20%–75%**

& No, Group Tours No, Mail order No, Catalogue No, Internet Sales No

Lincoln

Alexon Sale Shop
St Benedicts Square, Lincoln, Lincolnshire
Tel: 01522 545220

Wide range of clothes for ladies

Hours Mon–Sat 9–5:30

Discount

Labels Alexon, Eastex

40%–70%

Lincoln

Stage 2
Tritton Retail Park, Tritton Road, Lincoln, Lincolnshire,
LN6 7YA
Tel: 01522 560303

All stock is from Freemans catalogue sold on at discount prices. Group tours by appointment

Hours Mon–Fri 10–8:00, Sat 9–6, Sun 10–4,
Bank Holidays 10–4

Public Transport Bus

Discount

Labels Varied top brands

see text

Parking Yes, & Yes, Group Tours Yes, Mail order No,
Catalogue No, Internet Sales No

Saxilby

Magpie Fabrics

22 Bridge Street, Saxilby, Lincoln, Lincolnshire, LN1 2PZ
Tel: 01522 702137

Curtain and upholstery fabrics at low price on stock. Fabrics to order. Sanderson, Hico, Blendworth plus many more. Paper and bedding

Hours Tue–Fri, Mon and Wed half day

➤ On canal front, next to 'Ship Inn'

Public Transport Saxilby train station

Discount

see text

& No, **Group Tours** No, **Mail order** Yes, **Catalogue** No, **Internet Sales** No

Great Yarmouth

Alexon Sale Shop

Theatre Plain, Great Yarmouth, Norfolk
Tel: 01493 332146

Wide range of clothes for ladies

Hours Mon–Sat 9–5:30

Discount

Labels Alexon, Eastex

40%–70%

Great Yarmouth

Mrs Pickering's Dolls' Clothes

The Pines, Decoy Road, Potter Heigham, Great Yarmouth, Norfolk, NR29 5LX
Tel: 01692 670407
Email: dolls.clothes@virgin.net
Web site:
http://freespace.virgin.net/dolls.clothes/index.html

A wide selection of well-made dolls' clothes, which are easy to put on and take off. All popular dolls are catered for, including Baby Born, Tiny Tears, Sindy, Barbie, Ken, Action Man, Shelly, as well as teddies. Special outfits, like school uniforms to match the child's, can be made on request

➤ Mail order only

Discount

see text

& No, **Group Tours** No, **Mail order** Yes, **Catalogue** Yes, **Internet Sales** No

Norwich

Robert Cole Shoes

90 Catton Grove Road, Norwich, Norfolk, NR3 3AA
Tel: 01603 789639 Fax: 01603 789639

Over 4000 pairs of shoes on display. Large range of footwear by famous brands – Lotus, Hotter, Equity, Riva, Loake, Hush Puppies. Full children's fitting service

Hours Mon–Sat 9–5:30, Sun 10.30–4.30

Closed Christmas Day only

➤ Main Norwich ring road (North). Junction with Catton Grove Road

Public Transport Several buses

Discount

Labels Lotus, Hotter, Riva, Loake, Equity, Hush Puppies

10%–25%

Parking 20 Spaces, & No, **Group Tours** Yes, **Mail order** Yes, **Catalogue** No, **Internet Sales** No

Irthlingborough

Doc Shop

Nene Park, Station Road, Irthlingborough,
Northamptonshire
Tel: 01933 6522000

The latest range of Dr. Martens footwear and accessories

Hours Contact for opening hours

See ad on page 203

Discount
see text

Northampton

Doc Shop

Barn Way, Lodge Farm Industrial Estate, Northampton,
Northamptonshire
Tel: 01604 591174

The latest range of Dr. Martens footwear and accessories

Hours Contact for opening hours

See ad on page 203

Discount
see text

Central England & Mid Wales Northamptonshire

Wollaston

Doc Shop

71 High Street, Wollaston, Northamptonshire
Tel: 01933 666144

The latest range of Dr. Martens footwear and accessories

Hours Contact for opening hours

See ad on page 203

Discount

see text

Newark

Weston Mill Pottery

Navigation Yard, Millgate, Newark, Nottinghamshire,
NG24 4TY
Tel: 01636 676835 Fax: 01636 611342
Email: info@wmpot.co.uk
Web site: www.wmpot.co.uk

Seconds and end of lines at discounted prices. Large range of hand thrown garden pots. Wide selection of imported planters all at discounted prices. We supply many high street stores

Hours Mon–Sat 9–5, Sun and Bank Holidays 11–5

Closed Christmas for approx. two weeks

➡ From A1, follow bypass around Newark in the Nottingham direction. From A46 from Lincoln, follow bypass around Newark as above. From Nottingham on A46, reach large roundabout with 'Lord Ted' pub. Take Newark exit. Past Marina, Millgate is on left (one way), nav. yard at end of Millgate on left

Public Transport 2 local train stations. Bus station around corner

Labels N/A

Discount

20%–80%

Parking 2 + Street, & No, **Group Tours** No, **Mail order** Yes, **Catalogue** No, ✗ Local bars and cafes, **Internet Sales** Yes

Nottingham

Change of A Dress

294 Broxtowe Lane, Nottingham, Nottinghamshire,
NG8 5NB
Tel: 01159 291531 Fax: 01159 296688

Change of A Dress is a 'mecca' for the fashion conscious and the penny wise. Our spacious salon offers a unique collection of designer clothes including Armani, Chanel, Dior, YSL, Escada, etc. Car parking allows for 6 cars plus space in pub next door

Hours Mon–Sat 9:30–5

Closed All Bank Holidays

➡ 3 mins from J6 of the M1 motorway

Public Transport 1 minute away

Labels Armani, Escada, Mondi, Chanel, Laurel, Dior, Basler

Discount

see text

& Yes, **Group Tours** Yes, **Mail order** Yes, **Catalogue** No, ✗ Refreshments on site, **Internet Sales** Yes

Nottingham

Essential Items

Church House, Plungar, Nottingham, Nottinghamshire,
NG13 0JA
Tel: 01949 861172 Fax: 01949 861320

Designers and manufacturers of upholstered stools and ottomans, windowseats, bed-end stools. Special filing cabinet ottoman. All made to measure, covered in customers own fabric, tapestries etc. All makers of soft furnishings, handsewn curtains, re-upholstery etc. No overheads so prices very low

Hours Mon–Sun 8–8

Closed Christmas and New Year

➡ Showroom approximately 4 miles from Bingham off the A52 between Nottingham and Grantham

Public Transport Buses and trains from Grantham, Nottingham

Discount

see text

Parking 10 Spaces, & No, **Group Tours** No, **Mail order** Yes, **Catalogue** Yes, ✗ Refreshments on site, **Internet Sales** No

page 204

Nottingham

Renaissance

31 Wollaton Road, Beeston, Nottingham,
Nottinghamshire, NG9 2NG
Tel: 0115 9220653 Fax: 0115 9482133

Highest quality, pristine clothes and accessories – from
T-shirts to occasion wear, from M & S to Armani. Most
items no more than 2 years old

Hours Mon–Sat 9–5:30, Fri late until 7, Sun 11–4

Closed Bank Holidays

➡ Junction 25 on M1. Off A52 Derby to Nottingham Road

Public Transport Buses and trains

Discount

50%–75%

Labels Paul Smith, Jigsaw, Jacques
Vert, Armani, Next, Karen Millern
Betty Barclay, Gap, Mondi

Parking Public, ♿ Yes, **Group Tours** No, **Mail order** No,
Catalogue No, ✗ Pubs and tea rooms, **Internet Sales** No

Brecon

Stewart Seconds

Unit 4, Bethel Square Shopping Centre, Brecon, Powys,
LD3 7HU
Tel: 01874 610260

Branded merchandise from major chainstores for all the
family

Hours Mon–Sat 9–6

Discount

40%–70%

Builth Wells

Seconds Out

West Street, Builth Wells, Powys
Tel: 01547 520649

Clothes for all the family

Hours Mon–Sat 10–4

Discount

see text

Knighton

Seconds Out

22 Broad Street, Knighton, Powys
Tel: 01547 520649

Clothes for all the family

Hours Mon–Fri 9–5, Sat 9–4

Discount
see text

Newtown

Catalogue Bargain Shop

Old Kerry Road, Newtown, Powys, SY16 1BJ
Tel: 01686 628283

Merchandise from ex-catalogue stock including men's, ladies' and children's clothes, furniture, food, sportswear, electrical and household goods, toys, decorating and sports equipment

Hours Mon–Sat 9–5, Sun 10:30–4:30

Labels Kays, G. Universal

Discount
see text

Newtown

Laura Ashley Sale Shop

Bear Lane, Newtown, Powys
Tel: 01686 626549

Laura Ashley fashion for women and home furnishings

Hours Mon–Fri 9:30–5:30, Sat 9–5:30

Discount
see text

Newtown

Seconds Out

15 Shortbridge Street, Newtown, Powys
Tel: 01686 624388

Clothes for all the family

Hours Mon–Fri 9–5, Sat 9–4

Discount
see text

Rhayader

Welsh Royal Crystal

5 Brynberth Industrial Estate, Rhayader, Powys, LD6 5EM
Tel: 01597 811005 Fax: 01597 811129
Email: sales@welshcrystal.demon.co.uk
Web site: www.welshcrystal.demon.co.uk

Most types of crystalware from giftware to bespoke trophies, tableware to bowls and vases. Items are hand-made on our premises

Hours Mon–Sat 9–5, Sun 10–5

Closed Christmas Day, Boxing Day, New Year's Day

➡ Factory is on outskirts of Rhayader on the A44 Leominster Road

Public Transport Rhayader

Discount

Labels Own

10%–25%

Parking 30 Spaces, & Yes, **Group Tours** Yes, **Mail order** Yes, **Catalogue** Yes, ✕ Refreshments on site, **Internet Sales** Yes

Welshpool

Silver Scenes

Berriew, Welshpool, Powys, SY21 8QA
Tel: 01686 640695 Fax: 01686 640683
Email: scenes@netcomuk.co.uk

Well laid out factory shop with full range of Silver Scenes designs, including frames, pill boxes, clocks and jewellery. We also stock card and wrapping paper

Hours Mon–Fri 9–5, Mon to Sat May to September

Closed Christmas, New Year and all Bank Holidays

➡ A483 Welshpool to New Town, turn right towards Berriew situated on left side of road on edge of village

Public Transport Bus

Discount

see text

& Yes, **Group Tours** Yes, **Mail order** Yes, **Catalogue** Yes, ✕ Lion Hotel, Talbot Hotel, in Berriew, **Internet Sales** Yes

Ludlow

E Walters Factory Shop

The Old Fire Station, Old Street, Ludlow, Shropshire, SY8 1NR
Tel: 01584 875595

Largest trousers manufacturer, sells ends of line, cancelled orders; also golf wear, trainers

Hours Mon–Fri 9–5, Sat 9–4

Discount

30%–40%

Newport

Catalogue Surplus Centre Ltd

28–30 St Mary's Street, Newport, Shropshire, TF10 7AB
Tel: 01952 825889

Ex-catalogue merchandise including shoes for all the family

Hours Mon–Sat 9–5

Discount

see text

Matalan

Unit 1, Meole Brace Retail Park, Hereford Road,
Shrewsbury, Shropshire, SY3 9NB
Tel: 01743 363240

Fashion and homewares shop for all the family

Hours Mon–Fri 10–8, Sat 9:30–5:30, Sun 10–6

Discount up to

50%

Windsmoor Sale Shop

16 High Street, Shrewsbury, Shropshire, SY1 1SP
Tel: 01743 244980

Women's clothes. Sells last year's stock

Hours Mon–Fri 9–5:30, Sat 9:30–5:30

Discount up to

50%

Yes & Co

Unit 4, Riverside Precinct, Riverside, Shrewsbury,
Shropshire, SY1 1BY
Tel: 01743 356 761

Ladies' fashion, with men's and children's available in
selected stores at the lowest prices. More than 150
different lines in every store. 40 new lines coming into
every store every week. We are specialists in High Street
and designer fashion names at the lowest prices.
Whatever your style, whatever your choice, be it elegance
or casual, there's always something for all at Yes & Co.
DOESN'T IT FEEL GOOD TO PAY LESS?

Hours Telephone 0151 547 2224 for information

See ad on page 263

Discount

see text

Fashion Factory

Park Street, Wellington, Shropshire, TF1 3AE
Tel: 01952 260489 Fax: 01952 260530
Email: fashion_factory@hotmail.com

Complete range of ladies' day and leisurewear, lingerie,
sunglasses, reading glasses and giftware. Labels such as
Gossard, Berlei, Roman Originals, Eleganze, Foster Grant,
Christian Marcus, Steilman

Hours Mon–Sat 9:30–5:30, Sun 11–4.30

Closed Christmas Day and Easter Sunday

➡ Located in Wellington, suburb of Telford, 3 miles off
M54 (J6) motorway. From motorway (J6) follow signs to
Whitchurch. At hospital traffic island turn left to
Wellington. At next junction turn left. Store is located
quarter mile on right

Public Transport Train station half mile. Bus stop 200m

Discount

Labels Gossard, Steilman,
Eleganze, Berlei, Focus, Naturana,
Roman Originals, Christian Marcus

20%–70%

♿ Yes, **Group Tours** Yes, **Mail order** No, **Catalogue** No,
✗ Public house, 'Red Lion', next door, **Internet Sales** No

Telford

Fashion Factory

The Maltings, King Street, Wellington, Telford,
Shropshire, TF1 3AE
Tel: 01952 260489

Range of mens and womenswear

Hours Mon–Sat 9:30–5:30, Sun 11–5

Discount up to

70%

Telford

Matalan

Unit J, The Wrekin Retail Park, Wellington, Telford,
Shropshire, TS1 2DE
Tel: 01952 641080

Fashion and homewares shop for all the family

Hours Mon–Fri 10–8, Sat 9–6, Sun 10–4

Discount up to

50%

Telford

Wrekin Workwear Factory Shop

Unit 41, Snedshill Trading Estate, Telford, Shropshire,
TF2 9NH
Tel: 01952 615976

Clothes for men and women

Hours Mon–Thu 10–5, Fri 10–3.30

Discount

see text

Burton-on-Trent

Georgian Crystal Factory Shop

Silk Mill Lane, Tutbury, Burton-on-Trent, Staffordshire,
DE13 9LE
Tel: 01283 814534 Fax: 01283 520186

Household goods. Crystal glass can be seen being made
on the ground floor

Hours Mon–Sat 9–5, Sun 10–4

Closed Christmas and New Year

➜ Main road out of Burton to Tutbury, then signposted
with the tourist information brown signs to the village of
Tutbury

Public Transport Bus service

Discount

see text

Labels Own label

& Yes, **Group Tours** Yes, **Mail order** Yes, **Catalogue** Yes,
✕ Plenty of refreshments in the village, **Internet Sales** No

Burton-on-Trent

Matalan

Unit A, Lichfield Street, Burton-on-Trent, Staffordshire, DE14 3ZZ
Tel: 01283 540856

Fashion and homewares shop for all the family

Hours Mon–Fri 10–8, Sat 9–6, Sun 11–5

Discount up to
50%

Burton-on-Trent

Webb Ivory Ltd

Queensbridge Works, Queen Street, Burton-on-Trent, Staffordshire, DE14 3LP
Tel: 01283 566371

Men's, women's and children's clothes, furniture, sportswear, electrical and household goods, toys, decorating items and sports equipment. All from the Webb Ivory catalogue

Hours Mon–Fri 9–5, Sat 9–2

Discount up to
50%

Cannock

Fashion Factory

Wyrley Brook Park, Vine Lane, Bridgetown, Cannock, Staffordshire, WS11 3XF
Tel: 01543 466000

Range of mens and womenswear

Hours Mon–Sat 9:30–5:30, Sun 11–5

Discount up to
70%

Cannock

Five Star Dress Agency

7–8 Bridgetown Business Centre, North Street, Bridgetown, Cannock, Staffordshire
Tel: 01543 571397

Good selection of designer wear for women

Hours Tue–Sat 10–4

Labels Planet, L. Ashley, Next, Wallis, Windsmoor, F. Usher

Discount
see text

Cannock

New Life

Martindale, Hawk's Green, Cannock, Staffordshire,
WS11 2XN
Tel: 01543 468888

Men's, ladies' and children's clothes, furniture,
sportswear, electrical and household goods, toys,
decorating and sports equipment. Charity shop sells
new merchandise donated by High Street shops and
nearly new

Hours Mon–Sat 9:30–9, Sun 10–4

Labels YSL, River Island,
Mothercare

Discount

see text

Cannock

Slimma

Wolverhampton Road, Cannock, Staffordshire
Tel: 01543 462571

Ladieswear. Over-runs and seconds

Hours Mon–Sat 9:30–4:30

Discount
see text

Cheadle

Slimma

7 Cross Street, Cheadle, Staffordshire
Tel: 01538 751455

Women's clothes. Over-runs and seconds

Hours Mon, Tues, Thur and Fri 9–5, Wed 9–1, Sat 9–4

Discount
see text

Leek

Joshua Wardle Factory Shop

Cheadle Road, Leekbrook, Leek, Staffordshire, ST13 7AZ
Tel: 01538 382451

Men's, women's and children's chainstore clothes, most of
which are not seconds

Hours Mon–Fri 9:30–4, Sat 10–3

Labels M & S, BHS, Abella,
Ladybird

Parking Yes

Discount
see text

Central England & Mid Wales Staffordshire

Leek

Slimma

James Street, Leek, Staffordshire
Tel: 01538 388096

Ladieswear. Over-runs and seconds

Hours Mon–Fri 9–5, Sat 9–3

Discount

Lichfield

Decor Supplies

Units 21 & 23, Britannia Way, Lichfield, Staffordshire, WS14 9VY
Tel: 01543 263327 Fax: 01543 263327

Wall coverings and paints

Hours Mon–Sat 8–5:30, Sun 10–4

Closed Christmas and New Year

➡ A38 from Lichfield towards Burton on Trent. Come off at first slip road, A5192 signposted Lichfield industrial estate. Bear left at T-junction, right at roundabout

Public Transport Train Lichfield–Trent Valley

Discount

Labels Coloroll, Dulux, Crowsons, Crown, Sanderson, Kingfisher, Vymura, Harlequin, Gallery

Parking 30 Spaces, & Yes, **Group Tours** Yes, **Mail order** No, **Catalogue** No, ✗ Café on same site, **Internet Sales** No

Oldbury

Matalan

Portway Road, Portway Green, Oldbury, Staffordshire, B69 2BZ
Tel: 0121 544 4899

Fashion and homewares shop for all the family

Hours Mon–Fri 10–8, Sat 9–6, Sun 11–5

Discount up to

50%

Rugeley

John Partridge Outlet Store

Power Station Road, Trent Meadows, Rugeley, Staffordshire, WS15 2HS
Tel: 01889 584438

Specialist in hard-wearing outdoor clothing for men and women

Hours Mon–Fri 9–5, Sat 9–4

Discount

30%–70%

Stafford

Matalan

Units 5 & 6, Queensville Retail Park, Silkmore Lane,
Stafford, Staffordshire, ST17 4SU
Tel: 01785 226211

Fashion and homewares shop for all the family

Hours Mon–Fri 10–8, Sat 9.30–5.30, Sun 10–6

Discount up to

50%

Stafford

Schott Factory Shop

Drummond Road, Astonfields Industrial Estate, Stafford,
Staffordshire, ST16 3EL
Tel: 01785 223166 Fax: 01785 223522

Schott Zwiesel is Europe's largest manufacturer of blown
crystal glassware – established over 100 years ago. The
Factory Shop stocks fine cut, plain and coloured crystal,
crystal giftware including vases, decanters and bowls,
exclusive hand-made glassware and oven-to-table heat
resistant glassware – all at up to 70% off normal retail
prices. Mainly perfects with a bargain corner

Hours Wed–Fri 10–4:30, Sat 10–3

Closed Christmas Day, Boxing Day and New Year period

➡ From M6 J14 follow the A513 for three-quarters of a
mile. At roundabout go straight ahead towards
Uttoxeter. After half a mile turn right at sign to Common
Road and Astonfields Industrial Estate. 1 mile bear left
into Astonfields Road. Drummond Road first left. Factory
shop is on right at end of Drummond Road

Discount

Labels Schott Zwiesel, Schott
Studio, Jaenaer Glas,
Christinenhutte, Wagenfeld, Heron

10%–70%

Parking Unlimited, ♿ Yes, **Group Tours** No, **Mail order** Yes,
Catalogue No, ✗ Yes, enquire in shop, **Internet Sales** No

Stafford

Shoe Shed

Castlefields, Newport Road, Stafford, Staffordshire,
ST16 1BQ
Tel: 01785 211311

Shoes and clothes for the whole family, and some
housewares

Hours Mon–Sat 9–5:30, Sun 10–4

Discount up to

30%

Stoke-on-Trent

Direct Specs

1 Church House, Old Hall Street, Hanley, Stoke-on-Trent,
Staffordshire, ST1 3AU
Tel: 01782 263038

Spectacles and sunglasses. Most designer names

Hours Mon–Sat 9–5

Discount

see text

Stoke-on-Trent

Fashion Direct

151–153 Marsh Street, Hanley, Stoke-on-Trent,
Staffordshire, ST1 5HR
Tel: 01782 266660

Labels for all the family

Hours Mon–Sat 9–5:30, Sun 11–5

Discount

Labels Klass, Blast, Double Two,
Cote & Cote

30%–50%

Stoke-on-Trent

Freeport Outlet Mall

Pit Lane, Talke Pits, Stoke-on-Trent, Staffordshire, ST7 1XD
Tel: 01782 774113 Fax: 01782 775664

Mens, ladies and childrenswear, furniture, food,
sportswear, household goods and toys. Stock includes
Adidas, Calvin Klein, Christian Dior, Ellesse, Kickers, Lee,
Next, Nike, Thorntons, Wedgwood, YSL

Hours Mon–Sat 10–8, Sun 11–5

Closed Christmas Day and New Year's Day

➜ Exit M6 at J16 on to the A500 and follow directions to
Kidsgrove

Public Transport Train from Stoke followed by 15 minute
taxi ride

Discount

Labels YSL, Carlton, Ben Sherman,
Calvin Klein, Iceberg, Pierre
Cardin, Bally, Head, Puma

20%–70%

Parking 1000 Cars, Yes, **Group Tours** Yes, **Mail order** No,
Catalogue No, ✗ Refreshments on site, **Internet Sales** No

Stoke-on-Trent

Leading Labels Ltd

Unit 18/19, Freeport Stoke, Jamage Road, Talke Pits,
Stoke-on-Trent, Staffordshire, ST7 1XD
Tel: 01782 774822 Fax: 01782 774928

A huge selection of quality mens and ladieswear over an
extensive range of sizes. Top brand names and designer
labels all at discounted prices

Hours Mon–Sun, Various opening hours depending on
site, Sun various

Closed Christmas Day

Discount

Labels Ben Sherman, Kangol,
Whimsey, Kläss, Chilli Pepper,
Roman Originals, Double Two

20%–75%

 No, **Group Tours** No, **Mail order** No, **Catalogue** No,
Internet Sales No

Matalan

Wolstanton Retail Park, Wolstanton, Stoke-on-Trent,
Staffordshire, ST5 1DY
Tel: 01782 711731

Fashion and homewares shop for all the family

Hours Mon–Fri 10–8, Sat 9–6, Sun 11–5

Discount up to

50%

Thorntons

Unit 11, Outlet Mall, Pit Lane, Talke Pits, Stoke-on-Trent,
Staffordshire, ST7 1QE
Tel: 01782 787793

The factory outlet stores sell three different product
categories: misshapes, discounted lines and standard
lines. Misshapes are packed into assorted bags and offer a
saving of between 35%–55%. Discount lines are offered
at a discount of 25%–50%. Standard lines are also on sale
at normal prices

Hours Opening times dependent upon individual factory
outlet centre

Discount

Labels Thorntons

25%–55%

& No, **Group Tours** No, **Mail order** Yes, **Catalogue** Yes,
✗ Most outlet centres have food courts, **Internet Sales** Yes

TK Maxx

The Potteries Shopping Centre, Hanley, Stoke-on-Trent,
Staffordshire, ST1 1PP
Tel: 01782 207509

Men's, women's and children's clothes and household
goods. American concept has everything under one roof
for the whole family

Hours Mon–Fri 9–5:30, Sat 9–6, Sun 11–5

Discount up to

60%

Parking Yes, & Yes

Webb Ivory Ltd

Potteries Shopping Centre, Hanley, Stoke-on-Trent,
Staffordshire, ST1 1PP
Tel: 01782 202570

Men's, women's and children's clothes, furniture,
sportswear, electrical and household goods, toys,
decorating items and sports equipment. All from the
Webb Ivory catalogue

Hours Mon–Sat 9–5:30, Thur late until 8

Discount up to

50%

Tamworth

Alexon Sale Shop

34 George Street, Tamworth, Staffordshire
Tel: 01827 310041

Last season's stock for women

Hours Mon–Sat 9–5:30

Labels Alexon, Eastex, A. Harvey

Discount

40%–70%

Tamworth

Direct Specs

39 Lower Gungate, Tamworth, Staffordshire, B79 7AS
Tel: 01827 50233

Spectacles and sunglasses. Most designer names

Hours Mon–Sat 9–5

Discount

see text

Tamworth

Jaeger Factory Shop

42–43 Church Street, Tamworth, Staffordshire, B79 7DE
Tel: 01827 52828

Contemporary classics from Jaeger at excellent prices for men and women

Hours Mon–Sat 9:30–5:30

Discount

see text

Tamworth

Matalan

Unit 7, Ventura Shopping Centre, Ventura Park Road, Bone Hill Drive, Tamworth, Staffordshire, B78 3HB
Tel: 01827 50900

Fashion and homewares shop for all the family

Hours Mon–Fri 10–8, Sat 9:30–5:30, Sun 10–6

Discount up to

50%

Tamworth

Webb Ivory Ltd

6 Market Street, Tamworth, Staffordshire
Tel: 01827 60266

Men's, women's and children's clothes, furniture, sportswear, electrical and household goods, toys, decorating items and sports equipment. All from the Webb Ivory catalogue

Hours Mon–Sat 9–5

Discount up to

50%

Parking Yes

Exning

Shuffles

16 Oxford Street, Exning, Newmarket, Suffolk, CB8 7EW
Tel: 01638 578297

Fashionable, good quality, nearly new and new ladieswear

Hours Tue–Sat 10–4

Closed Christmas and New Year

➡ Village location 3 miles west of Newmarket

Public Transport Newmarket

Discount

Labels All labels – condition being the priority

see text

Parking On street, & Yes, **Group Tours** No, **Mail order** No, **Catalogue** No, ✗ Coffee shop, bakers, pubs, **Internet Sales** No

Ipswich

Suffolk Carpet Weavers

Unit D, Hill Farm Estate, Witnesham, Ipswich, Suffolk, IP6 9EW
Tel: 01473 785111 Fax: 01473 785843

Fine quality 80% wool twist pile carpet. 80 colours in stock. Any quality, any width service. Special dye service. Rugs made to order. Prices per square metre

Hours Mon–Fri 9–5, Sat 9–1

Closed Bank Holidays, Christmas and New Year

➡ 4 miles north of Ipswich on B1077

Public Transport None

Discount

Labels Own brand

45%–70%

Parking 30 Spaces, & Yes, **Group Tours** Yes, **Mail order** Yes, **Catalogue** No, ✗ 'Barley Mow' public house, **Internet Sales** No

Leamington Spa

Into Clothing

144 The Parade, Leamington Spa, Warwickshire
Tel: 01926 430407

Sells ladies' clothing

Hours Mon–Sat 9–5

Discount up to

70%

Leamington Spa

Second Time Around

13B Park Street, Leamington Spa, Warwickshire,
CV32 4QN
Tel: 01926 889811

Middle of the range new and nearly-new women's
clothes – mostly top high street brands and some
designer wear. Also small pieces of furniture

Hours Tue–Fri 10:30–5:15, Sat 10–5:30

Discount

see text

Leamington Spa

The Dressing Room

20A Regent Street, Leamington Spa, Warwickshire,
CV32 5EH
Tel: 01926 882154

Clothes and lots of accessories, including luggage for
both men and women

Hours Tue–Sat 10–5:30

Labels Versace, P Costelloe,
Armani

Discount

see text

Nuneaton

Forget-Me-Not

The Wedding Centre, 5–7 Lutterworth Road,
Attleborough Green, Nuneaton, Warwickshire, CV11 4LD
Tel: 024 7637 5555 Fax: 024 7637 4455

Designer bridalwear

Hours Mon–Fri 9:30–5, Sat by appointment

Discount

see text

Nuneaton

The Factory Shop

CV Clothing Ladies and Childrens Wear, Bosworth Road,
Barlestone, near Nuneaton, Warwickshire, CV13 0EL
Tel: 01455 290 6685

Constantly updating the range of clothing for all the
family

Hours Mon–Sat 10–4

Discount

see text

Rugby

M C Hitchen & Sons Ltd

14–16 North Street, Rugby, Warwickshire, CV21 2AF
Tel: 01788 565116

Littlewoods clearance shop selling men's, ladies' and children's clothes, sportswear, electrical and household goods and sports equipment

Hours Mon–Wed 9:30–5:30, Thur–Sat 9–5:30

Labels Nike, Berlei, Gossard, Adidas, Timberland, Caterpillar

Discount

40%–60%

Stratford-upon-Avon

Matalan

Unit E, Maybird Centre, Birmingham Road, Stratford-upon-Avon, Warwickshire, CV37 0HZ
Tel: 01789 262223

Fashion and homewares shop for all the family

Hours Mon–Fri 10–8, Sat 10–5:30, Sun 10–6

Discount up to

50%

Stratford-upon-Avon

Top Drawer as New

19–20 Wood Street, Stratford-upon-Avon, Warwickshire, CV37 6JF
Tel: 01789 269766

Wide variety of carefully selected as-new ladieswear and accessories for the discerning woman

Hours Tue–Sat 10–4:30

Labels Escade, Max Mara, Jaeger

Discount

see text

Warley

Scoops

567–569 Bearwood Road, Smethwick, Warley, Warwickshire, BA1 1DA
Tel: 0121 434 3086

Grattan clearance shop selling men's, women's and children's clothes, sportswear, electrical and household goods, toys, decorating and sports equipment

Hours Mon–Sat 9–5:30

Labels Grattan

Discount

30%–50%

Warwick

Arkwrights Mill

Hatton Country World, Dark Lane, Hatton, Warwick,
Warwickshire, CV35 8XA
Tel: 01926 843022 Fax: 01926 842761
Email: hatton@hattonworld.com

Arkwrights Mill stock clothing ranging from ladies
casualwear through to formal dress. We stock a wide size
range from 10–24 and clothes are suitable for all ages.
Menswear range from casual clothes to shirts and
trousers suitable for the office. We also have a wide
range of outdoor coats including waterproofs, fleeces
and lightweight jackets. Our accessories provide the
completion to any outfit with hats, scarves, hair
accessories, purses and handbags

Hours Mon–Sun 10–5

Closed Open until 2 pm Christmas Eve and New Year
1999. Closed Jan. 1st 2000

➡ Hatton Country World is five minutes from J15 off the
M40 via the A46 (towards Coventry) and signed off the
A4177 Warwick to Solihull Road

Public Transport Hatton train station

Discount

30%–50%

Parking 450 Spaces, ⅙ Yes, Group Tours Yes,
Mail order No, Catalogue No, Internet Sales No

Warwick

The Cuckoo's Nest

70 Smith Street, Warwick, Warwickshire, CV34 4HU
Tel: 01926 496804

Wide range of ladies' clothing. No garment is more than
two years old. Mobile telephone 07836 647400

Hours Mon–Sat 9:30–5

Labels M & S, P. Cardin

Discount

see text

Bilston

Catalogue Bargain Shop

59 High Street, Bilston, West Midlands, WV14 0BJ
Tel: 01746 763282

Merchandise from ex-catalogue stock including men's,
ladies' and children's clothes, furniture, food, sportswear,
electrical and household goods, toys, decorating and
sports equipment

Hours Mon–Sat 9–5:30, Sun 11–5

Labels Kays, G. Universal

Discount

see text

Bilston

Catalogue Bargain Shop

95 Church Street, Bilston, West Midlands, WV14 0BJ
Tel: 01902 353624

Merchandise from ex-catalogue stock including men's,
ladies' and children's clothes, furniture, food, sportswear,
electrical and household goods, toys, decorating and
sports equipment

Hours Mon–Sat 9–5:30, Sun 9:30–3:30

Labels Kays, G. Universal

Discount

see text

Birmingham

Bags by Anne Marie Direct

89 Cecil Street, Birmingham, West Midlands, B19 3SU
Tel: 0121 359 1777

Bags

Hours Mon–Sat 10–4

Labels A. Marie

Discount see text

Birmingham

Dress Exchange

1003A Alcester Road South, The May-Pole, Birmingham,
West Midlands, B14 5JA
Tel: 0121 474 5707

Middle to up-market designer wear, and accessories for women

Hours Mon–Sat 10–5

➜ above Three Cooks

Labels M & S, Escada, Max Mara, Ghost, Jasper Conran, Armani, Valentino

Discount see text

Birmingham

Encore

48–52A St Mary's Row, Moseley, Birmingham, West
Midlands, B13 8JG
Tel: 0121 442 4888

Womens and menswear with accessories

Hours Mon–Fri 9:30–5, Sat 9:30–4:45

Labels Ghost, J. Conran, Valentino, Mondi, Armani, Boss, YSL, M & S

Discount see text

Birmingham

Encore

48–52A St Marys Row, Moseley, Birmingham, West
Midlands, B13 8JG
Tel: 0121 442 4888

Nearly new clothing and accessories for both men and women. A wide choice from High Street to Designer names, e.g. Next, M & S, Principles to Armani, Maxmara, YSL

Hours Mon–Sat 9:30–5

Closed Bank Holidays

➜ Approx. 20 minutes bus journey from city centre off the main Alcester Road in Moseley

Public Transport No. 50 and No. 35 buses

Labels Hugo Boss, Maxmara, Armani, Ferretti, J. Muir, Jaeger, Cerruti, Mondi, K. Millen

Discount 30%–50%

Parking Restricted, & No, **Group Tours** Yes, **Mail order** No, **Catalogue** No, ✕ Coffee shop nearby, **Internet Sales** No

Birmingham

Jeff & Annabel's Diamond Gallery

35 Warstone Lane, Hockley, Birmingham, West Midlands, B18 6JQ
Tel: 0121 236 5799

Jewellery

Hours Mon–Sat 9–5

Discount up to

30%

Birmingham

M C Hitchen & Sons Ltd

236 Hawthorn Road, Kingstanding, Birmingham, West Midlands, B44 8PP
Tel: 0121 373 1276

Littlewoods clearance shop selling men's, ladies' and children's clothes, sportswear, electrical and household goods and sports equipment

Hours Mon–Sat 9:15–5:30

Labels Nike, Berlei, Gossard, Adidas, Timberland, Caterpillar

Discount

40%–60%

Birmingham

M C Hitchen & Sons Ltd

299 Coventry Road, Birmingham, West Midlands, B10 0RA
Tel: 0121 772 1637

Littlewoods clearance shop selling men's, ladies' and children's clothes, sportswear, electrical and household goods and sports equipment

Hours Mon–Sat 9:30–5:30, Sun 11–4

Labels Nike, Berlei, Gossard, Adidas, Timberland, Caterpillar

Discount

40%–60%

Birmingham

M Latif & Sons

New Canal Street, Digbeth, Birmingham, West Midlands, B5 5PL
Tel: 0121 643 2822

Household and electrical goods

Hours Mon–Sat 9:30–5:30, Thur late until 8, Sun 10–2:30

Labels M & S

Discount

see text

Birmingham

Moulinex Swan Krups Shop

35 Rocky Lane, Aston Cross, Birmingham, West Midlands,
B6 5RQ
Tel: 0121 380 0635

Seconds, obsolete and reconditioned stock: jug kettles,
fryers, food processors, steamers, irons, toasters, coffee
makers and many more bargains

Hours Mon–Fri 10–4, Sat 9–1

See ad on page 223

Discount

25%–50%

Parking Plenty

Birmingham

Next to Nothing

104 Corporation Street, Birmingham, West Midlands
Tel: 0121 233 0022

Men's, women's and children's clothes, household goods
and shoes. Surplus stock from Next

Hours Mon–Fri 10–5:30, Sat 11–5

Labels Next

Discount up to

50%

Birmingham

PJ Gold Depot Ltd

37 Vyse Street, Birmingham, West Midlands, B18 6JY
Tel: 0121 554 6165 Fax: 0121 554 2438

Jewellery

Hours Mon–Sat 9–4

Discount up to

30%

Birmingham

Preview

Burlington Court, New Street, Birmingham,
West Midlands, B2
Tel: 0121 643 2007 Fax: 0121 644 5232

Upmarket designer boutique-showroom for women

Hours Mon–Sat 9:30–5:30

Discount up to

75%

Birmingham

Principles

9 The Pavilions Shopping Centre, Lower Ground Level,
High Street, Birmingham, West Midlands
Tel: 0121 643 7005

Sells ends of lines for men and women

Hours Mon–Sat 9:30–6, Thur late until 7

Discount up to

50%

Birmingham

Slaters Menswear

3 Cannon Street, Birmingham, West Midlands, B2 5EP
Tel: 0121 633 3855

Full range of menswear

Hours Mon–Sat 8:30–5:30

Labels Odermark, Bulmer,
Valentino, Charlie's Co, C. Gray

Discount

see text

Birmingham

The Dress Exchange

1003 Alcester Road, Maypole, Birmingham, West
Midlands, B14 5JA
Tel: 0121 474 5707

Women's new and nearly-new from M & S to Valentino

Hours Mon–Sat 10–5

Labels Valentino, Max Mara,
Reldan, Jaeger, B Barclay, Yarell,
Mani, Mondi

Discount

see text

Birmingham

V & F Parker Ltd

(Arden Jewellery), 51 Vise Street, off Great Hampton
Street, Birmingham, West Midlands, B18 6HS
Tel: 0121 554 3587

Stocks more than 3,000 lines of jewellery

Hours Mon–Fri 9:30–5, Sat 9:30–3

Discount

see text

Brierley Hill

Bairdwear Menswear

Level Street, Brierley Hill, West Midlands, DY5 1UB
Tel: 01384 77102

Menswear seconds and overmakes

Hours Mon–Sat 10–4

Discount

40%–60%

Brownhills

Scoops

63 High Street, Brownhills, West Midlands, W58 6HH
Tel: 01543 372933

Men's, women's and children's clothes, sportswear, electrical and household goods, toys, decorating items and sports equipment. Grattan clearance shop

Hours Mon–Sat 9–5:30

Labels Grattan

Discount

30%–50%

Coventry

Matalan

Gallagher Retail Park, Stoney Station Road, Coventry, West Midlands
Tel: 024 7663 7320

Fashion and homewares shop for all the family

Hours Telephone for opening hours

Discount up to

50%

Coventry

Nutcracker Factory Direct

1a City Arcade, Coventry, West Midlands, CV1 3HY
Tel: 024 762 24602 Fax: 024 765 50313

Leading chain-store bedding and curtains at large discounted prices. Seconds and clearance ranges

Hours Mon–Sat 9–5:30

Closed Christmas Day, Boxing Day, Bank Holidays

➟ Near Argos superstore. City centre

See ad on page 227

Labels M & S, Debenhams, BHS, Designers Guild

Discount

25%–50%

& Yes, **Group Tours** No, **Mail order** Yes, **Catalogue** No, **Internet Sales** No

Coventry

Stage 2

Austin Drive, Court House Green, Coventry,
West Midlands, CV6 7NS
Tel: 024 766 81520

All stock is from Freemans catalogue sold on at discount prices. Group tours by appointment

Hours Mon–Fri 10–8, Sat 9–6, Sun 10–4,
Bank Holidays 10–4

➡ At city centre follow signs for Bell Green. At roundabout take third turning into Austin Drive

Public Transport Bus

Discount

Labels Varied top brands

50%–65%

Parking Yes, & Yes, **Group Tours** Yes, **Mail order** No,
Catalogue No, **Internet Sales** No

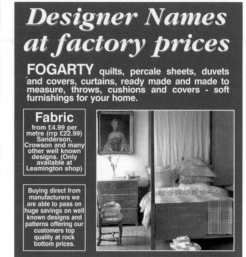
Dudley

TK Maxx

Upper Mall, Merryhill Shopping Centre, Dudley, West Midlands
Tel: 01384 77878

Men's, women's and children's clothes and household goods. American concept has everything under one roof for all the family

Hours Mon–Fri 10–8, Thur late night until 9, Sat 9–7, Sun 11–5

Discount up to

60%

Parking Yes, & Yes

Halesowen

Direct Specs

36 Douglas Road, Halesowen, West Midlands, B62 9HX
Tel: 0121 561 4940

Spectacles and sunglasses. Most designer names

Hours Mon–Sat 9–5

Discount

see text

Oldbury

H L Linen Bazaars

Churchbridge, Oldbury, West Midlands
Tel: 0121 552 1437 Fax: 0121 552 0107

Good quality branded goods. Slight seconds.
Discontinued lines. Job lots in sheets, duvets, towels,
blankets, tablecloths, tea towels, duvet covers, etc.

Hours Mon–Sat 9–5:30

Closed Bank Holidays and some Saturdays (telephone
before making journey)

➡ 200 yards from J2 M5 motorway. At large island follow
signs to Oldbury. Turn left into Park Street at first traffic
lights. Turn right into Birchfield Lane and go to end of
cul-de-sac

Public Transport Sandwell and Dudley rail station. Several
buses, routes 404, 217, 417, 218

Discount

see text

Labels Dorma, Slumberdown, J.P.
Stevens, Sheridan, Bianca, own
labels

Parking Plenty, ♿ No, **Group Tours** No, **Mail order** Yes,
Catalogue Yes, ✗ Pubs and restaurants, **Internet Sales** No

Rowley Regis

E Walters Factory Shop

42 High Street, Blackheath, Rowley Regis, West Midlands

Largest trousers manufacturer, sells end of lines, cancelled
orders; also golf wear, trainers

Hours Mon–Fri 9:30–5:30, Sat 9–4

Discount
30%–40%

Solihull

Gowns Galore

1 Old Warwick Road, Hockley Heath, Solihull, West
Midlands, B94 6HH
Tel: 01564 783003

Specialist in designer ball gowns, cocktail wear and
accessories

Hours Mon–Sat 9–5, Tues late until 8

Discount
see text

Stourbridge

Cambio

168A Lower High Street, Stourbridge, West Midlands, DY8 1TT

Nearly-new designer wear, as well as some new end of lines designer wear for women

Hours Mon–Sat 9:30–5

Labels R. Ozbek, L. Feraud, B. Barclay

Discount

Stourbridge

Catalogue Bargain Shop

78 High Street, Stourbridge, West Midlands, DY8 1DX
Tel: 01384 374544

Merchandise from ex-catalogue stock including men's, ladies' and children's clothes, furniture, food, sportswear, electrical and household goods, toys, decorating and sports equipment

Hours Mon–Sat 9–5:30, Sun 10:30–4:30

Labels Kays, G. Universal

Discount

Stourbridge

Dennis Hall Tudor Crystal

Kiosk 8, Merry Hill Centre, Merry Hill, Stourbridge, West Midlands
Tel: 01384 483218 Fax: 01384 75761
Email: sales@tudorcrystal
Web site: www.tudorcrystal.co.uk

Titanic glassware, stemware, decanters, rose bowls, salad bowls, vases, lamps, tankards, tray sets, comports, glass sweets

Hours Mon–Fri 10–8, Thur 10–9, Sat 9–7, Sun 11–5

Closed Christmas Day

➡ Signs for Merry Hill shopping complex

Public Transport Stourbridge, Dudley, Halesowen

Discount

♿ Yes, **Group Tours** Yes, **Mail order** Yes, **Catalogue** Yes,
✗ Local eating places in centre, **Internet Sales** No

Stourbridge

Stuart Crystal Factory Shops & Visitor Centres

Redhouse Glassworks, Stourbridge, West Midlands, DY8 4AA
Tel: 01384 828282

Fantastic all year round value on 1st and 2nd quality crystal. Engraving and gift wrap service. Extensive range of crystal millennium gifts. Our outlets are situated in the following areas: Stourbridge – West Midlands, Crieff – Perthshire, Chepstow – South Wales, plus many other locations throughout the country. Look out for special events and promotions throughout the year

Hours Please call for information

See ad on page 229

Discount up to

50%

Sutton Coldfield

Catalogue Bargain Shop

182 The Parade, Sutton Coldfield, West Midlands,
WS1 1PB
Tel: 01922 722286

Merchandise from ex-catalogue stock including men's,
ladies' and children's clothes, furniture, food, sportswear,
electrical and household goods, toys, decorating and
sports equipment

Hours Mon–Sat 9–3:30, Sun 10:30–4:30

Labels Kays, G. Universal

Discount

see text

Sutton Coldfield

Deja Vu

5 Boldmere Road, Sutton Coldfield, West Midlands,
B73 5UY
Tel: 0121 321 3110

Women's clothes. Everything from M & S to top labels. No
more than 4 years old. All in pristine condition

Hours Mon–Sat 10–5, Wed half day

Labels M & S, Wallis, Country
Casuals, Jaeger, Elvi, Windsmoor,
Jacques Vert, Mondi, Escada

Discount
20%–50%

& No, **Group Tours** Yes, **Mail order** No, **Catalogue** No,
Internet Sales No

Sutton Coldfield

The Changing Room at Four Oaks

11 Mere Green Road, Four Oaks, Sutton Coldfield,
West Midlands, B75 5BL
Tel: 0121 308 1848

Exclusive dress agency, also selling accessories

Hours Mon–Sat 10–5

Labels Versace, Moschino,
Armani, G. Rech, L. Feraud, C.
Dior

Discount
see text

Walsall

Catalogue Bargain Shop

17 Bradford Street, Walsall, West Midlands, WS1 1PB
Tel: 01922 722286

Merchandise from ex-catalogue stock including men's, ladies' and children's clothes, furniture, food, sportswear, electrical and household goods, toys, decorating and sports equipment

Hours Mon–Sat 9–5:30, Sun 10:30–4:30

Labels Kays, G. Universal

Discount

see text

Walsall

Matalan

Unit 9, Broadwalk Retail Park, Bescot Crescent, Walsall, West Midlands, WS1 4DK
Tel: 01922 615188

Fashion and homewares shop for all the family

Hours Telephone for opening hours

Discount up to
50%

Walsall

Walsall Leather Museum

Littleton Street West (Ring Road), Walsall, West Midlands, WS2 8EQ
Tel: 01922 721153 Fax: 01922 725827

Walsall is the centre of the British leathergoods industry and our shop offers an unrivalled range of locally-made belts, purses, wallets, bags and small leathergoods, many at substantially discounted prices

Hours Tue–Sat 10–5, Sun 12 noon–5. November to March close at 4.

Closed 24th–26th December, New Year, Easter Sunday

➡ On Walsall ringroad, on north (Bloxwich) side of town centre. Well signposted from ringroad

Public Transport Walsall railway station 5 minutes walk. Walsall bus station 5 minutes walk

Discount up to
60%

Parking Public car park, & Yes, **Group Tours** Yes, **Mail order** No, **Catalogue** No, ✗ On site, **Internet Sales** No

Wolverhampton

Matalan

Birmingham Road, Howard Street, Wolverhampton, West Midlands, WV2 2LQ
Tel: 01902 352813

Fashion and homewares shop for all the family

Hours Mon–Fri 10–8, Sat 9:30–5:30, Sun 10–6

Discount up to
50%

SPENCER'S

Bed and Breakfast 2000

The new full colour guide to British B&B

The brand new Spencer's B&B features a fantastic range of properties from all over Britain and Ireland. It's an easy-to-use guide that can solve your holiday and short-break problems in a few minutes.

Over 1000 places to stay are included, all illustrated in colour. There's a description of every property and full details of prices and facilities. Plus a fully-indexed full-colour route planning and map section, a feature of all Spencer's guides.

The focus is on high-quality high-value accommodation. Whether it's a short break in the Cotswolds or Yorkshire Dales, a seaside break in Wales or Cornwall, overnighting on business or holiday, or a place to stay when visiting London…whatever your need Spencer's can provide the solution.

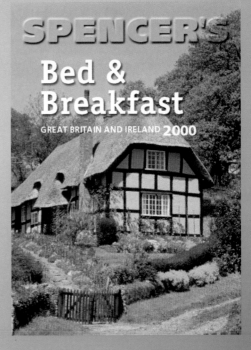

SPENCER'S
Bed &
Breakfast
GREAT BRITAIN AND IRELAND 2000

Format:	210x148mm
No. of pages:	256pp
ISBN:	1 900327 52 X
Price:	£6.99
Publication date:	April 2000

West One Publishing
Kestrel House, Duke's PLace
Marlow, Bucks SL7 2QH

tel: 01628 487722

www.WestOneWeb.com

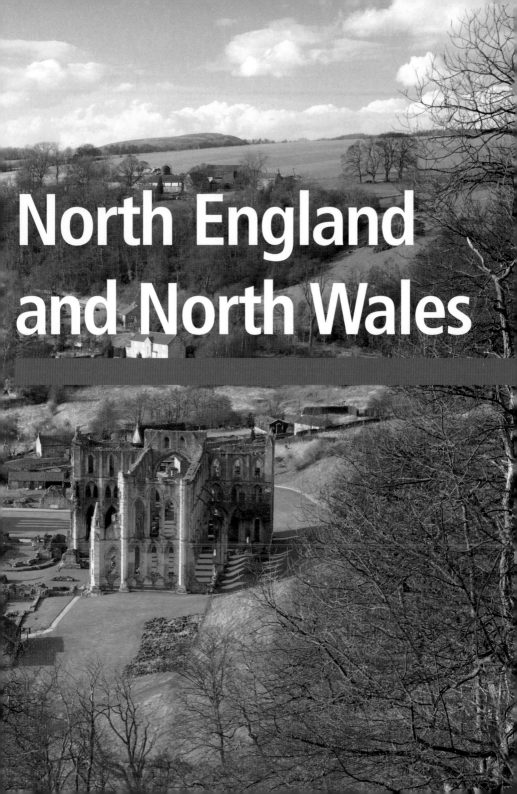

North England
and North Wales

Chester

China Chase

Long Byre, Borras, Nr Chester, Cheshire, LL13 9TL
Tel: 01978 856400 Fax: 01978 856400

Royal Doulton, Wedgwood, Spode, Royal Worcester, etc. English china available in out of production patterns. Only discontinued patterns stocked. Also interested in buying china. Internet sales soon

Hours Mon–Sat 9–6

Closed Public holidays

➜ Telephone to see if pattern in stock to save wasted journey

Public Transport Wrexham station

Discount **10%–25%**

Labels Royal Doulton, Wedgwood, Spode, Royal Worcester, Royal Grafton, Colclough, Minton

♿ No, **Group Tours** No, **Mail order** Yes, **Catalogue** No, **Internet Sales** Yes

MasterCard, VISA

Chester

Montgomery Tomlinson

Broughton Mill Road, Bretton, Chester, Cheshire, CH4 0BY
Tel: 01244 661363

Company manufacturing soft furnishings. Mainly cancelled orders, some seconds. 50% off normal prices

Hours Tue–Fri 10–4:30, Sat 9:30–4:30

Closed Lunch 12:30–1 daily, Bank Holidays

➜ About 3 miles west of Chester

Public Transport Buses from city centre to Bretton

Discount from **50%**

Parking Yes, ♿ Yes, **Group Tours** No, **Mail order** No, **Catalogue** No, ✕ Chester city centre or local pub, **Internet Sales** No

Chester

Something Different

44 Lower Bridge Street, Chester, Cheshire, CH1 1RS
Tel: 01244 317484

Designer label and some High Street labels too. Also new clothing i.e. Phool. Specialists in wedding outfits. 25 years old in 2000

Hours Mon–Sat 9:30–5, Sun 11–4

Closed Christmas and New Year

➜ From the cross turn into Bridge Street. Go across traffic lights into Lower Bridge Street. We are on the right hand side

Discount **see text**

Labels Escada, Louis Feraud, Max Mara, Valentino, Umberto Ungaro, Laurel, Betty Barclay

♿ No, **Group Tours** No, **Mail order** No, **Catalogue** No, **Internet Sales** No

MasterCard, Switch, VISA, Delta, American Express

Chester

Special Event

44 Lower Bridge Street, Chester, Cheshire, CH1 1RS
Tel: 01244 340757

Evening wear for hire or sale. Size 8 to 26. Alterations possible at no extra cost

Hours Mon–Sat 9:30–5, Sun 11–4

Closed Christmas, New Year and Bank Holidays

➜ From the cross turn into Bridge Street. Go across traffic lights into Lower Bridge Street. We are on the right hand side above Something Different

Discount **see text**

Labels Tadashi, After Shock, Roots, Touch of Class, Katerina, Creative Creations, Ariela

♿ No, **Group Tours** No, **Mail order** No, **Catalogue** No, **Internet Sales** No

Congleton

Florakits Limited

Worral Street, Congleton, Cheshire, CW12 1DT
Tel: 01260 271371 Fax: 01260 270741
Email: sales@florakits.co.uk
Web site: www.florakits.co.uk

Floral sundries, silk and dried flowers, ribbons, baskets, candles, glassware, pottery, terracotta, silk and dried arrangements, trees and plants, Daler-Rowney, quilling, stencilling, glass paints, silk and silk paints, fabric paints, art and craft materials

Hours Mon–Sat 8–5, Sun 9–4

Closed Christmas and New Year

➡ Warehouse is situated behind the leisure centre at the end of Worrall Street in Congleton

Public Transport Main bus station in Congleton – 200 yards away

Discount see text

Labels Daler-Rowney, Bolsius, Oasis

Parking 10 Spaces, & Yes, Group Tours Yes, Mail order Yes, Catalogue Yes, ✗ On site, café 100 yds, Internet Sales Yes

Congleton

RH Lowe

The Roldane Mills, Mill Green, Congleton, Cheshire, CW12 1JO
Tel: 01260 277911

Wide range of childrenswear, ladies' and men's fashions. Lingerie and nightwear, leisurewear, footwear, luggage and leather goods. Homeware including towels and bedding. Chainstore end of lines and seconds

Hours Mon–Sat 9:30–4:30, Sun 12–4:30, Bank Holidays 9:30–4:30

Closed Christmas Day, Boxing Day and New Year's Day

➡ On north side of Congleton, quarter of a mile from town centre

Public Transport Easy walk from town centre

Discount see text

Parking Yes, & Yes, Group Tours Yes, Mail order No, Catalogue No, ✗ Teas in town, café 100 yds, Internet Sales No

Congleton

Victoria Lighting/The Clothes Peg

Victoria Mill, Foundry Bank, Congleton, Cheshire, CW12 1DT
Tel: 01260 281071 / 297593

This mill encompasses several shops including Victoria Lighting and The Clothes Peg. Enjoy shopping in a recently refurbished Victorian Mill

Hours Mon–Sat 9–5

Closed Christmas Day and Boxing Day, Bank Holidays

➡ On north-east side of Congleton, quarter of a mile from town centre

Public Transport 10 minutes walk from town centre

Discount see text

Labels Famous named merchandise

Parking Outside, & No, Group Tours Yes, Mail order No, Catalogue No, ✗ On site, Internet Sales No

for leisure...

www.WestOneWeb.com

...great

expectations

Crewe

Yes & Co

32/34 Victoria Street, Crewe, Cheshire, CW1 2JE
Tel: 01270 213 135

Ladies' fashion, with men's and children's available in selected stores at the lowest prices. More than 150 different lines in every store. 40 new lines coming into every store every week. We are specialists in High Street and designer fashion names at the lowest prices. Whatever your style, whatever your choice, be it elegance or casual, there's always something for all at Yes & Co. DOESN'T IT FEEL GOOD TO PAY LESS?

Hours Telephone 0151 547 2224 for information

See ad on page 263

Discount

see text

Ellesmere Port

Cheshire Oaks Designer Outlet Village

Cheshire Oaks, Kinsey Road, Ellesmere Port, Cheshire, L65 9JJ
Tel: 0151 357 3633

Men's clothes, women's clothes, children's clothes, sportswear, electrical, household goods, footwear, Designer outlet village

Hours Mon–Sat 10–6, Thur late until 8, Sun and Bank Holidays 11–5

Closed Christmas Day

➡ Easy to find, 6 miles north of Chester city centre and a short distance south of Ellesmere Port

Public Transport Buses from Ellesmere Port and Chester

See ad on page 275

Discount from

30%

Parking 2000 Spaces, & Yes, **Group Tours** Yes, **Mail order** No, **Catalogue** No, ✗ On site, **Internet Sales** No

Ellesmere Port

Thorntons

Unit 37, Cheshire Oaks, Designer Outlet Village, Kinsey Road, Ellesmere Port, South Wirral, Cheshire, L65 9JJ
Tel: 0151 3555637

The factory outlet stores sell three different product categories: misshapes, discounted lines and standard lines. Misshapes are packed into assorted bags and offer a saving of between 35%–55%. Discount lines are offered at a discount of 25%–50%. Standard lines are also on sale at normal prices

Hours Opening times dependent upon individual factory outlet centre

Discount

Labels Thorntons

25%–55%

& No, **Group Tours** No, **Mail order** Yes, **Catalogue** Yes, ✗ Most outlets have food courts, **Internet Sales** Yes

Ellesmere Port

Velmore

Thornton Road Industrial Estate, Ellesmere Port, Cheshire, L65 5ER
Tel: 0151 357 1212

Women's clothes. Leading chainstore seconds only sold here, at factory shop prices

Hours Tue–Thu 10:30–3, Fri 10:30–2, Sat 9–1

Closed Monday, Bank Holidays, Christmas and New Year

➡ About three-quarters of a mile east of town centre

Public Transport Local buses, Ellesmere Port train station

Discount

see text

Parking Street, & Yes, **Group Tours** Yes, **Mail order** No, **Catalogue** No, ✗ Teas in town, **Internet Sales** No

Ellesmere Port

Yes & Co

Unit 11 Mercer Way, Ellesmere Port, South Wirral,
Cheshire, L65 0AP
Tel: 0151 357 3782

Ladies' fashion, with men's and children's available in
selected stores at the lowest prices. More than 150
different lines in every store. 40 new lines coming into
every store every week. We are specialists in High Street
and designer fashion names at the lowest prices.
Whatever your style, whatever your choice, be it elegance
or casual, there's always something for all at Yes & Co.
DOESN'T IT FEEL GOOD TO PAY LESS?

Hours Telephone 0151 547 2224 for information

See ad on page 263

Discount

Knutsford

Just One Night

11 Brook Street, Knutsford, Cheshire, WA16 8EB
Tel: 01565 633059

Over 300 evening outfits to hire (from £50–£95) or buy
(from £45–£250) in sizes 8–22. Ballgowns, party dresses
and cocktailwear. Stock changes each season. From simple
dresses to grand ballgowns we have the dress of your
dreams. Accessories also available

Hours Mon and Fri 10–6, Tues and Thur 10–8. Wed 10–3.
Sat 10–4 pm

Closed Christmas Day, Boxing Day, New Year's Day, Bank
Holidays

➡ Junction 19 off M6, follow signs to Knutsford or
Macclesfield. Turn right at roundabout in Knutsford town
centre. Turn left at British Rail station, follow road to
next set of lights. We are on the right. Own car park

Public Transport British Rail Knutsford station –
3 minutes walk away

Discount

Labels J. Charles, Serenade,
Bernshaw, La Regina, Zvanzino,
Asable, Mairin, Ariella, Foxy Frocks

Parking 4 Spaces, & Yes, Group Tours No, Mail order Yes,
Catalogue Yes, ✕ Local rest'nts, cafés, Internet Sales No

Macclesfield

A Shufflebotham and Son

8 Gunco Lane, Macclesfield, Cheshire, SK11 7JK
Tel: 01652 423304

Exclusive designer seconds in furnishing and upholstery
fabrics

Hours Mon–Fri 9–5:30, Sat 10–1

Closed Bank Holidays and Christmas

➡ Near south-east end of town

Public Transport 10 minutes walk from train station

Discount

Parking Lots, & Yes, Group Tours Yes, Mail order Yes,
Catalogue No, ✕ Refreshments on site, and Arighi Bianchi
coffee shop 5 minutes away, Internet Sales No

Macclesfield

Designer Warehouse

Paradise Mill, Park Lane, Macclesfield, Cheshire, SK11 6TJ
Tel: 01625 511169 Fax: 0161 449 7842

Ends of lines and samples, cancelled orders and
overmakes of up-to-the-minute designer wear for
women. Top designer labels. At least 50% off normal
retail prices

Hours Mon–Sat 9:30–5:30

Closed Bank Holidays, Christmas Day, Boxing Day and
New Year's Day

➡ In the town centre, next to Paradise Mill Silk Museum
which is well signed

Public Transport 10 minutes walk from train station.
5 minutes from bus station

Discount up to

50%

Parking Street, & Yes, Group Tours Yes, Mail order No,
Catalogue No, ✕ Café 200 yd, Internet Sales No

Macclesfield

Room Service Interiors

38 Charlotte Street, Macclesfield, Cheshire, SK11 6JA
Tel: 01625 613955

Curtain and upholstery fabrics by top British and
International designers. End of lines and seconds.
Rolls at half usual price

Hours Mon–Tue 9:30–5, Wed 10–5, Thur–Sat 9–5:30

Closed Bank Holidays, Christmas Day, Boxing Day and
New Year's Day

➡ In tangle of little streets in old town centre

Public Transport Easy walk from bus and train station

Discount

see text

Parking Car park, & Yes, **Group Tours** No, **Mail order** No,
Catalogue No, ✗ Good local cafés, **Internet Sales** No

Macclesfield

The Fent Shop

Pickford Street Mill, Pickford Street, Macclesfield,
Cheshire, SK11 6HY
Tel: No telephone in shop

Huge range of haberdashery, craft items and fabrics.
Large range of rolls and remnants at vastly reduced
prices.

Hours Mon, Tues, Thur 9:30–4:30, Wed 9:30–12:30,
Fri 9:30–3:30, Sat 9–1

Closed Bank Holidays, Christmas Day, Boxing Day and
New Year's Day

➡ In the tangle of little streets in the old town centre,
facing and on downhill side of the Pickford Centre
(discount giant) supermarket car park

Public Transport Easy walk from bus and train stations

Discount

see text

Parking Public car park, & Yes, **Group Tours** Yes,
Mail order No, **Catalogue** No, ✗ Teas in supermarket next
door, **Internet Sales** No

Northwich

Yes & Co

69 Witton Street, Northwich, Cheshire, CW9 5DW
Tel: 01606 352 318

Ladies' fashion, with men's and children's available in
selected stores at the lowest prices. More than 150
different lines in every store. 40 new lines coming into
every store every week. We are specialists in High Street
and designer fashion names at the lowest prices.
Whatever your style, whatever your choice, be it elegance
or casual, there's always something for all at Yes & Co.
DOESN'T IT FEEL GOOD TO PAY LESS?

Hours Telephone 0151 547 2224 for information

See ad on page 263

Discount

see text

Runcorn

Yes & Co

Unit 38, Orchard Walk, Halton Lea Shopping Centre,
Runcorn, Cheshire, WA7 2BU
Tel: 01928 796 732

Ladies' fashion, with men's and children's available in
selected stores at the lowest prices. More than 150
different lines in every store. 40 new lines coming into
every store every week. We are specialists in High Street
and designer fashion names at the lowest prices.
Whatever your style, whatever your choice, be it elegance
or casual, there's always something for all at Yes & Co.
DOESN'T IT FEEL GOOD TO PAY LESS?

Hours Telephone 0151 547 2224 for information

See ad on page 263

Discount

see text

Warrington

Yes & Co

22–26 Buttermarket Street, Warrington, Cheshire, WA1 2LL
Tel: 01925 576 151

Ladies' fashion, with men's and children's available in selected stores at the lowest prices. More than 150 different lines in every store. 40 new lines coming into every store every week. We are specialists in High Street and designer fashion names at the lowest prices. Whatever your style, whatever your choice, be it elegance or casual, there's always something for all at Yes & Co. DOESN'T IT FEEL GOOD TO PAY LESS?

Hours Telephone 0151 547 2224 for information

See ad on page 263

Discount

see text

Widnes

Yes & Co

10 Albert Square, Widnes, Cheshire, WA8 6JW
Tel: 0151 424 8951

Ladies' fashion, with men's and children's available in selected stores at the lowest prices. More than 150 different lines in every store. 40 new lines coming into every store every week. We are specialists in High Street and designer fashion names at the lowest prices. Whatever your style, whatever your choice, be it elegance or casual, there's always something for all at Yes & Co. DOESN'T IT FEEL GOOD TO PAY LESS?

Hours Telephone 0151 547 2224 for information

See ad on page 263

Discount
see text

Alston

Hi-Pennine Outdoor Shop

Market Square, Alston, Cumbria, CA9 32W
Tel: 01434 381742

Men's, women's and children's outdoor clothing

Hours Mon–Sun 9:30–4:30

Closed Sundays in winter

➡ Market Square area

Public Transport Bus

Discount
see text

Parking Limited, ♿ Yes, **Group Tours** No, **Mail order** Yes, **Catalogue** No, **Internet Sales** No

Cleator

The Kangol Factory Shop

Cleator, Cumbria, CA23 3DJ
Tel: 01946 810312 Fax: 01946 811087

Factory shop is always stocked with a huge selection of the world-famous range of Kangol headwear for formal and casual wear – both men's and ladies'. Also in stock a range of ther products, including Kangol-branded merchandise. Factory tours by arrangement (Monday to Thursday). Coach parties welcome

Hours Mon–Sat 9–5, Sun 11–4, telephone for Christmas and Bank Holiday opening hours

See ad on page 243

Discount
see text

Group Tours Yes

Kendal

K Village

Netherfield, Lound Road, Kendal, Cumbria, LA9 7DA
Tel: 01539 732363

Full range of shops selling men's, ladies' and children's clothing, furniture, food, sportswear, electrical and household goods, toys decorating, sports equipment and shoes

Hours Telephone for opening hours

See ad on page 153

Discount

see text

Sedbergh

Farfield Clothing

The Old School, Sedbergh, Cumbria, LA10 5AS
Tel: 01539 620169 Fax: 01539 621716
Email: jean@farfield.co.uk

'Tough Customer' range of children's fleece jackets etc. Farfield range of adult fleece and fibre jackets etc.

Hours Mon–Sat 9:30–5

Closed Christmas and New Year

➜ Junction 37 M6. A684 to Sedbergh. Off main street, past Joss Lane car park

Public Transport Train – Oxenholme, Kendal

Discount

Labels Tough Customer, Farfield, all own brand, manufactured on premises

see text

Parking 10 Spaces, & Yes, **Group Tours** Yes, **Mail order** Yes, Catalogue Yes, ✗ In town, **Internet Sales** Yes

Hornsea

Freeport Outlet Village

Rolston Road, Hornsea, East Riding, HU18 1UT
Tel: 01964 534211

Mens, ladies and childrenswear, sportswear, household goods, toys. Stock includes Adidas, Calvin Klein, Christian Dior, Ellesse, Kickers, Lee, Next, Nike, Thorntons, Wedgwood, YSL

Hours Mon–Sun 9:30–6

Closed Christmas Day and New Year's Day

➜ Take the M62 to J38. Follow signs for Beverley, then take the A1035 to Hornsea

Public Transport Bus routes 230, 240, 246 and 824 from Hull

Discount

Labels YSL, Calvin Klein, Adidas, Lee, Craghopper, Tog 24, Laura Ashley, Wedgwood, Hallmark

20%–70%

Parking 1100 Spaces, & Yes, **Group Tours** Yes, **Mail order** No, Catalogue No, ✗ On site, **Internet Sales** No

Ashton-under-Lyme

Barden Mill Shop

Cavendish Street, Ashton-under-Lyme, Greater Manchester, OL6 7QL
Tel: 0161 343 7696

Full range of discount clothing for men, ladies and children. Most garments are overmakes for chainstores or ex High Street merchandise

Hours Mon–Sat 10–5

Closed Bank Holidays

➜ On the south edge of Ashton town centre, towards Dukinfield

Public Transport Two minutes walk from bus station. Bus No. 219 runs past

Discount

see text

Parking Yes, & Yes, **Group Tours** Yes, **Mail order** No, Catalogue No, ✗ In town

Bolton

AP Supplies

Unit 7, Lever Bridge Mills, Radcliffe Road, Darcy Lever, Bolton, Greater Manchester, BL3 1RV
Tel: 01204 394981 Fax: 01204 531767

Twist pile carpets 80/20% wool/nylon. Wide selection of colours

Hours Mon–Fri 8–4:30, Sat 9–3

Closed Bank Holidays, Christmas Day, Boxing Day and New Year's Day

➡ On the south-east side of Bolton

Public Transport Buses from Bolton town centre

Discount **see text**

Parking Yes, & Yes, **Group Tours** No, **Mail order** No, **Catalogue** No, ✗ Nearby pubs, cafés, teashops in Bolton

Bolton

Baird Outerwear Brands

Fletcher Street, Bolton, Greater Manchester, BL3 6PR
Tel: 01204 32311

Ladies' and men's rainwear and casualwear. Perfects, seconds, ends of lines on sale

Hours Mon–Sat 10–4

Closed Christmas and New Year

➡ About quarter mile south-west of Bolton station

Public Transport 15 minutes walk from town centre

Discount **see text**

Labels Dannimac, Cloud Nine, Telemac, Thomas Marshall, Baracuta

Parking Street, & Yes, **Group Tours** Yes, **Mail order** No, **Catalogue** No, ✗ In Bolton, **Internet Sales** No

Bolton

Dewhurst Dent

Union Mill, Vernon Street, Bolton, Greater Manchester
Tel: 01204 399619

Ready made curtains, dress fabrics, trimmings and linings. 40% off normal retail prices

Hours Mon–Wed 10–5, Thur 10–7:30, Fri and Sat 10–5, Sun 10–4

Closed Some Bank Holidays. Telephone for Christmas, New Year and Easter

➡ In a large mill close to the city centre (on the north-west side). Vernon Street leads off St Georges Road (B6226/A613)

Public Transport Bus Nos. 501, 502, 518, 519, 575 from town centre or train station

Discount

Parking Yes, & No, **Group Tours** Yes, **Mail order** No, Catalogue No, ✕ Various cafés in town, **Internet Sales** No

Bolton

The Coathanger Clothing & Camping Co

215 Fletcher Street, Bolton, Greater Manchester, BL3 6NG
Tel: 01204 397886

Wide range of high quality outdoor clothing and camping equipment for all the family

Hours Mon–Sat 9–5

Closed Wednesday, Bank Holidays, 1st week September, Christmas Day, Boxing Day and New Year's Day

➡ About third mile south-west of Bolton station

Public Transport Bus/train

Discount

Parking Street, & No, **Group Tours** No, **Mail order** Yes, Catalogue No, ✕ On site, and in town, **Internet Sales** No

Bolton

Willsmart Factory Shop

St Pauls Mill, Caroline Street, Bolton, Greater Manchester, BL3 6UQ
Tel: 01204 64215 Fax: 0161 745 3837

Men's, women's and children's clothing

Hours Mon–Sat 9:30–5:00

Public Transport Buses 582/559/12/571/572 from town centre.

Discount

Labels Mixed, varied

& Yes, **Group Tours** Yes, **Mail order** No, **Catalogue** No, ✕ Local pub and cafés, **Internet Sales** No

Broadbottom

Tiviot Prints

Lymefield Mill, Broadbottom, near Hyde, Greater Manchester, SK14 6AF
Tel: 01457 764399

Printed cloth

Hours Thu–Fri 10–4, Sat 10–3:30

Closed Bank Holidays, Christmas and New Year

➡ About 3 miles west of Glossop canal and railway

Public Transport Trains from Manchester/Glossop to Broadbottom; buses from Hyde/Glossop

Discount

Parking Yes, & Yes, **Group Tours** No, **Mail order** No, Catalogue No, ✕ Local pubs. Tearooms in Glossop, **Internet Sales** No

Bury	Bury

Antler

Pilot works, Alfred Street, Bury, Greater Manchester, BL9 9EF
Tel: 0161 764 5241

Wide selection of luggage, cases, bags and attaché cases, picnic hampers and leather goods. End of season ranges, quality seconds and samples

Hours Tue–Sat 10–4

Closed Monday, Easter Friday and Saturday, Christmas and New Year

➡ South-east of Bury town centre, not far from M66 exit 2

Public Transport Train or bus to Bury then local buses Nos. 92, 93, 70, 135, 136, 138, 790

Discount
see text

& No, **Group Tours** No, **Mail order** No, **Catalogue** No,
✕ Teas in town centre, **Internet Sales** No

Whitfords Bury Boot & Shoe Co

Brandleholme Road, Bury, Greater Manchester, BL8 1BQ
Tel: 0161 238 4209

Shoes for people who have difficulty finding correct fittings. Heavy duty corsetry, dresses, coats and underwear etc. Also items for people with disabilities

Hours Mon–Sat 9–5

Closed Bank Holidays, Christmas and New Year

➡ On the B6214 north-west of Bury

Public Transport Bus No. 474 (to Ramsbottom) from Bury interchange, ask for Whitfords Bury Boots

Discount
25%–50%

& Yes, **Group Tours** No, **Mail order** Yes, **Catalogue** Yes,
✕ Teas in town

Chadderton

Gorse Mill Lighting

Gorse Mill, Gorse Street, Broadway, Chadderton, Greater Manchester, BL9 9RK
Tel: 0161 628 4202

Modern and traditional light fittings. Average saving 50% off normal retail price

Hours Mon–Fri 9–4:30, Sat and Sun 10–4, Bank Holidays 10–4

Closed Easter Sunday, Christmas Day, Boxing Day and New Year's Day

➡ Between Middleton and Oldham, off A663 in a huge, conspicuous mill

Public Transport Buses from Oldham and from Manchester to Chadderton

Discount

see text

Parking 300 Spaces, & Yes, Group Tours Yes, Mail order No, Catalogue No, ✗ On site, Internet Sales No

Failsworth

Pifco Factory Shop

Princess Street, Failsworth, Greater Manchester, M35 0HS
Tel: 0161 947 3117

Small electrical goods. Most of our goods are at factory prices

Hours Mon–Fri 9–4:30, Sat 9–12:30

Closed Tuesday, Bank Holidays, Christmas–New Year's Eve

➡ On the A62 Manchester–Oldham Road

Public Transport 3 minutes walk from Failsworth train station. Oldham–Manchester buses stop nearby

See ad on page 245

Discount

see text

Labels Pifco, Salton, Carmen, Russell Hobbs, Tower, Mountain Breeze

Parking Yes, & Yes, Group Tours No, Mail order No, Catalogue No, ✗ Teas in Failsworth, Internet Sales No

Hazel Grove

Mood Factory Shopping

36/38 London Road, Hazel Grove, Greater Manchester, SK12 1LF
Tel: 0161 456 9876 / 0161 482 4544

Ladies' and gents' clothing. Most of our stock is current season's lines, with about 80% manufactured by ourselves. Prices on average are 30% lower than High Street. Fashion shows can be arranged

Hours Mon–Sat 9:30–5:30, Sun 11–4

Closed Christmas Day and New Year's Day, Bank Holidays

➡ In the centre of Hazel Grove

Public Transport Hazel Grove train station. Bus No. 192 stops outside shop

Discount

see text

Parking Yes, & Yes, Group Tours Yes, Mail order No, Catalogue No, ✗ Nearby Co-op and cafés, Internet Sales No

Hazel Grove

Wynsors World of Shoes

56/57 London Road, Hazel Grove, Greater Manchester, SK12 1LF
Tel: 0161 456 2632

Men's, ladies' and children's fashion shoes. Car park adjacent to Kwik Save

Hours Mon–Wed 9–5:30, Thur and Fri 9–8, Sun and Bank Holidays 10–4

Closed Christmas Day and New Year's Day

➡ In the centre of Hazel Grove

Public Transport Hazel Grove train station. Bus No. 192 stops outside shop

Discount

see text

& Yes, Group Tours Yes, Mail order No, Catalogue No, ✗ Teas in Co-op shopping giant, Internet Sales No

Horwich

Halbro Sportswear

Lee Lane, Horwich, Greater Manchester, BL6 7JE
Tel: 01204 696476

Huge range of rugby jerseys, including replicas of those worn by UK and overseas teams. Most items are slightly imperfect at greatly reduced prices

Hours Tues, Thur, Fri 10–5, Sat 10–2

Closed Monday, Wednesday, Easter, Christmas–New Year, Bank Holidays

➡ At the west end of Horwich on the B6226

Public Transport Any bus to Horwich

Discount

Parking Public, & Yes, **Group Tours** Yes, **Mail order** No, **Catalogue** No, ✕ Local cafés, pubs, rest'nts, **Internet Sales** No

Horwich

The Towel Mill Shop

Vicoria Mill, Chorley New Road, Horwich, Greater Manchester, BL6 6ER
Tel: 01204 695611

Wide range of towels in all colours and sizes. Bathrobes, skirts, blouses, knitwear, tops and men's shirts. Near perfects and current stock manufactured by this company, sold here at discounted prices

Hours Mon–Fri 9–4:30, Thur late until 7, Sat 10–3

Closed Christmas–New Year, some Bank Holidays

➡ A short way south of the town centre

Public Transport Local buses

Discount

Parking Yes, & No, **Group Tours** No, **Mail order** No, **Catalogue** No, ✕ Teas in Horwich, **Internet Sales** No

Hyde

Ashtons

Newton Street, Hyde, Greater Manchester, SK14 4NP
Tel: 0161 368 1961

Towels, bed linen, baby products, blankets

Hours Mon–Wed 9–6:30, Thur 9–6, Fri 9–12:30

Closed Bank Holidays, Easter, Friday and Monday first week in October, Christmas–New Year

➡ In the huge mill just north of M67 exit 3

Public Transport Local trains and buses

Labels Ashtons, Christys

Discount

Parking Road, & Yes, **Group Tours** No, **Mail order** No, **Catalogue** No, ✕ Teas in Hyde, **Internet Sales** No

Hyde

Providence Reproductions

Providence Mill, Alexandra Street, Hyde, Greater Manchester, SK14 1DX
Tel: 0161 366 6184

Vast selection of period-style furniture, specialists in solid mahogany. Repair and polishing services

Hours Mon–Sat 9–5, Sun 10–4, Bank Holidays 10–4

Closed Christmas Day and Boxing Day

➡ West side of Hyde, south of M67 exit 3, near Hyde central station

Public Transport 10 minutes walk from town centre

Discount

Parking In Mill Yard, & Yes, **Group Tours** No, **Mail order** No, **Catalogue** No, ✕ Teas in Hyde, **Internet Sales** No

Hyde

Super Seconds

24 Reynold Street, Hyde, Greater Manchester, SK14 1LU
Tel: 0161 368 3376

High quality men's and women's designer and High Street chainstore wear

Hours Mon–Sat 10–5

Closed Tuesday, Bank Holidays, Christmas Day, Boxing Day and New Year's Day

➡ In the town centre at the side of the covered market. Next door but one to Iceland

Public Transport Five minutes walk from bus station

Discount

see text

Parking Public car park, ✦ Yes, **Group Tours** Yes, **Mail order** No, **Catalogue** No, ✗ In shopping mall, **Internet Sales** No

Hyde

The Mill Fabric Shop

Cartwright Street, Newton, Hyde, Greater Manchester, SK14 4QU
Tel: 0161 367 9337

Furnishing fabrics. Perfects plus seconds, most at half price or less. Prices from £1.50 per yard upwards

Hours Mon 10–5, Tues–Sat 9–5, Sun 10–4, open most Bank Holidays, telephone to check

Closed Easter Sunday, Christmas and New Year

➡ On the north-east side of Hyde

Public Transport Hyde central station. Bus Nos. 209 and 346 from bus station

Discount

see text

Parking Street, ✦ Yes, **Group Tours** Yes, **Mail order** No, **Catalogue** No, ✗ Pub on the corner, **Internet Sales** No

Kearsley

EBAC

221 Manchester Road, Kearsley, Greater Manchester, BL4 8QX
Tel: 01204 707953

Range of domestic appliances. First and seconds, various discounts. Prices from under £1

Hours October–March only: Thur 10–7, Fri 10–5, Sat 9–5

Closed April–September, also Monday–Wednesday during rest of the year

➡ Kearsley is north of M61 exits 2 and 3

Public Transport Bus Nos. 22, 28, 8, 9 from Bolton or Manchester stop 200 yards away

Discount

see text

Parking Street, ✦ No, **Group Tours** No, **Mail order** Yes, **Catalogue** No, ✗ On site, sandwich shop, **Internet Sales** No

Leigh

Yes & Co

Unit 11, Spinning Gate Shopping Centre, Ellesmere Street, Leigh, Greater Manchester, WN7 4PG
Tel: 01942 261 701

Ladies' fashion, with men's and children's available in selected stores at the lowest prices. More than 150 different lines in every store. 40 new lines coming into every store every week. We are specialists in High Street and designer fashion names at the lowest prices. Whatever your style, whatever your choice, be it elegance or casual, there's always something for all at Yes & Co. DOESN'T IT FEEL GOOD TO PAY LESS?

Hours Telephone 0151 547 2224 for information

See ad on page 263

Discount

see text

Littleborough

New England Design

Sladen Wood Mill, Todmorden Road, Littleborough,
Greater Manchester, OL15 9EW
Tel: 01706 371343

Household goods and made-to-measure suites etc., and
accessories

Hours Mon–Sat 10–5, Thur late until 8, Sun, Bank
Holidays 10–5,

Closed Christmas Day, Boxing Day and New Year's Day

➡ North of Littleborough (which is about 3 miles north-
east of Rochdale)

Public Transport On main Halifax–Burnley and Rochdale
bus route. Bus stop outside

Discount
see text

Parking Yes, ♿ Yes, **Group Tours** Yes, **Mail order** Yes,
Catalogue No, ✕ Tea rooms nearby, **Internet Sales** No

Manchester

Sanderson Clearance Outlet

2 Pollard Street, Manchester, Greater Manchester, M4 7DR
Tel: 0161 272 8501

Huge range of seconds and remnants in Sanderson
printed and plain fabrics; also carpets, wall-coverings, bed
linen, ready-made curtains and extensive range of gift
items

Hours Tues, Wed, Fri 10–6, Thur 10–7:30, Sat 10–5:30, Sun
10–4

Closed Mondays and Bank Holidays

➡ Conspicuous shop in the middle of Manchester. Pollard
Street is the A662, off Great Ancoats Street (A665)

Public Transport Bus Nos. 216 and 217. Trains to central
Manchester

Labels Sanderson

Discount
see text

Parking Yes, ♿ Yes, **Group Tours** No, **Mail order** Yes,
Catalogue No, ✕ City centre

Middleton

Color Blind

Unit 6, Middleton Central Industrial Estate, Oldham Road,
Middleton, Greater Manchester, M24 1AS
Tel: 0161 643 380

All blinds including ones made to order

Hours Mon–Wed, Fri 10–5, Sat 10–4

Closed Thursday, Bank Holidays and Christmas period

➡ Easy to find in small industrial estate along the road
from huge Warwick Mill on Oldham road, A669, through
Middleton

Public Transport Bus Nos. 17, 163, 59 from Manchester

Discount
see text

Parking Yes, ♿ No, **Group Tours** Yes, **Mail order** Yes,
Catalogue No, ✕ Café in Arndale Centre, **Internet Sales** No

Salford

Willsmart Factory Shop

Langley Mill, Langley Road, Salford, Greater Manchester,
M6 6JP
Tel: 01204 64215 Fax: 0161 745 3837

Men's, women's and children's clothing

Hours Mon–Sat 9:30–5:00

Public Transport Bus

Labels Varied

Discount
see text

♿ Yes, **Group Tours** Yes, **Mail order** No, **Catalogue** No,
Internet Sales No

Swinton

Yes & Co

9–11 The Parade, Swinton, Greater Manchester
Tel: 0161 793 8670

Ladies' fashion, with men's and children's available in selected stores at the lowest prices. More than 150 different lines in every store. 40 new lines coming into every store every week. We are specialists in High Street and designer fashion names at the lowest prices. Whatever your style, whatever your choice, be it elegance or casual, there's always something for all at Yes & Co. DOESN'T IT FEEL GOOD TO PAY LESS?

Hours Telephone 0151 547 2224 for information

See ad on page 263

Discount

Accrington

Bohemia Period Clothing

11 Warner Street, Accrington, Lancashire
Tel: 01254 231119

Retro clothing & antiques

Hours Mon–Sat 10:30–5:00

Closed Wednesdays and Bank Holidays

Public Transport Bus

Discount

& Yes, **Group Tours** No, **Mail order** No, **Catalogue** No, **Internet Sales** No

Accrington

Hamilton McBride

Shorten Brook Drive, Altham Business Park, Accrington, Lancashire, BB5 5YR
Tel: 01282 858206

Co-ordinated fashion home textiles, curtains, bed linen, table linen, table lamps and cushions

Hours Wed, Thur, Fri 10–5, Sat and Sun 12–5

Closed Christmas Day, Boxing Day and New Year's Day

➜ From Padiham: go west for Blackburn. At traffic lights take A678 for Accrington. From M65 exit 8: aim for Padiham. At first lights turn left. After half mile, opposite Walton Arms go into estate. Take second left, company 150 yards on right

Discount

see text

Parking Yes, & No, **Group Tours** No, **Mail order** Yes, **Catalogue** No, ✕ In Accrington, local pubs, **Internet Sales** No

Accrington

Karrimor International

Petre Road, Clayton-le-Moors, Accrington, Lancashire, BB5 5JZ
Tel: 01254 388466

Men's and women's clothes – perfects, seconds, ex-display, samples and ends of lines and sportswear

Hours Mon–Thu 11–7:30, Fri 11–5, Sat 9–12.30

Closed Bank Holidays, Christmas and New Year

➜ From M65 exit 7: follow signs to Clitheroe (A6185). Turn right at lights opposite GEC Industrial Estate. Petre Road is first on left. Karrimor is at the end of the road

See ad on page 281

Discount

Labels Gore-tex, Phoenix

Parking Yes, & Yes, **Group Tours** Yes, **Mail order** Yes, **Catalogue** Yes, ✕ In Accrington, **Internet Sales** No

Accrington

Optical Direct

5 Cunliffe Court (off Petre Road), Clayton Enterprise Park,
Clayton-le-Moors, Lancashire, BB5 5JF
Tel: 01254 395725

Over 1300 budget and designer frames; contact lenses.
Prices from £14.95 upwards

Hours Mon–Sat 9–5

Closed Christmas Day, Boxing Day and New Year's Day,
check for other Bank Holidays

➨ From M65 exit 7: follow signs to Clitheroe (A6185), go
right at lights opposite GEC Industrial Estate. Petre Road
is first left, Cunliffe Court is on right with unit 5 clearly
busy

Discount up to

50%

Parking Yes, & Yes, **Group Tours** Yes, **Mail order** Yes,
Catalogue No, ✕ On site, and Cafés and pubs

Accrington

Red Rose Velvets

Royal Mill, Victoria Street, Accrington, Lancashire,
BB5 0PO
Tel: 01254 392059

Velvet curtain fabric, velvet clothing fabric. Curtains
made-to-measure all in cotton. Accessories etc. We only
sell what we weave on the premises. Prices: £5.50 to
£7.50 per yard

Hours Mon–Fri 9:30–5, Sat 10–1

Closed Three days at Easter, last week of May, last 2
weeks of July, 3rd week in September, Christmas and New
Year

➨ In the town on the south-west side of main shopping
area

Public Transport Not far to walk from town centre

Discount

see text

& No, **Group Tours** Yes, **Mail order** Yes, **Catalogue** No,
✕ In town

Accrington

The Card & Gift Factory

Church Bridge Works, Mill Street, Church, near
Accrington, Lancashire, BB5 4EF
Tel: 01254 237324

Wide range of greeting cards, toys, gifts, etc. All items
are excess orders or returned items from catalogues, sold
at very low prices

Hours Mon–Fri 9:30–4:45

Closed Bank Holidays, Christmas and New Year

➨ From big roundabout underneath railway viaduct on
west side of Accrington: follow signs for (M65 Blackburn)
/Church. Look for factory shop sign

Public Transport Buses Nos. 5, 6, 7, 8. Church and
Oswaldtwistle train station 5 minutes walk

Discount

see text

Parking Yes, & Yes, **Group Tours** Yes, **Mail order** No,
Catalogue No, ✕ Teas at Oswaldtwistle Mill. Cafés in
Accrington, **Internet Sales** No

Anderton

Jorgus Carpets

Grimeford Mill, Grimeford Lane, Anderton, Lancashire,
PR6 9HK
Tel: 01257 452636

Plain wool carpets made on premises. Genuine mill shop
with everything made on site. Fitting service available.
Prices from £1.50 per sq. yd. upwards

Hours Mon–Fri 8–5, Sat 9.30–3, Sun 11–3

Closed Lunch 12–1 daily, Bank Holidays, Christmas and
New Year

➨ Short distance south of Adlington and almost in the
shadow of M61, between A6 and A673 (Grimeford Road
links these two roads)

Public Transport Horwich–Chorley buses stop near the
end of Grimeford Road

Discount

see text

Parking Large area, & Yes, **Group Tours** No,
Mail order Yes, **Catalogue** No, ✕ Teas in town

Bacup

E. Sutton & Sons

Newchurch Road, Bacup, Lancashire, OL13 0DP
Tel: 01706 875578

Massive range of branded footwear from own factory and all over the world

Hours Mon–Fri 10–5:30, Sat 9–5:30, Sun and Bank Holidays 10–4

Closed Christmas Day, Boxing Day and New Year's Day

➧ Easy to see on the Bacup–Rawenstall Road (A681), on the edge of Bacup

Public Transport Bus No. 464 within 20 metres (every 15 minutes)

Discount

Parking Large area, & Yes, Group Tours No, Mail order No, Catalogue No, ✗ On site, and Coffee and tea in Bacup

Barrowford

East Lancashire Towel Company

Park Mill, Halstead Lane, Barrowford (near Nelson), Lancashire, BB9 6HK
Tel: 01282 612193

Household goods. Jacquard woven towels, etc.

Hours Mon–Fri 8:30–5, Bank Holidays

Closed One week Easter, first 3 weeks July, 1 week September, 2 weeks Christmas

➧ On northern side of town, just off main road

Public Transport Regular local buses

Discount

Parking Outside Mill, & Yes, Group Tours Yes, Catalogue Yes, ✗ Refreshments on site, and Teas and traditional Lancashire meals served on site between 10 and 2

Blackburn

Graham & Brown

Davey Field Road, Roman Road Industrial Estate, Blackburn, Lancashire, BB1 2NR
Tel: 01254 582229

Wide selection of wallpapers and decorating accessories

Hours Mon–Sat 9:30–5, Sun 10–4

Closed Christmas and New Year period

➧ About 1.5 miles south of Blackburn

Public Transport Bus service

Discount

Parking Large area, & Yes, Group Tours No, Mail order No, Catalogue No, ✗ Local pubs etc in Blackburn

Blackburn

Ovalword

Bastfield Mill, Beach Street, Little Harwood, Lancashire, BB1 6LT
Tel: 01254 582735

Huge selection of wall coverings. Full range of accessories. Prices from 50p upwards

Hours Mon–Fri 9–5:30, Sat 9.30–5, Sun 10–4, open Bank Holidays

Closed Christmas Day and Boxing Day

➧ Little Harwood is on the north-east side of Blackburn

Public Transport Bus Nos. 212, 213, 214 and outer circle

Discount

Parking Yes, & Yes, Group Tours No, Mail order No, Catalogue No, ✗ Blackburn town centre

Blackburn

Sheltered Workshop for the Blind and Disabled

Mill Hill Street, Blackburn, Lancashire, BB2 2RA
Tel: 01254 52666

Textiles including curtains. 95% of goods manufactured on premises by blind and disabled workforce

Hours Mon–Fri 9–4, Sat 9–12

Closed Lunch 12.30–1.30 daily, Bank Holidays, last 2 weeks July, Christmas and New Year

➡ Near Mill Hill station

Public Transport Regular services from Blackburn station

Discount
see text

Parking Yes, ♿ Yes, **Group Tours** Yes, **Mail order** No, **Catalogue** No, ✗ Refreshments on site, **Internet Sales** No

Blackburn

Willsmart Factory Shop

Stonebridge Mill, Shed Street, Oswaldtwistle, Lancashire, BB5 3HY
Tel: 01204 64215 Fax: 0161 745 3837

Men's, women's and children's clothing

Hours Mon–Sat 9:30–5:00

Public Transport Bus

Discount
see text

Labels Varied

♿ Yes, **Group Tours** Yes, **Mail order** No, **Catalogue** No, **Internet Sales** No

Blackpool

Yes & Co

80/82 Talbot Road, Blackpool, Lancashire, FY1 1LR
Tel: 01253 628 347

Ladies' fashion, with men's and children's available in selected stores at the lowest prices. More than 150 different lines in every store. 40 new lines coming into every store every week. We are specialists in High Street and designer fashion names at the lowest prices. Whatever your style, whatever your choice, be it elegance or casual, there's always something for all at Yes & Co. DOESN'T IT FEEL GOOD TO PAY LESS?

Hours Telephone 0151 547 2224 for information

See ad on page 253

Discount
see text

Burnley

Barden Mill

Barden Lane, Burnley, Lancashire, BB12 0DX
Tel: 01282 420333 Fax: 01282 420336

Menswear, ladieswear and childrenswear at a fraction of High Street prices. Some items are de-labelled but there are no seconds. Current and surplus High Street stock arriving every week, plus bedding, towels, curtains, luggage, gifts, books, furniture, pictures, shoes, wool, mirrors and even ice cream!

Hours Mon–Sat 10–5 May–October, Thur late until 8, Sun 11–5

Closed Christmas Day, News Year's Day 2000, Easter Sunday

➡ M65 to J8. A6068 towards Nelson. Go through 2 sets of traffic lights. From 2nd set go for 3.5 miles till you see large brown tourism sign for Barden Mill. Turn right immediately after sign

Public Transport No.5 bus to Reedley stops outside

See ad on page 269

Discount

Labels Baird menswear, Musbury fabrics, ex M & S stock, de-labelled High Street, Hothouse, ex Wallis **25%–70%**

Parking 150 Spaces, & Yes, Group Tours No, Mail order No, Catalogue No, ✗ On site, Internet Sales No

Burnley

Color Blind

Farrington Road, Rossendale Road Industrial Estate, Burnley, Lancashire, BB11 5ST
Tel: 01282 425504

Blinds in large range of styles: vertical, roller, pleated; conservatory roof blinds, venetian blinds in four slat widths

Hours Mon–Fri 10–5:30, Sat 10–4

Closed Bank Holidays, Christmas and New Year

➡ South-west of Burnley town centre

Public Transport From town, on each half hour: bus No. 1 to Rose Grove/Whitegate, ask for Farrington Road

Discount

see text

Parking Yes, & Yes, Group Tours Yes, Mail order Yes, Catalogue No, ✗ Kiosk nearby, Internet Sales No

Burnley

Jaytex Fabrics

129 Oxford Road, Burnley, Lancashire, BB11 3HM
Tel: 01282 428291

Quality materials at bargain prices. Upholstery service

Hours Tue–Fri 9:30–5, Sat and Bank Holidays please telephone

Closed Monday, Christmas and New Year

➡ On the southeast side of Burnley centre

Discount

see text

Parking Yes, & Yes, Group Tours No, Mail order Yes, Catalogue No, ✗ Towneley Hall, and park and café 500 yards away, Internet Sales No

Burnley

John Wilman

Widow Hill Road, Heasandford Industrial Estate, Burnley, Lancashire, BB10 2TK
Tel: 01282 427008

Wide range of co-ordinated wallpapers and accessories. Prices from £1.99 upwards

Hours Mon–Fri 9:30–5:30, Sat 9–5, Sun 10–4, Bank Holidays 10–5

Closed Christmas Eve, Christmas Day, Boxing Day, New Year's Day, Easter Sunday

➡ Off Eastern Avenue (A6114), major road on north-east side of town

Public Transport Bus to bottom of Widow Hill Road, then walk

Discount

see text

Parking Yes, & Yes, Group Tours No, Mail order No, Catalogue No, ✗ Refreshments on site, Internet Sales No

North England & North Wales

Burnley

Lambert Howarth & Sons

Finsley Mill, Finsley Gate, Burnley, Lancashire, BB11 2HI
Tel: 01282 471283

Men's, ladies' and children's shoes, boots, slippers, training shoes. Towels, 'bags', ladies, mens and childrenswear and accessories

Hours Mon–Fri 9:30–5, Sat 9–4, open some Bank Holidays

Closed Good Friday, Easter Monday, Christmas and New Year

➡ Close to town centre, backing on to canal. Probably easiest to look for tall black chimney with red stripes and water tank on roof with large sign 'Osbornia Shoe'

Public Transport Easy walking distance from centre of town

Discount

Parking Yes, ♿ Yes, Group Tours No, Mail order No, Catalogue No, ✗ Coffee across the road, Internet Sales No

Burnley

Oakmount Mill Shop

Wiseman Street, Burnley, Lancashire, BB11 1RV
Tel: 01282 414950

Wide range of dress fabrics, patterns and haberdashery. Curtain and sewing accessories and American craft cottons for patchwork

Hours Mon–Sat 9:15–5

Closed Bank Holidays, Christmas Day, Boxing Day and New Year's Day

➡ Close to town centre on the west side

Public Transport Burnley–Padiham buses pass end of Wiseman Street. Burnley train station about 400 m

Discount

♿ Yes, Group Tours No, Mail order No, Catalogue No, ✗ Good café at ASDA, Internet Sales No

Carnforth

Abbey Horn of Lakeland

Units 6A and 6B Holme Mills, Holme, Lancashire, LA6 1RD
Tel: 01524 782387

Shoe horns, spoons, spatulas, salad servers, horn ships, brushes and combs

Hours Mon–Fri 9–4

Closed Bank Holidays, Christmas and New Year

➡ Company is in industrial estate south of Holme

Public Transport Bus No. 55 from Kendal

Discount
see text

Parking Small area, ♿ No, Group Tours Yes, Mail order No, Catalogue No, ✗ Local pub, Internet Sales No

Castleton

Vectase Lighting

Unit 4B, Gorrels Way, Trans-Pennine Trading Estate, Castleton, Lancashire, GL11 9XY
Tel: 01706 341636

Light fittings. Both perfects and seconds on sale at wholesale prices

Hours Mon–Thu 9:30–4:30, Fri 9:30–2:45

Closed Bank Holidays, Christmas–New Year period

➡ A short distance north of M62 exit 20 and 2 miles south of Rochdale Centre

Discount
see text

Parking In front of shop, ♿ Yes, Group Tours No, Mail order No, Catalogue No, ✗ Teas in Castleton, Internet Sales No

Chorley

Curtain Choice

Corporation Street, Chorley, Lancashire, PR6 0HK
Tel: 01257 622290

Ready-made curtains and accessories. Clearance lines and slight seconds

Hours Mon–Fri 10–4:30, Sat 10–4

Closed Bank Holidays, Spring Bank Holiday weekend, Christmas, New Year, last 2 weeks July

➡ A short way north-east of Chorley town centre

Public Transport 15 minutes walk from town centre

Discount

see text

Parking Street, & Yes, Group Tours Yes, Mail order No, Catalogue No, ✗ Teas in Chorley, Internet Sales No

Chorley

John Wilman

George Street, Chorley, Lancashire, PR7 2BE
Tel: 01257 264011

Wide range of co-ordinated wallpapers, furnishing fabrics, lampshades and textiles, always special offers

Hours Mon–Fri 9:30–5:30, Sat 9–5, Sun 10–4, Bank Holidays 10–5

Closed Christmas Eve, Christmas Day, Boxing Day, New Year's Day, Easter Sunday

➡ On the south side of the town centre just off the A6

Public Transport Train station almost facing shop, 10 min walk to bus station

Discount

see text

Parking Yes, & Yes, Group Tours No, Mail order No, Catalogue No, ✗ Teas in Chorley, Internet Sales No

Chorley

R B Contacts (Wholesale)

Churchill Road, Brinscall, Chorley, Lancashire, PR6 8RO
Tel: 01254 832188/832177

Huge range of curtain fabrics by the yard. Full fitting and making-up service on site for curtains and accessories

Hours Mon–Fri 9–5, Sat 10–3, Sun 11–1, Bank Holidays 9–5

Closed Christmas and New Year's Day

➡ Five miles north-east of Chorley

Public Transport Hourly bus service from Chorley and Blackburn

Discount

see text

Parking Yes, & Yes, Group Tours No, Mail order No, Catalogue No, ✗ Teas in Brinscall, Internet Sales No

Cleveleys

Cresta Factory Outlet

8–12 Nutter Road, Cleveleys, near Blackpool, Lancashire, FY5 1BG
Tel: 01253 823257

Vast range of famous chainstore ladies', men's and children's clothing and shoes. Pottery, household goods. Genuine authentic designer wear.

Hours Mon–Sat 9:30–5:30, Wed and Thur until 6, Sun 10:45–4:45

Closed Christmas Day, Boxing Day and New Year's Day

➡ Nutter Road leads off the central shopping street in Cleveleys

Public Transport Lots of buses from Blackpool, stop nearby

Discount

Labels Armani, Calvin Klein, Ralph Lauren, Versace, Valentino, Boss, many more

see text

Parking Yes, & Yes, Group Tours Yes, Mail order No, Catalogue No, ✗ Cafés in Cleveleys, Internet Sales No

Clitheroe

Shireburn Carpets

Primrose Works, Primrose Road, Clitheroe, Lancashire, BB7 1BS
Tel: 01200 429066

Large range of quality tufted carpets

Hours Mon and Tues 9–5, Thur 9–8, Fri 9–4:30, Sat 10–4, open Bank Holidays

Closed Wednesday, Easter, Christmas, New Year

➜ On the southern edge of town

Public Transport Buses from Clitheroe, get off at Primrose Bridge

Discount see text

Parking Yes, ♿ Yes, **Group Tours** Yes, **Mail order** No, **Catalogue** No, ✕ Teas in Clitheroe, **Internet Sales** No

Colne

Boundary Mill Stores

Burnley Road, Colne, Lancashire, BB8 8LS
Tel: 01282 865229

Ladies' and men's quality wear from all over Europe. Also shoes and boots and home furnishings

Hours Mon–Fri 10–6, Sat and Bank Holidays 10–5, Sun 11–5

Closed Easter Sunday and Christmas Day

➜ A few yards off the A56, between Colne and Nelson, beside ASDA

Public Transport Main Colne–Burnley bus route, 2 minutes walk from Asda bus stop

Discount see text

Labels Alexon, Austin Reed, Jaeger, Christian Dior, Dannimac, Double Two, Farah, Fruit of the Loom

Parking Yes, ♿ Yes, **Group Tours** Yes, **Mail order** No, **Catalogue** No, ✕ Refreshments on site, **Internet Sales** No

MasterCard, Switch, VISA

Colne

Empress Mills (1927)

Hollin Hall Sewing Centre, Hollin Hall Mill, Colne, Lancashire, BB8 8SS
Tel: 01282 863181

Haberdashery, embroidery and quilting suplies. Fabric paints etc. There is a calendar of workshops for beginners and advanced sewing enthusiasts. Regular exhibitions held

Hours Mon–Fri 9–5, Sat and Sun 10–4

Closed Christmas Eve until 4th Jan

➜ This company is in Trawden, a village south-east of Colne

Public Transport Colne–Trawden bus

Discount see text

Parking Yes, ♿ Yes, **Group Tours** Yes, **Mail order** Yes, **Catalogue** Yes, ✕ Refreshments on site, **Internet Sales** No

MasterCard, VISA

Colne

Gardeners' Choice Mill Shop (LBS Group)

Standroyd Mill, Cotton Tree, Colne, Lancashire, BB8 7BW
Tel: 01282 873341

A–Z range of horticultural supplies and gardening sundries. Large florist

Hours Mon–Fri 9–5, Sat 9–4, some Bank Holidays 10–4

Closed Christmas Day and New Year's Day

➜ At the south-east end of town

Public Transport Bus No. 21 Colne–Trawden

Discount see text

Parking Yes, ♿ Yes, **Group Tours** Yes, **Mail order** Yes, **Catalogue** Yes, ✕ Teas in town, **Internet Sales** No

MasterCard, Switch, VISA

Colne

Hartleys Barley Mill Shop (& Mail Order)

Regent House, Whitewalls Industrial Estate, Colne, Lancashire, BB8 8LJ
Tel: 01282 868587 Fax: 01282 870679

Large selection of quality silks, dress, curtain and sheeting fabrics. Bedding, towels, other textile bargains

Hours Mon–Fri 9:30–4:30, Sat 9:30–12:30

Closed Bank Holidays, Christmas–New Year (telephone to check)

➡ Off the A56 between Nelson and Colne. Pass Asda on left then shop is 300 yards on the right

Public Transport On main Nelson–Colne bus route, 3 minutes walk from Asda bus stop

Discount

Parking Yes, & Yes, **Group Tours** No, **Mail order** Yes, **Catalogue** Yes, ✗ Nearby pub for lunch, **Internet Sales** No

Darwen

Silk Mill Shop

Anchor Mill, Moss Fold Road, Darwen, Lancashire, SK14 1LU
Tel: 01254 873333

Bridal and evening dress fabrics, plus patterns and trimmings. Prices: £5–£25 per metre

Hours Mon–Fri 10–5, Saturday 10:30–4

Closed Christmas and New Year. Telephone to check Bank Holidays

➡ At the north end of Darwen just off the A666

Public Transport Any bus on the main Darwen–Blackburn route. Bus stop 100 m from shop

Discount

Parking Yes, & No, **Group Tours** No, **Mail order** No, **Catalogue** No, ✗ Pub half a mile away, **Internet Sales** No

Fleetwood

Briggs & Shoe Mines

Freeport Shopping Village, Fleetwood, Lancashire, SK14 1LU
Tel: 01253 773355

Family footwear by famous makers at greatly reduced prices

Hours Every day 10–6, Thur and Fri late until 8

Closed Christmas Day and Boxing Day

➡ Easy to find in the outlet centre at the 'top right of the Fleetwood peninsula' adjacent to the marina

Public Transport Public transport from Blackpool to Fleetwood

Discount

Parking Yes, & Yes, **Group Tours** Yes, **Mail order** Yes, **Catalogue** No, ✗ Refreshments on site, **Internet Sales** No

Fleetwood

Freeport Outlet Village

Anchorage Road, Fleetwood, Lancashire, FY7 6AE

Mens, ladies and childrenswear, sportswear, household goods and toys. Stock includes Adidas, Calvin Klein, Christian Dior, Ellesse, Kickers, Lee, Next, Nike, Thorntons, Wedgwood, YSL

Hours Mon–Sun 10–6, Thur and Fri late until 8

Closed Christmas Day and New Year's Day

➡ Junction 32 off M5, on to M55, off at J3 and then follow A585 to Fleetwood

Public Transport Blackpool Transport No.14 bus. Nearest railway Poulton-le-Fylde

Discount

20%–70%

Parking 800 Cars, & Yes, **Group Tours** Yes, **Mail order** No, **Catalogue** No, ✗ Refreshments on site, **Internet Sales** No

Fleetwood

Thorntons

Fleetwood Freeport Village, Anchorage Road, Fleetwood, Lancashire, FY7 6AE
Tel: 01253 770710

The factory outlet stores sell three different product categories: misshapes, discounted lines and standard lines. Misshapes are packed into assorted bags and offer a saving of between 35%–55%. Discount lines are offered at a discount of 25%–50%. Standard lines are also on sale at normal prices

Hours Opening times dependent upon individual factory outlet centre

Labels Thorntons

Discount
25%–55%

& No, **Group Tours** No, **Mail order** Yes, **Catalogue** Yes, ✗ Most centres have food courts, **Internet Sales** Yes

Fleetwood

Wynsors World of Shoes

Dock Street, Fleetwood, Lancashire, FY7 6JW
Tel: 01253 779871

Massive range of branded footwear from own factory and all over the world. Mainly perfects, some seconds, special lines at lowest prices in the country. Also, handbags, sportsbags and accessories

Hours Mon–Sat 9–5:30, Thur late until 8, Sun 10–4

Closed Easter Sunday, Christmas Day, Boxing Day and New Year's Day

➡ Easy to find at the 'top right of the Fleetwood peninsula'

Public Transport Bus and tram stops at pier head, 100 yards

Discount

Parking Yes, & Yes, **Group Tours** Yes, **Mail order** No, **Catalogue** No, ✗ On site, others nearby, **Internet Sales** No

Garstang

Country Vogue

Garstang Road, Claughton-on-Brock, Garstang, Lancashire, PR3 0PH
Tel: 01995 640622

Quality upmarket ladies' clothing. Perfects and overmakes. 'Classics for Less' range gives excellent value

Hours Every day 10–5. Open Bank Holidays

Closed Christmas–New Year period

➡ Just off the A6, south of Garstang

Public Transport Buses from Lancaster, Blackpool and Preston stop outside The Brockholes Arms pub

Discount
30%–50%

Parking On forecourt, & Yes, **Group Tours** Yes, **Mail order** Yes, **Catalogue** Yes, ✗ In Garstang, **Internet Sales** No

Great Harwood

The Bedding Box

Harwood House, Glebe Street, Great Harwood, Lancashire, BB6 7AF
Tel: 01254 888338

Continental quilts, pillows, duvet covers, pillowcases, curtains made-to-measure, tie-backs, lampshades, mattress covers, also fabrics by the yard. Chainstore items at very reasonable prices

Hours Mon–Fri 9–5, Sat 9:30–4:30, Sun 11–4:30

Closed Christmas Day, Boxing Day and New Year's Day

➡ In the centre of town

Public Transport Any bus to town

Discount

Parking Yes, & Yes, **Group Tours** No, **Mail order** Yes, **Catalogue** Yes, ✗ In the town, **Internet Sales** No

North England & North Wales Lancashire

Haslingden

Winfields

Hazel Mill, Blackburn Road, Haslingden, Rossendale, Lancashire, BB4 5DD Tel: 01706 227916 Fax: 01706 214280
Email: sales@winfields.co.uk
Web site: www.winfields.co.uk

Footwear, fashion, sports gear or homewares, Winfields has the answer and all at discount prices you won't believe! Perfects, seconds and clearance lines in a wide variety of quality goods at value for money prices; many items are at half the usual High Street price – with over 70 000 sq. ft. Winfields is factory shopping at its best!

Hours Mon–Fri 10–5:30, Thur late until 8, Sat 9–5:30, Sun 11–5

Closed Christmas Day and Easter Sunday

➡ From the roundabout where the A680 and A56 (the extension of M66 from Manchester) join, turn south towards Haslingden. After a few yards, Winfields entrance is clearly signposted on the left

Public Transport Buses No. 4 (Accrington–Bacup), No. 464 (Accrington–Rochdale), No. 701 (Clitheroe–Manchester)

Discount up to

Labels Kappa, Kickers, Caterpillar, Pod, Rockport, Adidas, Lipsy, Diabless, Tamaris, and many more **50%**

Parking 600 Spaces, 20 Coaches, & Yes, Group Tours Yes, Mail order No, Catalogue No, ✗ On site, Internet Sales Yes

Helmshore

Musbury Fabrics

Park Mill, Holcombe Road, Helmshore, Lancashire, BB4 4NQ
Tel: 01706 221318

Co-ordinated household textiles. Firsts, seconds and ends of runs at keen factory prices

Hours Every day 9:30–4:30 including Bank Holidays

Closed Christmas Day, Boxing Day and New Year's Day

➡ Six miles south of Accrington and eight miles north of Bury

Public Transport Helmshore circular buses from Rawtenstall and Haslingden stop outside

Discount **see text**

Parking Car park, & Yes, Group Tours No, Mail order Yes, Catalogue Yes, ✗ Textile museum, Internet Sales No

Lancaster

Standfast

Caton Road, Lancaster, Lancashire, LA1 3PB
Tel: No telephone in shop

Seconds in printed fabrics, including many well-known Designer names

Hours Mon–Fri 9:30–1, Sat 10–12:30

Closed Bank Holidays, Christmas and New Year

➡ Nearly 1 mile north of town

Public Transport None

Discount **see text**

Parking Yes, & Yes, Group Tours No, Mail order No, Catalogue No, ✗ Refreshments on site, and In Lancaster, Internet Sales No

Lancaster

The Factory Shop Ltd

Lancaster Leisure Park, Wyresdale Road, Lancaster, Lancashire, LA1 3LB
Tel: 01524 846079

Clothing and footwear for all the family

Hours Mon–Sat 10–5, Sun 11–5

Closed Christmas Day and Boxing Day

➡ On the east side of town

Public Transport Bus No. 253 from Lancaster bus station

Discount **see text**

Parking Yes, & Yes, Group Tours Yes, Mail order Yes, Catalogue Yes, ✗ Refreshments on site, Internet Sales No

Leyland

Holmes for Foam

Heald House Road, Leyland, Lancashire, PR5 2JB
Tel: 01772 422377

Foam cut to any size and shape. Also curtains and accessories

Hours Mon–Thu 8:30–5, Fri and Sat 8:30–4

Closed Bank Holidays, Christmas and New Year

➡ On the B5248 south of town centre and next to M6

Public Transport 2 miles from Leyland train station

Discount

see text

Parking Yes, & Yes, **Group Tours** No, **Mail order** Yes, **Catalogue** No, ✕ In nearby village, **Internet Sales** No

Lytham

Fylde Footwear

Units A & B, Waterfront Marine, Dock Road, Lytham, Lancashire, FY8 5AQ
Tel: 01253 730060

Fashionwear for all the family. Branded names and well-known High Street shoes. Household goods including crockery, towels and bedding. Some seconds available. Prices from £1 upwards

Hours Mon–Fri 9:30–5, Sat 9–4, Sun 10–4

Closed Bank Holidays, Christmas–New Year (telephone to check)

➡ In the industrial estate east of town centre

Public Transport Bus Nos. 11, 11a and 22 from Blackpool and Lytham to the end of Dock Road

Discount up to

75%

Parking Yes, & Yes, **Group Tours** Yes, **Mail order** Yes, **Catalogue** No, ✕ Good range in Lytham, **Internet Sales** No

Morecambe

Briggs & Shoe Mines

205 Marine Road West, Morecambe, Lancashire, LA3 1TE
Tel: 01524 419293

Wide selection of branded clearance footwear at reduced prices for all the family

Hours Summer: Mon–Sat 10–8, Sun 10:30–4:30, Winter: Mon–Sat 10–5:30, Sun 10:30–4:30

Closed Christmas Day

➡ On the promenade between Victoria Pavilion and old railway station, next to Woolworths

Public Transport Train station 5 minutes walk

Discount

see text

Labels 60 brands stocked

Parking Yes, & Yes, **Group Tours** Yes, **Mail order** Yes, **Catalogue** No, ✕ Along promenade, **Internet Sales** No

Morecambe

Yes & Co

32/33 Arndale Centre, Morecambe, Lancashire, LA4 5DH
Tel: 01524 400 610

Ladies' fashion, with men's and children's available in selected stores at the lowest prices. More than 150 different lines in every store. 40 new lines coming into every store every week. We are specialists in High Street and designer fashion names at the lowest prices. Whatever your style, whatever your choice, be it elegance or casual, there's always something for all at Yes & Co. DOESN'T IT FEEL GOOD TO PAY LESS?

Hours Telephone 0151 547 2224 for information

See ad on page 263

Discount

see text

Nelson

Pendle Village Mill

Hollin Bank, Brierfield, Nelson, Lancashire, BB9 5NF
Tel: 01282 605004

Wide range of quality clothes, first class footwear, household textiles, three-piece suites, carpets, much more

Hours Mon–Sat 9–5:30, Sun and Bank Holidays 10–4

Closed Easter Sunday, Christmas Day

➡ Brierfield is between Nelson and Burnley. This mill is close to M65 exit 12

Public Transport 5–10 minutes walk from town centre

Discount

Parking Yes, & Yes, **Group Tours** Yes, **Mail order** No, **Catalogue** No, ✗ Refreshments on site, **Internet Sales** No

Birkenhead

Yes & Co

207 Grange Road, Birkenhead, Merseyside, L41 2PH
Tel: 0151 647 3050

Ladies' fashion, with men's and children's available in selected stores at the lowest prices. More than 150 different lines in every store. 40 new lines coming into every store every week. We are specialists in High Street and designer fashion names at the lowest prices. Whatever your style, whatever your choice, be it elegance or casual, there's always something for all at Yes & Co. DOESN'T IT FEEL GOOD TO PAY LESS?

Hours Telephone 0151 547 2224 for information

See ad on page 263

Discount

Liverpool

Yes & Co

125 Mariners Way, Bootle Strand, Liverpool, Merseyside, L20 4ST
Tel: 0151 944 2625

Ladies' fashion, with men's and children's available in selected stores at the lowest prices. More than 150 different lines in every store. 40 new lines coming into every store every week. We are specialists in High Street and designer fashion names at the lowest prices. Whatever your style, whatever your choice, be it elegance or casual, there's always something for all at Yes & Co. DOESN'T IT FEEL GOOD TO PAY LESS?

Hours Telephone 0151 547 2224 for information

See ad on page 263

Discount

Liverpool

Yes & Co

166–167 St Johns Precinct, Liverpool, Merseyside, L1 1NF
Tel: 0151 707 2526

Ladies' fashion, with men's and children's available in selected stores at the lowest prices. More than 150 different lines in every store. 40 new lines coming into every store every week. We are specialists in High Street and designer fashion names at the lowest prices. Whatever your style, whatever your choice, be it elegance or casual, there's always something for all at Yes & Co. DOESN'T IT FEEL GOOD TO PAY LESS?

Hours Telephone 0151 547 2224 for information

See ad on page 263

Discount

YES & Co
WHY PAY MORE?

ELEGANCE OR CASUAL

WHATEVER YOUR CHOICE IS, THERE IS SOMETHING FOR EVERYONE

DOESN'T IT FEEL GOOD TO PAY LESS?

WITH 19 STORES THROUGHOUT THE NORTH WEST OF ENGLAND, AND NEW STORES OPENING IN YOUR AREA SOON, THERE HAS TO BE A YES & CO FOR YOU.

FOR INFORMATION ABOUT YOUR NEAREST YES & CO STORE, CALL 0151 547 2224

Liverpool

Yes & Co

27 Bellevale Shopping Centre, Bellevale, Liverpool, Merseyside, L25 2RG
Tel: 0151 498 4270

Ladies' fashion, with men's and children's available in selected stores at the lowest prices. More than 150 different lines in every store. 40 new lines coming into every store every week. We are specialists in High Street and designer fashion names at the lowest prices. Whatever your style, whatever your choice, be it elegance or casual, there's always something for all at Yes & Co. DOESN'T IT FEEL GOOD TO PAY LESS?

Hours Telephone 0151 547 2224 for information

See ad on page 263

Discount
see text

Liverpool

Yes & Co

60 Walton Vale, Liverpool, Merseyside, L9 2BU
Tel: 0151 523 1213

Ladies' fashion, with men's and children's available in selected stores at the lowest prices. More than 150 different lines in every store. 40 new lines coming into every store every week. We are specialists in High Street and designer fashion names at the lowest prices. Whatever your style, whatever your choice, be it elegance or casual, there's always something for all at Yes & Co. DOESN'T IT FEEL GOOD TO PAY LESS?

Hours Telephone 0151 547 2224 for information

See ad on page 263

Discount
see text

Bangor

Matalan

Unit 1A and 1B, Caernarfon Road, Bangor, North Wales, LL57 4SU

Fashion and homewares shop for all the family

Hours Mon–Fri 10–8, Sat 9:30–5:30, Sun 10–8

Discount
see text

Colwyn Bay

Hughes Lighting

Mochore Business Park, Colwyn Bay, North Wales, LL28 5HA
Tel: 01492 547789

Manufacturer of table lamps and lamp shades. Comprehensive range of light fittings.

Hours Mon–Sat 10–4

Closed Bank Holidays

➡ South-west of Colwyn Bay off the A547

Public Transport No reliable bus service

Discount
see text

Parking Yes, &. Yes, **Group Tours** No, **Mail order** No, **Catalogue** No, ✗ Plenty of places nearby, **Internet Sales** No

Denbigh

Wetherall

Diamond Buildings, Love Lane, Denbigh, North Wales,
LL16 3LF
Tel: 01745 815592

Top quality ladieswear. Significant price reductions – all
items at factory prices

Hours Mon–Sat 9–5, Open Bank Holidays

Closed Christmas and New Year

➡ Easy to find in a one-way street which leads off the
main road through town

Public Transport Any bus to Denbigh

Discount

see text

Parking Street, & Yes, Group Tours Yes, Mail order Yes,
Catalogue Yes, ✗ Several places in town, Internet Sales No

Holywell

Abakhan Fabrics

Coast Road, Llanerch-y-Mor, Mostyn, Holywell, North
Wales, CH8 9DX
Tel: 01745 562100 Fax: 01745 562101
Email: promo@abakhan-fabrics.co.uk

Fabrics, craft supplies, art supplies, gifts, trimmings and
haberdashery, readymades and soft furnishings, knitting
yarns, new home and garden department, special offer
shop, bridal fabrics and accessories, kids adventure play
area, coffee shop, tourist information

Hours Mon–Sat 9–5:15, Thur late until 8. Sun 10:30–4:30,
open Bank Holidays

Closed Christmas Day, Boxing Day, New Year's Day,
Easter Day

➡ On A548 Coast Road between Queensferry and
Prestatyn

Public Transport Bus stop outside. Flint station 10 mins
away

Discount

10%–70%

Parking 500 Spaces, & Yes, Group Tours Yes, Mail order Yes,
Catalogue No, ✗ On site coffee shop, Internet Sales No

Llandudno

Catalogue Bargain Shop

6–8 Madoc Street, Llandudno, North Wales, LL30 2TP
Tel: 01492 877561

Merchandise from ex-catalogue stock including men's,
ladies' and children's clothes, furniture, food, sportswear,
electrical and household goods, toys, decorating and
sports equipment

Hours Mon–Sat 9–5, Sun 10–4

Labels Kays, G. Universal

Discount

see text

Llandudno

Stewart Seconds

23 Mostyn Street, Llandudno, Gwynedd, North Wales,
LL30 2NL
Tel: 01492 870733

Branded merchandise from major chain stores for all the
family

Hours Mon–Sat 9:30–5:30

Discount

40%–70%

Mostyn

Abakhan Fabrics

Coast Road, Llanerch-y-mor, Mostyn, Clywd, North Wales, CH8 9DX
Tel: 01745 560312

household goods,

Hours Mon–Sat 9–5:15, Thur 9–8, Sun and Bank Holidays 9–4:30

Closed Easter Sunday, Christmas Eve, Christmas Day, Boxing Day and New Year's Day

Public Transport Trains and buses

Discount

see text

Parking Yes, & Yes, **Group Tours** Yes, **Mail order** Yes, **Catalogue** No, **Internet Sales** No

Porthmadog

Stewart Seconds

144 High Street, Porthmadog, Gwynedd, North Wales, LL49 9NU
Tel: 01766 514166

Branded merchandise from major chainstores for all the family

Hours Mon–Sat 9–5:30, Sun 11–4

Discount

40%–70%

Pwllheli

Stewart Seconds

Ymaes, Pwllheli, Gwynedd, North Wales, LL53 5HG
Tel: 01758 701130

Branded merchandise from major chainstores for all the family

Hours Mon–Sat 9–5:30

Discount

40%–70%

Rhyl

Kids Stock And Exchange

Unit 2, Wellington Road, Rhyl, North Wales, LL18 1BD
Tel: 01745 330115

Prams and baby products of every brand. Special discounts and offers available

Hours Mon–Sat 10–5

Closed Christmas, New Year

➔ Wellington Road. Next main Post Office, Police Station and Town Hall

Public Transport Bus station and Train station Kinmel Street

Labels Bebecar, Pierre Cardin, Monbebe, Chicco, Waki, Jane, Kingswood, Clair de Lune

Discount

5%–50%

Parking None, & Yes, **Group Tours** No, **Mail order** No, **Catalogue** Yes, **Internet Sales** No

St Asaph

The Tweedmill Factory outlets at Llannerch Park

Llannerch Park, St Asaph, North Wales, LL17 0UY
Tel: 01745 730072 Fax: 01745 731008
Email: enquiries@tweedmill.co.uk

Choose from over 50 000 garments for men and women. Menswear: Wolsey, French Connection, Tom Sayers, Regatta, Double Two, Farah, Calvin Klein, James Barry, Easy Jeans, Best Direction, Glenmuir, Levi's. Womenswear: Paco, Roman Originals, Hide Park Leather, Honey, Camille, Levi's Easy Jeans, Klass. 5,000 pairs of shoes for men, women and children: Hush Puppies, Loake, Sterling & Hunt, Rieker, Hotter, Lotus. Home accessories department: Dartington Crystal, Staffordshire Tableware, Churchill's, etc.

Hours Mon–Sat 9:30 am–6, Sun 11–5

Closed Christmas Day only

➡ Just off the A55 at St Asaph, 2 miles south of St Asaph on the A525 St Asaph to Denbigh Road. Next door to the golf driving range

Public Transport End of road – Trefnant (bus stop)

Discount
Labels Dartington Crystal, Roman Originals, Levis, Churchills, Paco, Double Two, Hush Puppies **5%–50%**

Parking 200 Spaces, ♿ Yes, Group Tours Yes, Mail order No, Catalogue No, ✗ On site, Internet Sales No

Wrexham

Scoops

7–10 Rhosddu Road, Wrexham, North Wales, LL11 1AR
Tel: 01978 266450

Grattan clearance shop selling men's, ladies' and children's clothes, furniture, sportswear and equipment, electrical and household goods, toys and decorating

Hours Mon–Sat 9–5:30

Discount **30%–50%**

North England & North Wales

Wrexham

Velmore Ltd

1–2 Jaeger House, 141 Holt Road, Wrexham, Clwyd, North Wales, LL13 9DY
Tel: 01978 363456

Ladieswear. Overmakes and seconds

Hours Mon, Wed, Fri 10:30–3

Discount

see text

Fulford

Thorntons

Unit 5, Designer Outlet Village, Naburn Retail Park, Fulford, York, North Yorkshire, YO19 4TA
Tel: 01904 679227

The factory outlet stores sell three different product categories: misshapes, discounted lines and standard lines. Misshapes are packed into assorted bags and offer a saving of between 35%–55%. Discount lines are offered at a discount of 25%–50%. Standard lines are also on sale at normal prices

Hours Opening times dependent upon individual factory outlet centre

Labels Thorntons

Discount

25%–55%

& No, **Group Tours** No, **Mail order** Yes, **Catalogue** Yes, ✗ Most centres have food courts, **Internet Sales** Yes

Harrogate

Everything But The Baby

19 Knaresborough Road, Harrogate, North Yorkshire, HG2 7SR
Tel: 01423 888292

We stock an extensive range of quality second-hand prams, nursery equipment, clothes and maternity wear, including all the major brand names at sensible, affordable prices offering real value for mummy!

Hours Mon–Sat 10–4, Wednesday 10–1

Closed Christmas and New Year

➡ 2 minutes from A59/A61 junction. We are opposite Harrogate Hospital on A59

Public Transport Bus stop outside door, from town centre

Labels Silver Cross, Mamas & Papas, Graco, M & S, Mini-man, Next, Mothercare, Fisher Price, Chicco

Discount

see text

Parking 4 Spaces, & Yes, **Group Tours** No, **Mail order** No, **Catalogue** No, **Internet Sales** No

Ingleton

Daleswear Factory Shop

High Street, Ingleton, North Yorkshire, LA6 3AD
Tel: 015242 42373

High quality outdoor and leisurewear, plus Altberg boots. Seconds and clearance lines

Hours Mon–Sat 9–5, Sun 9:30–5, including Bank Holidays

Closed Christmas Day, Boxing Day and New Year's Day

➡ Ingleton village is on the A65, 28 miles north-west of Skipton and 6 miles south-east of Kirkby Lonsdale

Public Transport None

Labels Polartec, Porelle, Kingsdale, Gold Flash, SRT, Altberg

Discount

see text

Parking High Street, & No, **Group Tours** Yes, **Mail order** Yes, **Catalogue** Yes, ✗ Teas in Ingleton, **Internet Sales** No

Leyburn

The Tea Pottery

Business Park, Harmby Road, Leyburn, Wensleydale, North Yorkshire, DL8 5QA
Tel: 01969 623839 Fax: 01969 624079
Email: info@teapottery.co.uk
Web site: www.teapottery.co.uk/indexhtm

We manufacture our own uniquely designed novelty teapots. Although eagerly sought out by collectors throughout the world, our teapots make excellent gifts. From the favourite Aga to a welsh dresser, a shopping trolley to a caravan we make teapots of every kind imaginable – except ordinary ones. See behind the scenes, then browse through our range of teapots in the shop, where it is also possible to buy high-quality seconds at advantageous prices

Hours Mon–Sun 9–5

Closed Christmas Day, Boxing Day, New Year's Day

➡ From centre of Leyburn, take A684 towards Bedale. The Tea Pottery is on the left as you leave town, on Leyburn Business Park

Public Transport Leyburn

Discount

25%–30%

Parking 30 Spaces, & Yes, Group Tours No, Mail order Yes, Catalogue Yes, ✕ On site, and in Leyburn, Internet Sales Yes

Nether Poppleton

Leading Labels Ltd

Unit 2, Millfield Lane, Nether Poppleton, North Yorkshire, YO26 6PB
Tel: 01904 782721 Fax: 01904 784701

A huge selection of quality mens and ladieswear over an extensive range of sizes. Top brand names and designer labels all at discounted prices

Hours Mon–Sun, Various opening hours depending on site, Sun various

Closed Christmas Day

Discount

Labels Ben Sherman, Kangol, Whimsey, Kläss, Chilli Pepper, Roman Originals, Double Two

20%–75%

& No, Group Tours No, Mail order No, Catalogue No, Internet Sales No

North Stainley

Leading Labels Ltd

Lightwater Shopping Village, North Stainley, Nr Ripon, North Yorkshire, HG4 3HT
Tel: 01765 635453 Fax: 01765 635453

A huge selection of quality mens and ladieswear over an extensive range of sizes. Top brand names and designer labels all at discounted prices

Hours Mon–Sun, Various opening hours depending on site, Sun various

Closed Christmas Day

Discount

Labels Ben Sherman, Kangol, Whimsey, Kläss, Chilli Pepper, Roman Originals, Double Two

20%–75%

& No, Group Tours No, Mail order No, Catalogue No, Internet Sales No

York

Priestleys

1 Norman Court, 11 Grape Lane, York, North Yorkshire, YO1 2HY
Tel: 01904 623114

A wide and extensive range of all types of vintage clothing. All in first class order, ready to wear and at discount prices

Hours Mon–Sat 11–5:30

Closed Sundays, Christmas, New Year's Day

➡ Very central York, just off Low Peter Gate

Public Transport Buses, train station

Discount

20%–30%

Parking None, & No, Group Tours No, Mail order No, Catalogue No, Internet Sales No

Barnsley

Naylor Clayware

Clough Green, Cawthorne, Barnsley, South Yorkshire,
S75 4AE
Tel: 01226 790591

Traditional craftsmanship

Hours Mon–Sun 9–5, Bank Holidays 9–5

Closed Christmas Day and Boxing Day

➡ From Denby: A635 east to Barnsley, after 3.5 miles
Naylor Clayware is on right

Public Transport Bus

Discount
see text

Parking Yes, ♿ Yes, **Mail order** No, **Catalogue** Yes,
Internet Sales No

Barnsley

Shaw Carpets

Huddersfield Road, Darton, Barnsley, South Yorkshire,
S75 5NH
Tel: 01226 390133 Fax: 01226 390549

Carpets, household goods, Carpets

Hours Mon–Sat 9:30–4:45, Thur open late until 7.30

Closed Christmas–New Year

➡ Enter Darton – shop is on right clearly signposted about
half a mile after you enter Darton

Public Transport Bus

Discount
see text

Parking Yes, ♿ No, **Group Tours** Yes, **Mail order** Yes,
Catalogue No, ✗ Darton service station, **Internet Sales** No

Doncaster

The Yorkshire Outlet

White Rose Way, Doncaster Lakeside, South Yorkshire,
DN4 5JH
Tel: 01302 366444

Full range of shops selling men's, ladies' and children's
clothing, furniture, food, sportswear, electrical and
household goods, toys decorating, sports equipment
and shoes

Hours Telephone for opening hours

See ad on page 153

Discount
see text

Doncaster

Thorntons

Unit 39, The Yorkshire Outlet, Doncaster, South Yorkshire,
DN4 5PH
Tel: 01302 320206

The factory outlet stores sell three different product
categories: misshapes, discounted lines and standard
lines. Misshapes are packed into assorted bags and offer a
saving of between 35%–55%. Discount lines are offered
at a discount of 25%–50%. Standard lines are also on sale
at normal prices

Hours Opening times dependent upon individual factory
outlet centre

Labels Thorntons

Discount
25%–55%

♿ No, **Group Tours** No, **Mail order** Yes, **Catalogue** Yes,
✗ Most centres have food courts, **Internet Sales** Yes

Doncaster

Tog 24

The Yorkshire Outlet, White Rose Way, Doncaster, South Yorkshire, DN4 5JH
Tel: 01302 364123 Fax: 01302 364123

Outdoor clothing for the whole family at up to 75% off the manufacturer's retail price. Brands included are Goretex, Polartec, Entrant Gill, etc.

Hours Mon–Sat 10 –6, Sun 11–5

Closed Christmas Day

➜ M18 J3. One mile from the motorway. All signposted

Public Transport Doncaster to outlet bus service No. 75

Labels Goretex, Entrant Gill, Polartec, Cool Max

Discount 25%–75%

♿ Yes, **Group Tours** Yes, **Mail order** Yes, **Catalogue** Yes, ✕ On site, and McDonalds, etc, **Internet Sales** No

MasterCard, Switch, VISA, Delta, American Express

Sheffield

Havenplan Ltd

The Old Station, Station Road, Killamarsh, Sheffield, South Yorkshire, S21 1EN
Tel: 0114 2489972 Fax: 0114 2489972

Antiques. Period doors, fire surrounds, inserts, stone troughs, chimney pots, post boxes, panelling, planking and 100s of unusual items for homes and gardens

Hours Tue–Fri 10–4 , Sat 10–3:30

Closed All Bank Holidays

➜ Junction 30 M1. A6135 towards Sheffield. Traffic lights turn right on to B6053. Roundabout straight forward. Roundabout turn right on to B6058 towards Killamarsh. Go under stone bridge, turn right, Havenplan situated towards top of road

Public Transport Local bus routes. Super tram

Discount see text

♿ No, **Group Tours** No, **Mail order** No, **Catalogue** No, ✕ Pubs, cafés, **Internet Sales** No

Sheffield

Osborne Silversmiths Ltd

Westwick Works, Solly Street, Sheffield, South Yorkshire, S1 4BA
Tel: 0114 272 4929

Cutlery

Hours Mon–Fri 9–4:30, Some Saturdays by appointment please telephone for further information

Closed Christmas, New Year, Bank Holidays, Spring Bank Holiday week and July annual shutdown

See ad on page 271

Discount see text

Sheffield

Outlet

Unit 160 Meadowhall, Sheffield, South Yorkshire

Top fashions. All labels. Designer brands. All at prices that are truly outrageous

See ad on page 53

Discount

see text

Addingham

The Fabric Shop

82 Main Street, Addingham, West Yorkshire, LS29 0PL
Tel: 01943 830982

Household goods,

Hours Mon 10–6, Tues, Wed, Fri 9–1, Thur 12 noon–4, Sat 10–4

Closed Christmas and New Year

➡ Take A65 into village, pass The Sailor Hotel on right, shop 150 yards on left opposite large square chimney

Public Transport Buses

Discount

see text

Parking Yes, & No, **Group Tours** No, **Mail order** No, **Catalogue** No, ✗ Refreshments on site, **Internet Sales** No

Batley

Bacchanalia

Skopos Mills, Bradford Road, Batley, West Yorkshire, WF17 5LZ
Tel: 01924 424000 Fax: 01924 359108

China tableware and gifts. Glass stemware and gifts. Cutlery formal and casual. Cookshop – gadgets, pans, etc. Gifts inc. Beanie Babies. Cards

Hours Mon–Sat 9:30–5:30, Sun 11–5

Closed Christmas Day, Boxing Day, New Year's Day

➡ M1 J40 – follow signs to Batley. M62 J27 or 28 – follow signs to Batley

Public Transport Batley railway station quarter mile. Batley bus station quarter mile

Discount up to

Labels T.T.C. China, Arthur Price, Gleneagles, Geo. Butler, Pimpernel, Speigelan, Johnson Bros.

70%

Parking 600+, & Yes, **Group Tours** Yes, **Mail order** No, **Catalogue** No, ✗ Refreshments on site, **Internet Sales** No

Batley

Beans of Batley

Skopos Mills, Bradford Road, Batley, West Yorkshire, WA7 6LZ
Tel: 01924 477717 Fax: 01924 477277

Huge range of men's and ladies' quality branded fashion

Hours Mon–Sun 10–5

Closed Easter, Christmas

➡ Into Batley – opposite large mill complex on right

Public Transport Trains, buses

Discount up to

Labels Mondi, Viyella, Klass

75%

Parking 600 Spaces, & Yes, **Group Tours** Yes, **Mail order** No, ✗ Refreshments on site

Batley

Skopos Mills Batley

Bradford Road, Batley, West Yorkshire, WA7 5LZ
Tel: 01924 485756

Vast choice of furnishings, fashion and footwear for all the family

Hours Mon–Sat 9:30–5:30, Sun 11–5

Closed Christmas Day

➡ A652 to Batley. At the traffic lights, large mill complex is immediately on right

Public Transport Trains

Discount
see text

& Yes, **Group Tours** Yes, ✕ Refreshments on site

Halifax

Frocks Dress Agency

16 Denholme Gate Road, Hipperholme, Halifax, West Yorkshire
Tel: 01422 202085

Women's clothes. Good quality, stylish clothing both new and nearly new

Hours Tue–Sat 10–4

Closed All Bank Holidays including Christmas Day and Boxing Day

➡ On main A644 Brighouse–Keighley road, quarter mile from Hipperholme traffic lights

Public Transport Below shop – 200 yards

Discount
see text

Parking Street, & Yes, **Group Tours** No, **Mail order** No, **Catalogue** No, ✕ Excellent pub, **Internet Sales** No

Leeds

BRK Crystal

Treefield Estate, Gildersome, Morley, West Yorkshire, LS27 7LB
Tel: 0113 252 2922 Fax: 0113 238 1445
Email: b_metcalfe@brk-group.co.uk
Web site: www.brk-group.co.uk

Hand-cut, hand-made 24% lead crystal. Giftware, stemware, decanters, small animals, etc. Special offers with discounts every month. Gift paper, gift tags and birthday/anniversary/wedding cards also available

Hours Mon–Fri 9–5, Sat 10–4

Closed Christmas, New Year, Easter, Spring Bank Holiday

➡ Just off the A62. From Gildersome roundabout towards Leeds, take the 2nd right turn, signed 'Crystal Shop'. Approx. quarter mile from J27 of M62, and 4.5 miles south west of Leeds centre

Public Transport Gildersome roundabout

Discount

Labels 'BRK' Crystal, 'Simon Elvin' Cards, 'Kingsley' Cards

5%–50%

Parking 10+ Spaces, & Yes, **Group Tours** Yes, **Mail order** Yes, **Catalogue** Yes, ✕ On site, **Internet Sales** Yes

Leeds

The Great Clothes Fashion Store

84 York Road, Leeds, West Yorkshire, LS9 9AA
Tel: 0113 2350808 Fax: 0113 2350668

Great Clothes sell this year's products, not discontinued or seconds. Current season stock at well below High Street prices

Hours Mon–Fri 9:30–9, Sat 9:30–6, Sun 9:30–4

Closed Christmas Day and Easter Sunday

➡ A64 bottom of York Road. Two minutes from city centre

Public Transport Outside door

Discount

Labels Levis, Nike, Gabicci, Adidas, Farrah, Ben Sherman, Reebok, Ellese

25%–50%

Parking 350 Spaces, & Yes, **Group Tours** Yes, **Mail order** No, **Catalogue** No, ✕ Full cafe in store, **Internet Sales** No

Shipley

The Shuttle Fabric Shop

Baildon Bridge, Otley Road, Shipley, West Yorkshire, BD17 7AA

Fabrics – dress and furnishing. Specialise in quilted fabrics, polar fleece, sherpa fleece

Hours Mon–Sat 9–5:50, Open all Bank Holidays except those listed below

Closed Christmas Day, Boxing Day

Public Transport Shipley railway station. Bradford–Ilkley bus passes the door

Labels Makewell

Discount up to **50%**

Parking 8 Spaces, ᕹ Yes, Group Tours Yes, Mail order No, Catalogue No, ✗ Within 3 minutes., Internet Sales No

Todmorden

Echo's

650A Halifax Road, Todmorden, West Yorkshire, OL14 6DN
Tel: 01706 817505

Period/Retro clothing

Hours Mon–Sat 10:30–5:00

Closed Wednesdays and all Bank Holidays

Public Transport Bus

Discount **see text**

ᕹ Yes, Group Tours No, Mail order No, Catalogue No, Internet Sales No

Wakefield

Craft Collection/Readicut Woods Mill Shop

Terry Mills, Westfield Road, Horbury, Wakefield, West Yorkshire, WF4 6HE
Tel: 01924 810812 Fax: 01924 810813

Craftware including needlecraft, rug making and doll making

Hours Mon–Sat 9–5

Closed Bank Holidays

➡ Signposted from J40 M1. Located at the north end of Horbury

Labels Readicut, Craft Collection, Leisure Arts, Anchor, FSK, Dimensions, Twilleys, Bucilla, J.C.A.

Discount up to **50%**

Parking 40 Spaces, ᕹ Yes, Group Tours Yes, Mail order Yes, Catalogue Yes, ✗ Several local facilities, Internet Sales No

Wakefield

Opportunities

13 Providence Street, Wakefield, West Yorkshire, WF1 3BG
Tel: 01924 290310

Two floors of nearly-new outfits, eveningwear, cruise wear, spearates, wedding outfits inc. shoes, hats, jewellery (new and nearly new). Louis Feraud, Calvin Klein, Morgan, Costelloe and many more designer labels. Children's Osh Kosh, Next. Easy sofas. Easy parking. Some evening events

Hours Mon–Sat 10–5:30

Closed Bank Holidays

➡ Wakefield Centre – near main Post Office off Northgate

Public Transport Bus station 2 mins. Train station 5 mins

Discount **see text**

Parking Nr car park, ᕹ Yes, Group Tours Yes, Mail order No, Catalogue No, ✗ Tea, coffee free, Internet Sales No

Scotland and North-East England

Aberdeen

Damart

36–40 Market Street, Aberdeen, Aberdeenshire
Tel: 01274 568211
Email: jdunn@damart.com

Women's clothing

Hours Mon–Sat 9–5:00

Closed Bank Holidays, Christmas and New Year

Public Transport Bus/train

Discount

see text

& Yes, **Group Tours** No, **Mail order** Yes, **Catalogue** Yes,
X Refreshments on site, **Internet Sales** No

Aberdeen

Elysees Dress Agency

4 Howburn Place, Aberdeen, Aberdeenshire, AB1 2XX
Tel: 01224 58857

A small shop with a very large selection of top of the
range daywear, eveningwear, casualwear. Also mother of
the bride and groom outfits. From Mani to Mondi. Top
quality garments selling for 50%–75% off retail prices.
On street parking at door

Hours Mon–Sat 10:30–5, Thur 10:30–6:30

Closed Christmas Day, Boxing Day, New Year's Day and
2nd and 3rd January 2000

➡ Off Holburn Street, next door to Blockbuster Video
shop

Public Transport Bus to door.

Discount

Labels Mani, Versace, Max Mara,
Caroline Chares, Frank Usher, Louis
Feraud, Donna Karan, Mondi

50%–75%

& No, **Group Tours** No, **Mail order** No, **Catalogue** No,
Internet Sales No

Alva

Inverallan Hand Knitters

Alva Industrial Estate, Alva, Clackmannanshire
Tel: 01259 762292

Women's and men's jumpers

Hours Mon–Fri 9–5:00 pm

Closed Scottish Bank Holidays

➡ A91 to Stirling, East of Alva

Public Transport Bus

Discount

see text

Parking 6 Spaces, & Yes, **Group Tours** No, **Mail order** Yes,
Catalogue Yes, **Internet Sales** Yes

Tillicoultry

Thorntons

Stirling Mills Factory Outlet, Unit 36, Stirling Mills,
Tillicoultry, Clackmannanshire, FK13 6NS
Tel: 01259 753875

The factory outlet stores sell three different product
categories: misshapes, discounted lines and standard
lines. Misshapes are packed into assorted bags and offer a
saving of between 35%–55%. Discount lines are offered
at a discount of 25%–50%. Standard lines are also on sale
at normal prices

Hours Opening times dependent upon individual factory
outlet centre

Discount

Labels Thorntons

25%–55%

& No, **Group Tours** No, **Mail order** Yes, **Catalogue** Yes,
X Most centres have food courts, **Internet Sales** Yes

Darlington

Coco
11 Grange Road, Darlington, Durham, DL1 5NA
Tel: 01325 383720

Moschino, Versace, Armani and Diesel at a fraction of the cost. Mondi suits from £60 to Ben Di Lisi ballgowns for £140. Patrick Cox shoes £25 and Morgan dresses £22. Real Coco Chanel handbag for £40

Hours Mon–Sat 10–5 pm

Closed Christmas and New Year

➡ Bear left of the Market Clock. Follow road round Binns Corner. Grange Road is second left turning

Public Transport We are five minutes from rail station and out of town bus station

Discount

Labels Armani, Versace, Mondi, Morgan, Moschino, Diesel, Laura Ashley, Monsoon, Patrick Cox — see text

Parking Close, & Yes, Group Tours Yes, Mail order No, Catalogue No, ✗ In the shopping complex, Internet Sales No

Darlington

Seymours of Darlington
East Row (1–3), Darlington, Durham, DL1 5PZ
Tel: 01325 355272 Fax: 01325 355272

All designs current and perfect unless otherwise stated. Huge variety of stock includes candlewicks to throws, duvet covers including children's, modern and sophisticated designs. Curtains ready-made and made to measure. Own-name wide range of sheets, valances, pillowcases in 50% polycotton or percale. Towels, bath sets, table-cloths. Sizes from bunk to superking. Large selection of pillows and duvets. Prices from economy to luxury with something for everyone. Group tours welcome but not organised

Hours Mon–Sat 9–5, Bank Holiday Mondays as above. Late Thur and some Sun approaching Christmas.

Closed Christmas and New Year

➡ Overlooking Market Square. Opposite town hall, near Dolphin Centre

Public Transport Most Darlington buses, 10 minutes from train station

Discount

Labels Dorma, Sandersons, Christy, Nimbus, Miller from Sweden, Hadida, Rectella Broomhill — 10%–33%

Parking 10–20 Spaces, & Yes, Group Tours Yes, Mail order No, Catalogue No, ✗ Nearby, Internet Sales No

North Berwick

Redress
31 High Street, North Berwick, East Lothian, EH39 4HH
Tel: 01620 87 5633

Shop stocks suits, wedding outfits, dresses, hats, shoes, bags, eveningwear and casualwear, including Tomasz Starsewski, Armani, YSL, Sisley, when available. Always reductions. Address from January 2000 will be 71 High Street, North Berwick

Hours Mon–Sat 10–4

Closed Thursday in winter

➡ Main shopping street in centre of town

Public Transport Buses regularly. Good rail service from Edinburgh

Discount

Labels Jaeger, Yarrell, Viyella, Country Casuals, Betty Barclay, Max Mara, Seiger, Jacques Vert — see text

& Yes, Group Tours No, Mail order No, Catalogue No, Internet Sales No

for hotels...
www.WestOneWeb.com
...great locations

Edinburgh

Belinda Robertson Cashmere

22 Palmerston Place, Edinburgh, City of Edinburgh,
EH12 5AL
Tel: 0131 225 1057 Fax: 0131 226 2148
Email: admin@belindarobertson.co.uk

Mens and ladieswear. Samples and overruns from latest
collections in over 120 colours, all in 100% cashmere.
Separates and coordinates, including capes, easy tops,
tunics, updated twin sets and a range of bottoms

Hours Mon–Fri 9–5:30, Sat 10–4

Closed Christmas and New Year

→ Opposite St Mary's Cathedral. 10 mins walk from city
centre

Public Transport Haymarket station – 2 minutes away.
Bus stops

Discount

20%–70%

Parking Plenty, & No, **Group Tours** Yes, **Mail order** Yes,
Catalogue No, ✕ Refreshments on site, **Internet Sales** No

Falkirk

J & W Carpets

Unit 5, Burnbank Road, Falkirk, Falkirk, SK2 7TE
Tel: 01324 610210 Fax: 01324 610210

All types of flooring

Hours Mon–Fri 9–8, Sat 9–6, Sun 9–5:30

Closed Christmas and New Year

Public Transport Bus

Discount

see text

Parking 10 spaces, & Yes, **Group Tours** No, **Mail order** No,
Catalogue No, **Internet Sales** No

Glasgow

Redress

51 Eastwoodmains Road, Glasgow, City of Glasgow,
GL16 6PW
Tel: 0141 638 5090

Women's and children's clothes. From M & S to Armani.
Jeans to ballgowns

Hours Mon–Sat 9:30–5:30

Closed Bank Holidays

Discount

see text

Labels Monsoon, Karen Millen,
Mondi, Escada, Betty Barclay,
Jaeger, Country Casuals, Planet

& Yes, **Group Tours** No, **Mail order** No, **Catalogue** No,
✕ Refreshments on site, and Coffee, **Internet Sales** No

Glasgow

The Address – Designer Exchange

3 Royal Exchange Court, , (off 17 Royal Exchange Square),
Glasgow, City of Glasgow, G1 3DB
Tel: 0141 221 6898 Fax: 0141 221 6898

An inviting shop in the heart of the city centre. This
exciting shop is full of new and nearly new designer
clothes and accessories, all at far below half price, from
Chanel, Armani, Versace, Moschino etc, to High Street
names such as Whistles, Jigsaw, Kookai, Karen Mitten,
etc. Stock turns around quickly with new items arriving
daily. Items come from all over the UK many from well
known celebrities

Hours Tue–Sat 10–6

Closed 2 weeks at Christmas

→ Between main shopping areas of Buchanan Street and
Queen Street, where you'll find Royal Exchange Square
and from No. 17 Royal Exchange Square enter the bend
which takes you directly to 3 Royal Exchange Court

Public Transport Queen Street train station, Central train
station – both main centre stations

Discount

50%–80%

& No, **Group Tours** Yes, **Mail order** No, **Catalogue** No,
Internet Sales No

Alnwick

Gladrags

51 Bondgate Within, Alnwick, Northumberland
Tel: 01665 602396

Designer dress labels

Hours Mon–Sat 10–4

Closed Wednesdays and Bank Holidays

➡ Above Wine Cellar, opposite Iceland

Discount

see text

& No, **Group Tours** No, **Mail order** No, **Catalogue** No,
Internet Sales No

Alnwick

Karrimor International

Unit 6c Coquetdale Trading Estate, Amble,
Northumberland, NA65 0PE
Tel: 01665 713869/513209

Men's and women's jackets. Camping equipment etc.

Hours Mon–Sat 10–6:00, Sun 10–4

Closed Bank Holidays

➡ Amble Industrial

See ad on page 281

Discount

see text

Parking 12 Spaces, & Yes, **Group Tours** No, **Mail order** Yes,
Catalogue Yes, **Internet Sales** No

Alnwick

Shark Group

Nordstrom House, North Broomhill, Amble,
Northumberland, NE65 9UJ Fax: 01670 761343

Wetsuits and water sports

Hours Mon–Fri 2 pm–4, Sat 10–2 noon in winter

Closed Bank Holidays

Public Transport Bus

Discount
see text

Parking 20 spaces, & No, **Group Tours** No, **Mail order** Yes,
Catalogue No, **Internet Sales** No

Comrie

Mari Donald Knitwear

Craiglea, Pudding Lane, Comrie, Crieff, Perth and Kinross,
PH6 2DB
Tel: 01764 670150 Fax: 01764 670150
Email: maridonald@lineone.net
Web site: http://website.lineone.net/~maridonald

Own design knitwear for children and adults. Sweaters
and cardigans with special buttons in natural yarns –
lambswool, silk, merino, cashmere and cotton. Made to
measure service available. Commissions welcome

Hours Mon–Fri 10–4:30, Sat 10–1

Closed Telephone to check if travelling from a distance

➡ North side of Drummond Street, between Comrie Hotel
and Esso garage

Public Transport Bus stop 20 m from Pudding Lane

Discount
see text

& Yes, **Group Tours** Yes, **Mail order** Yes, **Catalogue** Yes,
✗ Hotels and tea-rooms in village, **Internet Sales** Yes

Perth

Re Dress

43 New Row, off Glasgow Road, Perth, Perth and Kinross,
RH1 5QA
Tel: 01738 444447

Dress agency stocking middle to up-market range of
ladies' clothing and accessories. Wedding and
eveningwear. Day wear, shoes, hats, etc.

Hours Mon–Sat 10–4:30

Closed Public Holidays

➡ Off Glasgow Road or Old High Street

Public Transport Bus station. Railway station

Discount
10%–25%

& No, **Group Tours** No, **Mail order** No, **Catalogue** No,
Internet Sales No

Bridge of Weir

Redress

1 Prieston Road, Bridge of Weir, Renfrewshire, PA11 3AJ
Tel: 01505 615151 Fax: 01505 615151

From M & S to Armani. Jeans to ballgowns

Hours Mon–Sat 9:30–5:30

Closed Bank Holidays

➡ On M8 pass airport, take next turn-off, A737 for Irvine,
and follow directions to Bridge of Weir. We are opposite
Clydesdale Bank

Public Transport Bus

Discount
see text

Labels Monsoon, Karen Millen,
Mondi, Escada, Betty Barclay,
Jaeger, Country Casuals, Planet

& Yes, **Group Tours** No, **Mail order** No, **Catalogue** No,
✗ Refreshments on site, and Coffee, **Internet Sales** No

Glenpatrick Mill Shop

Open Sunday, Tuesday, Wednesday, Thursday 9.30am – 4.30pm.

Plenty of free parking

Telephone: (01505) 577009

A wide range of carpets, in plain colours and many patterns, mostly 80/20% wool/nylon ...

at prices that make you want to recarpet your home.

Johnstone

Glenpatrick Mill Shop

Stoddard Carpet Factory, Glenpatrick Road, Elderslie, Johnstone, Renfrewshire, PA5 9UJ
Tel: 01505 577009

A wide range of carpets, in plain and colours and many patterns, mostly 80/30% wool/nylon

Hours Sun, Tues, Wed and Thur 9.30–4.30

See ad on page 283

Discount

see text

Parking Plenty

for road maps...

www.WestOneWeb.com

...great offers

Hawick

Wiltonburn Country Cashmeres

Wiltonburn Farm, Hawick, Scottish Borders, TD9 7LL
Tel: 01450 372414 Fax: 01450 378098
Email: shell@wiltonburnfarm.u-net.com
Web site: smoothhound.co.uk/hotels/wiltonbu.html

Friendly personal attention given in our spacious barn showing designer cashmere knitwear for ladies and gentlemen, by internationally famous designer Valerie Louthan. Other Hawick knitwear in cashmere, lambswool, cotton and silks. Colourful locally-made jewellery, scarves, capes and gloves. Pretty hand-painted furniture and beautiful water-colours by Rose Hughes. B & B or S/c also available for extra discount. Small group tours welcome

Hours Mon–Sat 10–6, Sundays – telephone. (After hours welcome by appointment.)

Closed Winter months – please telephone in advance

➡ Take A7 out of Hawick towards Carlisle for 1 mile. Turn right on to B711, then immediate right again. Keep left around corner and on through 'no through road', for 1 mile. Wiltonburn is at end of road

Public Transport Hawick – 1 mile

Discount 25%–50%

Labels Valerie Louthan at Palm Beach plus others from French fashion houses

Parking 6 Spaces, & Yes, Group Tours Yes, Mail order Yes, Catalogue No, ✗ On site, and Sergio's, Internet Sales No

Strathaven

Encore

48 Waterside Street, Strathaven, South Lanarkshire, ML10 6AW
Tel: 01357 529779

New and 'as new' ladieswear – ranging from skirts/trousers/jackets to eveningwear and wedding outfits

Hours Mon–Sat 10–5

Closed Christmas and New Year

➡ Situated in small, attractive town, 8 miles from East Kilbride. Same distance from Hamilton, just off the A71 and close to M74

Public Transport Town centre

Discount 45%–75%

Labels Condici, Parigi, Medici, Tom Bowker, Jacques Vert, Mansfield, Frank Usher, Yarrell

Parking On street + public car parks, & Yes, Group Tours Yes, Mail order No, Catalogue No, ✗ Several tea rooms/coffee shops/bars/restaurants, Internet Sales No

Stirling

Sterling Mills Designer Outlet Village

Devonvale, Tillicoultry, Stirling, FK13 6HQ
Tel: 01259 752100 Fax: 01259 753684

Nike, Denby, Wrangler, Lee, Thorntons, Calvin Klein, Versace, Pacco, Double Two, Chilli Pepper and many quality designer brand names all with at least 30% discount, but up to 70% on some products

Hours Mon–Sun 10–6, Thur 10–8

Closed Christmas Day, New Year

See ad on page 285

Discount 30%–70%

Labels Nike, Wrangler, Calvin Klein, Ralph Lauren, Denby, Karrimor, Hush Puppies, Clarks, Samsonite

Parking 800 Spaces, & Yes, Group Tours Yes, Mail order No, Catalogue No, ✗ Refreshments on site, Internet Sales No

Middlesbrough

Designer Warehouse

20 Cumberland Road, Middlesbrough, Tees, TS5 6HZ
Tel: 01642 850651 Fax: 01642 852841
Web site: www.designerwarehouse.co.uk

Women and men's clothes

Hours Mon–Sat 9–5, Sun 11–5

Closed Christmas and New Year

➡ From A66 head up Linthorpe Road until you reach Linthorpe Village. Take last turning left which is signposted

Public Transport Outside, direct from town centre

Discount 50%–70%

Labels Dolce & Gabbanna, Stone Island, Versace, Valentino, DKNY, Exte, Ralph Lauren, Lacoste

Parking 150 Spaces, & No, Group Tours No, Mail order No, Catalogue No, Internet Sales Yes

LONDON

PARIS

MILAN

NEW YORK

TILLICOULTRY

At the Village, now open in Tillicoultry, you'll find more than 40 stores full of world famous designer labels. More than this, you'll find them with at least 30% off High Street prices, and sometimes as much as 70% off. They say the fashion world is one big village. It is, and it's at Tillicoultry, near Stirling. For details of stores and opening hours, call 01259 752100 (24 hours).

STERLING MILLS®
DESIGNER OUTLET VILLAGE

TILLICOULTRY, NEAR STIRLING, SCOTLAND.
www.sterlingmills.com

Stockton on Tees

Rock A Bye Baby

65 Larun Beat, Yarm, Stockton on Tees, Tees, TS15 9HR
Tel: 01642 898537

Cots, travel-cots, highchairs, car-seats, single and twin buggies, swing-cribs, Moses baskets, stairgates, fireguards, backpacks, swings, bouncers, toy packs, playpens, Christening gowns and outfits

Hours Always someone available to contact

Discount

Labels McClaren, Brevie, Britax

see text

&. No, **Group Tours** No, **Mail order** No, **Catalogue** No, **Internet Sales** No

Gateshead

Jockey Underwear Factory Shop

Eastern Avenue, Team Valley Trading Estate, Gateshead, Tyne and Wear, NE11 0PB
Tel: 0191 491 0088 Fax: 0191 491 0655
Email: mgibb@jockeyuk.com

Wide selection of branded men's and ladies' underwear, T-shirts, knitwear, socks, towels, bedding, baby accessories, swim/sportswear. Perfects and seconds

Hours Mon–Fri 9–4

Closed Christmas Day, New Year, Bank Holidays

➡ A1, Team Valley exit. First roundabout go straight over, second roundabout go right, then first right and on left hand side

Public Transport Bus from Gateshead to Team Valley

Discount up to

Labels Jockey, Lyle & Scott, Wolsey, Zorbit, Decotex, Aristoc, View From

70%

Parking 20 Spaces, &. No, **Group Tours** No, **Mail order** No, **Catalogue** No, **Internet Sales** No

Newcastle upon Tyne

Royal Quays Outlet Shopping Centre

Coble Dene, North Shields, Tyne and Wear, NE29 6DW
Tel: 0191 296 3743 Fax: 0191 258 3810

Over 40 outlets selling Designer and High Street brands within a pleasant shopping centre. All at discount prices

Hours Mon–Sat 10–6, Sun 11–5

Closed Christmas Day

➡ Situated off the A187 coast road to North Shields. Close to A19 and two minutes from the Tyne Tunnel

Public Transport Bus service to centre. Metro station half mile away

See ad on page 153

Discount

20%–50%

Parking 740 spaces, &. Yes, **Group Tours** Yes, **Mail order** No, **Catalogue** Yes, ✕ On site, and pub, **Internet Sales** No

North Shields

Leading Labels Ltd

Royal Quays Shopping Village, Unit 58/59, Coble Dene, North Shields, Tyne and Wear, NE29 6DW
Tel: 0191 2963862 Fax: 0191 2575792

A huge selection of quality mens and ladieswear over an extensive range of sizes. Top brand names and designer labels all at discounted prices

Hours Mon–Sun, Various opening hours depending on site, Sun various

Closed Christmas Day

Labels Ben Sherman, Kangol, Whimsey, Klàss, Chilli Pepper, Roman Originals, Double Two

Discount

20%–75%

&. No, **Group Tours** No, **Mail order** No, **Catalogue** No, **Internet Sales** No

North Shields

Thorntons

Unit 37, South Parade, Royal Quays Shopping, Coble Dene, North Shields, Tyne and Wear, NE29 6DN
Tel: 0191 2580623

The factory outlet stores sell three different product categories: misshapes, discounted lines and standard lines. Misshapes are packed into assorted bags and offer a saving of between 35%–55%. Discount lines are offered at a discount of 25%–50%. Standard lines are also on sale at normal prices

Hours Opening times dependent upon individual factory outlet centre

Discount
Labels Thorntons
25%–55%

& No, **Group Tours** No, **Mail order** Yes, **Catalogue** Yes, ✕ Most centres have food courts, **Internet Sales** Yes

Sunderland

M C Hitchen & Sons Ltd

19 Fawcett Street, Sunderland, Tyne and Wear, SR1 1RH
Tel: 0191 5640684 Fax: 0191 5640153

Littlewoods surplus stock from previous season's catalogue, also some Index all at minimum of 40% discount on catalogue price

Hours Mon–Sat 9:30–5:30

Closed Sundays and Bank Holidays

➜ Town centre

Public Transport Rail and buses stop in the street

Discount
Labels Reebok, Sony, CK, Philips, Esprit, Samsung – all as available
40%–80%

Parking In town, & Yes, **Group Tours** No, **Mail order** No, **Catalogue** No, ✕ Nearby cafés, **Internet Sales** No

Alexandria

Antartex Village Visitor Centre

Lomond Industrial Estate, Alexandria, West Dunbartonshire, G83 0TP
Tel: 01389 752 393 Fax: 01389 750 656

The Antartex Visitor Centre is a unique experience which combines the best of Scottish crafts and craftsmanship with quality woollens, sheepskin, leather goods and souvenirs. A golf, whisky and shoe shop with coffee shop and restaurant facilities make it the best in factory shopping

Hours Mon–Sun 10–6

Closed Christmas Day and New Year's Day

➜ From the A82 follow the brown tourist signs for the factory outlets and Antartex Village is situated a further 0.5 miles beyond the factory outlets – the same applies arriving into Balloch on the A811

Public Transport Alexandria and Balloch

Discount
Labels Adidas, MacGregor, Farah, Nike, Stylo, Double Two, Callaway, Regatta, Stead & Simpson
see text

Parking 100 Spaces, & Yes, **Group Tours** Yes, **Mail order** No, **Catalogue** No, ✕ Refreshments on site, **Internet Sales** No

Alexandria

Cocoon Coats

Lomond Industrial Estate, Alexandria, West
Dunbartonshire, G83 0TL
Tel: 01389 755511

Men's clothes, women's clothes, Fashion rainwear

Hours Mon–Fri 8:30–5:00, Sat and Sun 11–5

Closed Bank Holidays

Public Transport Bus

Discount
see text

Parking 25 spaces, & Yes, Group Tours No, Mail order Yes,
Catalogue Yes, Internet Sales Yes

Alexandria

Hermione Spencer

Unit 15, Lomond Trade Centre, Alexandria, West
Dunbartonshire
Tel: 01389 721542

Men's and ladies cashmere sweaters

Hours Mon–Fri 9–4:30

Closed Bank Holidays

Public Transport Bus

Discount
see text

& Yes, Group Tours No, Mail order No, Catalogue No,
Internet Sales Yes

Alexandria

Leading Labels Ltd

Loch Lomond Outlets, Unit 1, Main Street, Alexandria,
West Dunbartonshire, G83 0UG
Tel: 01389 607101 Fax: 01389 607104

A huge selection of quality mens and ladieswear over an
extensive range of sizes. Top brand names and designer
labels all at discounted prices

Hours Mon–Sun, Various opening hours depending on
site, Sun various

Closed Christmas Day

Discount
20%–75%

Labels Ben Sherman, Kangol,
Whimsey, Kläss, Chilli Pepper,
Roman Originals, Double Two

& No, Group Tours No, Mail order No, Catalogue No,
Internet Sales No

Alexandria

Loch Lomond Factory Outlets

Main Street, Alexandria, West Dunbartonshire, G83 0UG
Tel: 01389 710077

Full range of shops selling men's, ladies' and children's
clothing, furniture, food, sportswear, electrical and
household goods, toys decorating, sports equipment and
shoes

Hours Telephone for opening hours

See ads on pages 153 and 289

Discount
see text

Alexandria

Thorntons

Unit 5, Loch Lomond Centre, Main Street, Alexandria,
West Dunbartonshire, G83 0UG
Tel: 01389 729994

The factory outlet stores sell three different product categories: misshapes, discounted lines and standard lines. Misshapes are packed into assorted bags and offer a saving of between 35%–55%. Discount lines are offered at a discount of 25%–50%. Standard lines are also on sale at normal prices

Hours Opening times dependent upon individual factory outlet centre

Labels Thorntons

Discount
25%–55%

 No, **Group Tours** No, **Mail order** Yes, **Catalogue** Yes,
✗ Most centres have food courts, **Internet Sales** Yes

MasterCard   SWITCH   VISA   DELTA   Diners Club International   AMERICAN EXPRESS

Alexandria

Wellowear Ltd

Units 4 & 5, Block 2 Lomond Industrial Estate, Alexandria, West Dunbartonshire
Tel: 01389 757450

Children's clothes, factory and shop

Hours Mon–Fri 9–5, Sat 1–5, Sun 9–5

Closed Bank Holidays

Public Transport Bus

Discount

see text

& Yes, **Group Tours** No, **Mail order** No, **Catalogue** No, **Internet Sales** No

Edinburgh

Gleneagles Crystal

9 Simpson Road, East Mains Industrial Estate, Broxburn, West Lothian, EH52 5NP
Tel: 01506 852566 Fax: 01506 855735

Glass and crystal giftware. Occasional promotions. Viewing of cutter cutting the glass, coffee included

Hours Mon–Sat 10–5:00, Sun 11–4 and Bank Holidays

→ 5 minutes from Edinburgh airport

Public Transport Bus

Labels Own label

Discount

see text

Parking 35 Spaces, & Yes, **Group Tours** No, **Mail order** No, **Catalogue** Yes, ✗ Refreshments on site, **Internet Sales** No

Livingston

Thorntons

Unit B6, Five Sisters, Westwood, West Calder, Nr Livingston, West Lothian, EH55
Tel: 01501 762271

The factory outlet stores sell three different product categories: misshapes, discounted lines and standard lines. Misshapes are packed into assorted bags and offer a saving of between 35%–55%. Discount lines are offered at a discount of 25%–50%. Standard lines are also on sale at normal prices

Hours Opening times dependent upon individual factory outlet centre

Labels Thorntons

Discount

25%–55%

& No, **Group Tours** No, **Mail order** Yes, **Catalogue** Yes, ✗ Most centres have food courts, **Internet Sales** Yes

Westwood

Freeport Outlet Village

Westwood, West Lothian, GH55 8QB
Tel: 01501 763488 Fax: 01501 762409

Mens, ladies and childrenswear, sportswear, household goods and toys. Stock includes Adidas, Calvin Klein, Christian Dior, Ellesse, Kickers, Lee, Next, Nike, Thorntons, Wedgwood, YSL

Hours Mon–Sun

Closed Christmas Day and New Year's Day

→ Take M8 toJ4 then follow the tourist information signs to Freeport Village

Public Transport SMT on routes 98, 99, 198, 299, 275, 276

Labels YSL, Principles, Warners, Jumper, Iceberg, Mexx, Next, Tog 24

Discount

20%–70%

Parking 1200 Spaces, & Yes, **Group Tours** Yes, **Mail order** No, **Catalogue** No, ✗ On site, **Internet Sales** No

SPENCER'S

The British Golf Directory

Courses where you can turn up and play

This new Spencer's guide provides full details of golf courses the length and breadth of Britain. All are courses where you can turn up and play, from municipal courses to some of the grandest in the land. You don't need to be members or pay membership fees. Just the rate for the round.

Whether you are an old hand or one of the new wave of golf enthusiasts you will find Spencer's Directory an invaluable companion - for your home, for your car or for your holidays.

With full-colour throughout it's easy-to-use, highly practical and perfect for browsing.

Each entry has a full quarter-page, with a description of the course, and information on yardage, par, standard scratch score, directions and green fees. There's also a full-colour route-planning and map section - a feature of all Spencer's titles.

Format:	210x148mm
No. of pages:	112pp
ISBN:	1 900327 51 1
Price:	£4.99
Publication date:	April 2000

West One
PUBLISHING

West One Publishing
Kestrel House, Duke's PLace
Marlow, Bucks SL7 2QH

tel: 01628 487722

www.WestOneWeb.com

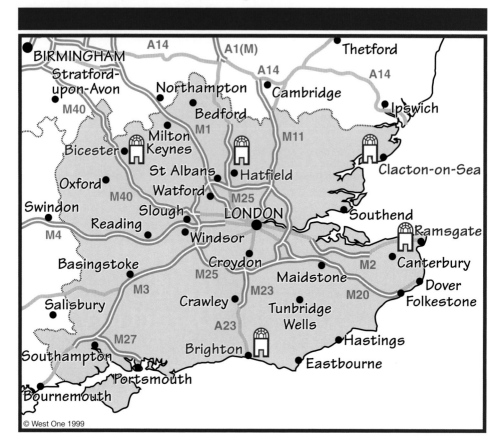

© West One 1999

Index : Companies

Company index

London & South-East England

Index : Products

London & South-East England

London & South-East England

Product index

South-West England & South Wales

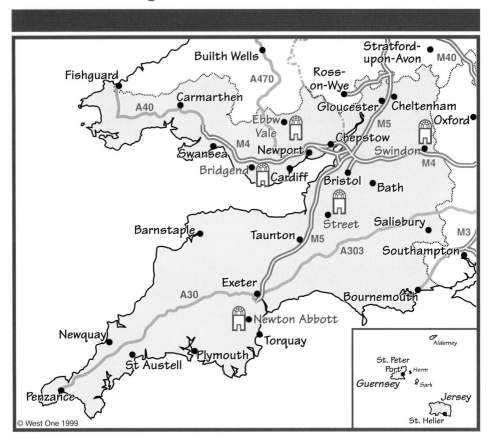

© West One 1999

Index : Companies

South-West England & South Wales

Index : Products

South-West England & South Wales

Product index

Central England and Mid Wales

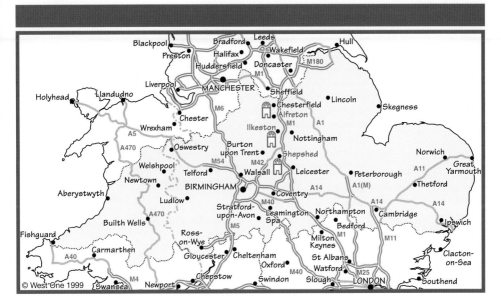

Index : Companies

Central England and Mid Wales

Company index

Index : Products

Product index

Product index

Women's clothes and accessories

Index : Companies

Index : Products

North England and North Wales

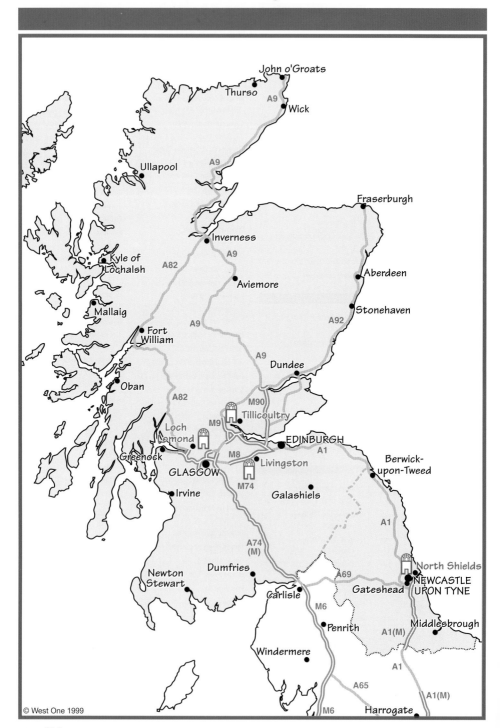

© West One 1999

Scotland and North-East England

Index : Companies

Index : Products

Scotland and North-East England

Key to Maps

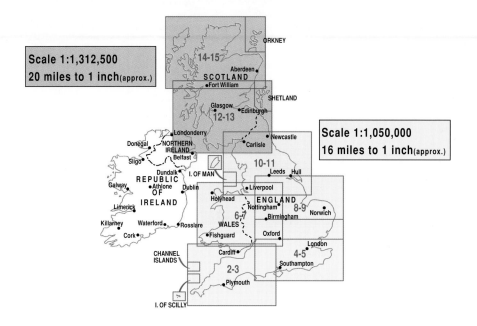

Scale 1:1,312,500
20 miles to 1 inch(approx.)

ORKNEY

14-15

Aberdeen
SCOTLAND
Fort William

SHETLAND

Glasgow Edinburgh
12-13

Londonderry
Donegal NORTHERN
IRELAND
Sligo Belfast

Newcastle
Carlisle

Scale 1:1,050,000
16 miles to 1 inch(approx.)

10-11

Dundalk I. OF MAN
REPUBLIC
Galway Athlone Dublin
OF
IRELAND
Limerick

Leeds Hull

Liverpool

ENGLAND
Holyhead
Nottingham
8-9
Birmingham Norwich
6-7
WALES
Fishguard Oxford

Killarney Waterford Rosslare

Cork

CHANNEL
ISLANDS

Cardiff
2-3

London
4-5
Southampton

Plymouth

I. OF SCILLY

Legend

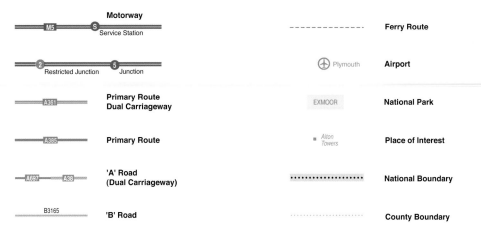

Motorway (M5) (S) Service Station	- - - - - - - - - - - **Ferry Route**
Restricted Junction (2) (5) Junction	(+) Plymouth **Airport**
A361 **Primary Route** **Dual Carriageway**	EXMOOR **National Park**
A385 **Primary Route**	■ Alton Towers **Place of Interest**
A697 A38 **'A' Road** **(Dual Carriageway)**	•••••••••••••••• **National Boundary**
B3165 **'B' Road**	.... **County Boundary**

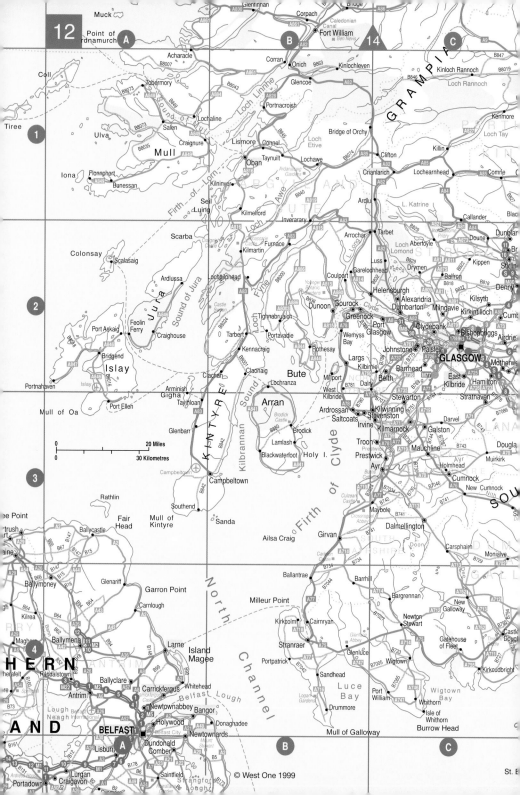

© West One 1999

INDEX TO GREAT BRITAIN

Abbreviations of County and new Unitary Authority names used in this index.

Aber	=	Aberdeenshire	Guer	=	Guernsey	Oxon	=	Oxfordshire
Arg	=	Argyll & Bute	Hants	=	Hampshire	Pemb	=	Pembrokeshire
Brid	=	Bridgend	Herts	=	Hertfordshire	S Lan	=	South Lanarkshire
Bucks	=	Buckinghamshire	High	=	Highland	S York	=	South Yorkshire
Camb	=	Cambridgeshire	IoM	=	Isle of Man	Shrop	=	Shropshire
Corn	=	Cornwall	IoW	=	Isle of Wight	Som	=	Somerset
Derb	=	Derbyshire	Jer	=	Jersey	Staf	=	Staffordshire
Dor	=	Dorset	Linc	=	Lincolnshire	Suff	=	Suffolk
Dur	=	Durham	Med	=	Medway Towns	W Isl	=	Western Isles
E York	=	East Riding of Yorkshire	New	=	Newport	W York	=	West Yorkshire
G Man	=	Greater Manchester	Norf	=	Norfolk	Wrek	=	The Wrekin
Glos	=	Gloucestershire	North	=	Northamptonshire			

A

Aberaeron 6 B3
Abercarn 3 E1
Aberchirder 15 F3
Aberdare 6 C4
Aberdaron 6 B2
Aberdeen 15 F3
Aberdyfi 6 C3
Aberfeldy 12 C1
Aberfoyle 12 C2
Abergavenny 7 D4
Abergele 6 C1
Aberporth 6 B3
Abersoch 6 B2
Abertillery 7 D4
Aberystwyth 6 C3
Abingdon 4 B2
Abington 13 D3
Aboyne 15 E4
Accrington 10 C4
Acharacle 12 A1
Achnasheen 14 C3
Acle 9 F3
Adderbury 4 B1
Adwick le Street 11 D4
Airdrie 12 C2
Alcester 4 A1
Aldeburgh 5 F1
Alderley Edge 7 E1
Aldermaston 4 B3
Aldershot 4 C3
Aldridge 7 F2
Alexandria 12 C2
Alford (Aber) 15 F3
Alford (Linc) 9 D1
Alfreton 8 B2
Allendale Town 10 C1
Alloa 13 D2
Alness 15 D3
Alnwick 13 F3
Alsager 7 E1
Alston 10 B1
Altnaharra 15 D1
Alton 4 B3
Altrincham 10 C4
Alyth 13 D1
Amble 13 F3
Ambleside 10 B2
Amersham 4 C2
Amesbury 4 A3
Amlwch 6 B1

Ammanford 6 C4
Ampthill 4 C1
Amulree 13 D1
Andover 4 B3
Annan 10 A1
Anstruther 13 E2
Appleby in Westmorland 10 B2
Arbroath 13 E1
Ardlui 12 C1
Ardlussa 12 A2
Ardrossan 12 B3
Ardvasar 14 B4
Arisaig 14 B4
Armadale 13 D2
Arminish 12 A2
Arnold 8 B2
Arrochar 12 B2
Arundel 4 C4
Ashbourne 7 F1
Ashburton 3 D3
Ashby-de-la-Zouch 7 F2
Ashford 5 E3
Ashington 13 F3
Ashton-under-Lyne 10 C4
Askrigg 10 C2
Aspatria 10 A1
Atherstone 7 F2
Atherton 10 B4
Attleborough 9 E3
Auchterarder 13 D1
Auchtermuchty 13 D1
Avebury 4 A2
Aviemore 15 D3
Avoch 15 D3
Avonmouth 3 E1
Axminster 3 E3
Aycliffe 11 D2
Aylesbury 4 C2
Aylsham 9 E2
Aynho 4 B1
Ayr 12 C3
Ayton 13 E2

B

Bacup 10 C4
Baile Ailein 14 B2
Bakewell 7 F1
Bala 6 C2
Baldock 4 C1
Baldslow 5 E4
Balfron 12 C2

Ballantrae 12 B4
Ballater 15 E4
Bamburgh 13 F3
Bampton 3 D2
Banbury 4 B1
Banchory 15 F4
Banff 15 F2
Bangor 6 C1
Banstead 5 D1
Bargoed 3 D1
Bargrennan 12 C4
Barking 5 D2
Barmouth 6 C2
Barnard Castle 10 C2
Barnet 5 D2
Barnoldswick 10 C3
Barnsley 11 D4
Barnstaple 2 C2
Barrhead 12 C2
Barrhill 12 B4
Barrow-in-Furness 10 A3
Barry 3 D1
Barton-upon-Humberside 11 E4
Basildon 5 D2
Basingstoke 4 B3
Bath 3 F1
Bathgate 13 D2
Battle 5 E4
Bawdsey 5 F1
Bawtry 11 E4
Beaconsfield 4 C2
Beaminster 3 E3
Beattock 13 D3
Beaulieu 4 B4
Beauly 15 D3
Beaumaris 6 C1
Beccles 9 F3
Bedale 11 D2
Bedford 4 C1
Bedlington 13 F4
Bedworth 8 B3
Beeston 8 B2
Beith 12 C2
Belford 13 F3
Belper 7 F1
Belton 11 E4
Bentley 11 D4
Bere Regis 3 F3
Berkhamsted 4 C2
Berwick-upon-Tweed 13 E2

Bethesda 6 C1
Bettyhill 15 D1
Betws-y-coed 6 C1
Beverley 11 E3
Bewdley 7 E3
Bexhill 5 E4
Bexley 5 D2
Bicester 4 B1
Biddulph 7 E1
Bideford 2 C2
Bigbury-on-Sea 2 C4
Biggar 13 D3
Biggleswade 4 C1
Billericay 5 D2
Billingham 11 D2
Billingshurst 4 C3
Bingham 8 B2
Bingley 10 C3
Birkenhead 10 B4
Birmingham 7 F3
Birsay 15 F1
Bishop Auckland 11 D1
Bishop's Castle 7 D3
Bishop's Stortford 5 D1
Bishop's Waltham 4 B4
Bishopbriggs 12 C2
Blackburn 10 B4
Blackford 12 C1
Blackpool 10 B3
Blackwaterfoot 12 B3
Blaenau Ffestiniog 6 C1
Blaenavon 7 D4
Blair Atholl 15 D4
Blairgowrie 13 D1
Blakeney (Glos) 7 E4
Blakeney (Norf) 9 E2
Blandford Forum 3 F2
Blaydon 10 C1
Blyth 13 F4
Bo'ness 13 D2
Bodmin 2 B3
Bognor Regis 4 C4
Boldon 11 D1
Bolsover 8 B2
Bolton 10 B4
Bonar Bridge 15 D2
Bootle 10 B4
Boroughbridge 11 D3
Borth 6 C3
Boscastle 2 B3
Boston 9 D2
Bothel 10 A1

Boughton 8 B2
Bourne 8 C3
Bournemouth 4 A4
Bourton-on-the-Water 4 A1
Bovey Tracey 3 D3
Bracadale 14 B3
Brackley 4 B1
Bracknell 4 C2
Bradford 10 C3
Bradford-on-Avon 3 F1
Braemar 15 E4
Braintree 5 E1
Bramhall 7 E1
Brampton 10 B1
Branderburgh 15 E2
Brandon 9 E3
Braunton 2 C2
Brechin 13 E1
Brecon 7 D4
Brentwood 5 D2
Bridge of Allan 12 C2
Bridge of Cally 13 D1
Bridge of Earn 13 D1
Bridge of Orchy 12 B1
Bridgend (Arg) 12 A2
Bridgend (Brid) 3 D1
Bridgnorth 7 E3
Bridgwater 3 E2
Bridlington 11 F3
Bridport 3 E3
Brigg 11 E4
Brighouse 10 C4
Brightlingsea 5 E1
Brighton 5 D4
Bristol 3 E1
Brixham 3 D4
Broad Haven 6 A4
Broadford 14 B3
Broadstairs 5 F2
Broadway 4 A1
Brodick 12 B3
Bromfield 7 D3
Bromley 5 D2
Bromsgrove 7 E3
Bromyard 7 E3
Brora 15 D2
Brough 10 C2
Broughton in Furness 10 A2
Broughton 13 D3
Brownhills 7 F2

Bruton 3 F2
Brynmawr 7 D4
Buckfastleigh 2 C3
Buckhaven 13 D2
Buckie 15 E2
Buckingham 4 B1
Buckley 7 D1
Bude 2 B2
Budleigh Salterton 3 D3
Builth Wells 7 D3
Bunessan 12 A1
Bungay 9 F3
Buntingford 5 D1
Burbage 4 A3
Burford 4 A2
Burgess Hill 5 D3
Burghead 15 E2
Burnham Market 9 E2
Burnham-on-Crouch 5 E2
Burnham-on-Sea 3 E2
Burnley 10 C3
Burntisland 13 D2
Burry Port 2 C1
Burslem 7 E1
Burton Bradstock 3 E3
Burton Latimer 8 C3
Burton upon Trent 7 F2
Burwell 9 D4
Burwick 15 F2
Bury St Edmunds 9 E4
Bury 10 C4
Bushey 4 C2
Buxton 7 F1

C

Caerleon 3 E1
Caernarfon 6 B1
Caerphilly 3 D1
Cairnryan 12 B4
Caister-on-Sea 9 F3
Caistor 11 F4
Callander 12 C1
Callington 2 C3
Calne 4 A2
Camberley 4 C3
Camborne 2 A4
Cambridge 5 D1
Camelford 2 B3
Campbeltown 12 B3
Cannich 14 C3
Cannock 7 F2
Canonbie 10 B1

Distance Chart

To find the distance from one town to another, follow the horizontal and vertical channels as appropriate to their point of intersection.

The larger bold figures are miles and the lighter figures are kilometres - thus the distance from Perth to York is 249 miles or 401 kilometres.

Distances are computed by the shortest practical routes, which are not necessarily those recommended by the Publisher.

Each cell below shows the distance in **miles / km**.

From \ To	Aberystwyth	Birmingham	Bristol	Cambridge	Cardiff	Carlisle	Dover	Edinburgh	Exeter	Fort William	Glasgow	Holyhead	Inverness	Leeds	Lincoln	Liverpool	London	Manchester	Newcastle	Norwich	Penzance	Perth	Sheffield	Southampton	Stranraer	York
Aberdeen	449/722	419/674	501/806	462/743	516/830	219/353	610/983	125/201	574/924	153/246	148/238	444/715	105/169	379/610	384/618	343/553	527/849	339/547	237/381	485/780	686/1104	82/132	359/578	553/891	236/380	317/510
Aberystwyth		123/198	132/212	226/364	113/182	243/391	325/523	341/549	205/330	450/724	338/544	107/172	488/786	183/295	194/312	121/195	213/343	140/225	286/460	283/455	317/510	386/621	156/251	207/333	354/570	222/357
Birmingham			89/143	107/172	110/177	194/312	202/325	291/468	162/261	400/644	288/463	156/251	453/729	133/214	94/151	98/158	120/193	87/140	204/328	163/262	275/443	337/542	89/143	130/209	301/484	132/212
Bristol				152/245	47/76	276/444	205/330	373/600	82/132	482/776	370/595	218/351	526/846	215/346	182/293	180/290	118/190	169/272	298/480	244/393	185/298	419/674	182/293	76/122	384/618	225/362
Cambridge					188/303	258/415	122/196	347/558	232/373	466/750	353/568	259/417	489/787	147/237	88/142	200/322	62/100	157/253	230/370	62/100	337/543	390/628	125/201	141/227	369/594	156/251
Cardiff						297/478	240/386	394/634	120/193	504/811	390/628	207/333	556/895	236/380	204/328	202/325	154/248	190/306	319/513	280/451	233/375	440/708	203/327	122/196	405/652	247/397
Carlisle							391/629	98/158	349/562	207/333	94/151	208/335	259/417	153/246	182/293	123/198	308/496	120/193	58/93	286/460	461/742	144/232	162/261	335/539	107/172	117/188
Dover								488/785	254/409	597/961	485/781	355/572	650/1046	280/451	209/336	296/476	79/127	284/457	350/563	175/282	356/573	534/859	252/406	152/245	499/803	277/446
Edinburgh									446/718	133/214	46/74	325/523	159/256	210/338	270/435	222/357	406/653	217/349	112/180	374/602	559/900	43/69	250/402	433/697	128/206	204/328
Exeter										556/895	443/713	291/468	608/978	288/463	255/410	253/407	175/282	242/389	371/597	324/521	112/180	492/792	255/410	109/175	457/735	298/480
Fort William											102/164	434/698	66/106	360/579	389/626	329/529	507/816	326/525	244/393	493/793	661/1064	97/156	369/594	542/872	186/299	323/520
Glasgow												321/517	176/283	247/397	277/446	219/352	403/649	213/343	149/240	380/612	556/895	50/80	257/414	429/690	86/138	211/340
Holyhead													481/774	167/269	205/330	101/163	264/425	126/203	277/446	316/509	403/649	371/597	161/259	297/478	337/542	206/332
Inverness														355/571	414/667	382/615	567/912	379/610	265/427	515/829	720/1159	116/187	389/627	595/958	259/417	347/559
Leeds															72/116	73/117	197/319	43/69	94/151	175/282	401/645	254/409	35/56	229/369	261/420	25/40
Lincoln																123/198	133/214	89/142	154/248	106/171	366/591	312/502	48/77	186/299	293/472	80/129
Liverpool																	213/343	34/55	184/296	219/352	366/589	266/428	79/127	240/386	230/370	108/174
London																		201/323	286/460	115/185	285/459	443/718	160/258	77/124	416/669	206/331
Manchester																			153/246	185/298	354/570	263/423	40/64	228/357	229/369	82/132
Newcastle																				257/415	484/779	155/249	134/216	317/510	161/259	88/143
Norwich																					436/702	430/692	152/245	202/325	394/634	185/298
Penzance																						604/974	368/592	223/359	569/916	410/661
Perth																							306/492	479/771	154/248	249/401
Sheffield																								201/323	270/435	61/93
Southampton																									443/713	244/393
Stranraer																										227/365

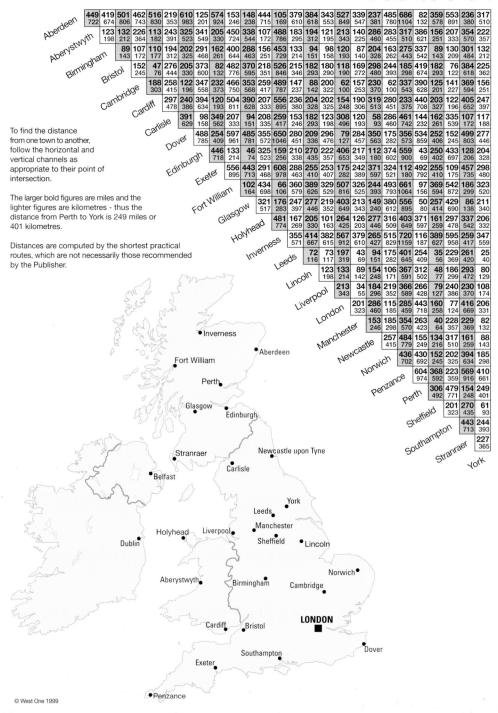

Contents

Introduction

Shopping for good quality items is now a more complicated and sophisticated activity than used to be the case. In addition to the traditional High Street, more and more shopping is conducted via brochures, catalogues, advertising and in specially created "Shopping Villages" in country areas away from the big cities. E-mail and the Internet have also brought computer shopping to the general populace. In the USA, Shopping Villages and the Internet have taken large shares of the general shopping market. This new way of buying goods is spreading around Europe, and especially the UK, at an impressive rate.

To cater for this burgeoning market, we have launched **Spencer's Labels for Less**.

Image is all important these days to the discerning shopper and, if you know where to turn, you can enjoy the assured quality and dashing style of designer labels at bargain prices.

Spencer's Labels for Less tells you where to find products from the world's finest designers at affordable prices – perfects, seconds, clearance and end of lines, bankrupt stock, good quality second-hand, hire-wear and much, much more.

The range of products covered within this guide is comprehensive, including designer clothing, children's wear and sportswear; hair-styling, perfume and toiletries; homeware, furnishings and electrical goods, even unusual teapots!

There are products from top designers, such as Versace, Calvin Klein and Nicole Farhi, own-brand labels of small exclusive companies and top High Street names.

What's more, these designer bargains can be found all over Great Britain: in out-of-town shopping centres, in new "Shopping Villages", northern and midland cities, small country towns, and even on farms, as well as in Mayfair and Knightsbridge.

Whether your child is longing for a particular brand of trainers, sold at an exorbitant price in the High Street, or you need an outfit for an important company function, or you want that perfect piece of furniture to set off your new home, open the covers of **Spencer's Labels for Less** and find out how and where to save money.

Using Spencer's Labels for Less

The listings in this book have been organised for ease of use. The companies are arranged geographically and alphabetically to allow you to find out what's available in your local area. Alternatively, if you are interested in a particular company or product, you can look it up in one of the two indices.

1 The book has been split into five sections corresponding to five regions of Great Britain (see the map on p.7). These are named on the top outside corner of each page and are colour coded as follows:

> **London and South-East England – purple**
> **South-West England and South Wales – pink**
> **Central England and Mid Wales – red**
> **North England and North Wales – blue**
> **Scotland and North-East England – green**

2 Each of these regions has been split into counties or larger geographical areas, such as the West Midlands. These are arranged alphabetically and are listed on the inner top corner of each page.

3 Within each county or region the towns are listed alphabetically. They appear in the coloured bands above each advertisement

4 Finally, within each town, the companies have been arranged alphabetically, and the name appears at the top of each advertisement.

for example

So if you want to find out what's available in Cambridge, for example, first turn to the red Central England and Mid Wales section. Then look at the county/area names and turn to Cambridgeshire. Finally, within the pages for Cambridgeshire, look up Cambridge.

Alternatively if you want a particular product or company, look in the relevant index on pages 292–316. The indices are split into the five separate regions and are colour-coded to match the listings.

The company index tells you the page number on which each company is listed.

In the product index you can find which companies sell a particular product and the page numbers on which they are listed.

page 6

Map of *Spencer's Labels for Less* regions

Scotland &
North East England

North England &
North Wales

Central England &
Mid Wales

London &
South East England

South West England &
South Wales

CHANNEL
ISLANDS

© West One 1999